Student Companion with Complete Solutions for

An Introduction to Genetic Analysis

FIFTH EDITION

by

Anthony J. F. Griffiths, Jeffrey H. Miller,

David T. Suzuki, Richard C. Lewontin,

and William M. Gelbart

Diane K. Lavett

Emory University

W. H. Freeman and Company

New York

Printed in the United States

ISBN 0-7167-2475-8

3 4 5 6 7 8 9 0 HC 9 9 8 7 6 5 4

Contents

Preface to the First Edition   v

Preface to the Second Edition   vi

Introduction: **How to Think Like a Geneticist**   viii

How To Read Like A Geneticist   ix

How to Solve Problems Like A Geneticist   x

How to Learn Genetics   xii

Chapter   1   **Genetics and the Organism**   1

Chapter   2   **Mendelian Analysis**   4

Working With Probability   5

A Systematic Approach to Problem Solving   22

Chapter   3   **Chromosome Theory of Inheritance**   24

Chapter   4   **Extensions of Mendelian Analysis**   38

Chapter   5   **Linkage I: Basic Eukaryotic Chromosome Mapping**   75

Chapter   6   **Linkage II: Special Eukaryotic Chromosome Mapping Techniques**   102

Some Tough Advice on How to Study Genetics   131

Chapter   7   **Gene Mutation**   132

Chapter   8   **Chromosome Mutation I: Changes in Chromosome Structure**   141

Chapter   9   **Chromosome Mutation II: Changes in Number**   161

Chapter   10   **Recombination in Bacteria and Their Viruses**   174

Chapter   11   **The Structure of DNA**   186

Chapter   12   **The Nature of the Gene**   193

Chapter   13   **DNA Function**   207

Chapter   14   **Recombinant DNA**   215

Chapter   15   **Applications of Recombinant DNA**   220

Chapter 16   **The Structure and Function of Eukaryotic Chromosomes**   229

Chapter 17   **Control of Gene Expression**   236

Chapter 18   **Mechanisms of Genetic Change I: Gene Mutation**   243

Chapter 19   **Mechanisms of Genetic Change II: Recombination**   250

Chapter 20   **Mechanisms of Genetic Change III: Transposable Genetic Elements**   257

Chapter 21   **The Extranuclear Genome**   262

Chapter 22   **Developmental Genetics: Cell Fate and Pattern Formation**   273

Chapter 23   **Developmental Genetics: Topics in Gene Regulation and Differentiation**   279

Chapter 24   **Quantitative Genetics**   285

Chapter 25   **Population Genetics**   296

Preface to the First Edition

Unlike many solutions manuals, *Student Companion with Complete Solutions for An Introduction to Genetic Analysis,* Fourth Edition attempts to provide a logical approach to solving genetics problems. While explaining the reasoning behind each answer given, the book also recognizes that what is obvious to geneticists is seldom apparent to the beginning student.

The *Companion* was written from the perspective of a teacher who is standing in front of a blackboard, trying to explain a problem to a class of beginning genetics students. Because I have been in that position many times, my students have taught me exactly where it is that difficulties will occur. I have tried to anticipate each of those potential obstacles in the explanations that follow.

The *Companion* has been tested in the classrooms at the State University of New York at Cortland and at Emory University. In addition, Dr. Anthony J. Pelletier of the Department of Molecular, Cellular, and Developmental Biology of the University of Colorado at Boulder has independently worked all the problems presented in the text. His careful, thorough work resulted in the detection of many errors, and he has my deepest respect and gratitude for his magnificent effort. Although Dr. Pelletier provided this invaluable service, he should not, however, be held responsible for any errors that may still remain. Those errors are mine, and I hope that all users of the *Companion* will feel free to communicate directly with me about any mistakes that they detect.

Diane K. Lavett

Department of Biological Science

The State University of New York at Cortland

Preface to the Second Edition

As with the first edition, all new problems in this second edition have been checked by another geneticist, in this case Michael T. Lewis and Mignon C. Fogarty of the Department of Biology at the University of California, Santa Cruz. Their sincere desire to see an answer book with no wrong answers has been much appreciated, and I thank them for their dedication to our common goal. They however, should not be held responsible for any errors that still remain; the errors are mine.

To the users of this text: Do not assume that just because an answer appears in a printed text that it is correct. If you do not follow an answer in this book and you have an answer of your own that you think is correct, please write me directly and give me the benefit of your thinking. You could be right, you know.

This edition has been written while on leave from SUNY Cortland and while a Visiting Scholar in the Department of Biology at Emory University. I am indebted to the former for time and to the latter for space. I especially thank Ms. Joyce Woodward and Ms. Anne Kirk for their assistance so freely given and so unexpected because they had no obligation to do anything at all.

The people at Freeman are a wonderful group, dedicated to turning out the best books possible. As they turn to their next projects, I wish them all authors who pay attention to deadlines and respond to requests. Janet Tannenbaum and Erica Seifert bore the brunt of the task, and they have my deep appreciation. I owe Patrick Shriner special thanks for his patience with me.

Now, to correct an omission from the last edition: for reasons I cannot comprehend, I failed to acknowledge Patrick Fitzgerald's guidance throughout the entire project. He was the one who talked me into doing the writing, the one who gave support and encouragement at each point that my frustrations reached a new high, and the one who somehow became a friend in the process.

Diane K. Lavett

Department of Biological Science   and   Department of Biology

The State University of New York at Cortland   Emory University

To my teacher,

Dr. Charles Ray, Jr.

Professor Emeritus of Genetics

Biology Department, Emory University

Introduction:
How To Think Like
A Geneticist

You will sharpen a number of skills as you work through your text-book and this *Companion*. Because genetics requires very careful reading, you should become a more careful reader by the end of your course of study. For example, a great deal of information is conveyed by the sentence, "Two mutants were crossed and a wild-type phenotype was observed in the male offspring." If you doubt the amount of information meant to be conveyed by that sentence, I will list it, even though the information may have little meaning for you until later:

1.   Two separate genes are involved.

2.   Both mutants are recessive.

3.   The mutant gene in the female is located on an autosome.

There are seldom superfluous words in a genetics problem. Consequently, you must learn to think about each word that is provided.

A second skill that will be sharpened as you progress through this course is systematic thought. To approach a problem in genetics in a haphazard manner is to enter quickly into the realm of chaos and confusion. I hope that this book will be of real assistance in sharpening your ability to think systematically.

A third skill that you should learn is what I call being gentle with your so-called mistakes. Our educational system has labeled as a mistake the failure to arrive at the correct answer on the first try. Yet, in genetics, as in all of science, progress is made by learning through trial and error what the explanation is *not*. No hypothesis can ever be proven in science, it can only be disproven or tentatively accepted. When you think in this way, I hope that you will begin to view your attempts to solve a problem as hypotheses that are being rejected rather than as errors. If you are not able to answer a particular problem, you need only to go back to your initial assumptions and revise them. Perhaps you have misread the problem. Perhaps you have not understood what the question is. Perhaps you have thought correctly but have made a simple mathematical error. An important point to keep in mind is that in any trial and error learning, there often must be a number of "trials." The only true mistake that you can make is to stop generating hypotheses and to give up.

HOW TO READ LIKE A GENETICIST

There is a big difference between studying and learning. Studying is the review of material already known; learning is an increase in the level of understanding. Most students confuse these two activities and equate all time spent reading the textbook with learning, when, in some instances, not even studying is occurring.

When I first pick up a book, I have to have a reason for opening it. When I was a student, very frequently my reason was simply that I was taking a course for which the book was required and I wanted to pass the course. Now, the first level of my reason is that I want to know what the authors are saying about the topic. I may, of course, have many other levels for wanting to read a specific book. If I do not want to know what the authors are saying, I will put down the book unopened. If your response to the textbook is that you do not want to know what is contained in it at any level, you should seriously think about why you are beginning a course of learning that holds no interest for you.

Once I open the book to a specific chapter, I skim through that chapter. I read the titles of the different sections. I look at the pictures and read the captions. I then read the chapter introduction and summary. I read some of the problems at the end of the chapter. With this cursory examination, I now know the general information that is presented in the chapter and the structure in which it will be presented. More importantly, I know whether the chapter contains the information that I am seeking. As a student reading a required text, I knew in a very general way the information that I was expected to master. Then and now, I ask myself what I already know about the material and ask myself questions that, from my little knowledge of the material, I would like to have answered. Only at this point am I ready to begin learning the material covered in the chapter.

Learning requires active reading, and most students are not accustomed to reading as carefully as is required for the learning of genetics and solving genetics problems. Ideally, as you read each sentence in the textbook you should ask yourself the following questions:

1.   What did the author say?

2.   What did the author mean?

3.   What is implied by what the author said and meant?

4.   Do I agree with both what the author meant and what is implied by what s/he meant?

5.   How does it connect with what I already know?

Until you can answer each of these questions with regard to a sentence, you should not read any further.

This type of reading is an exhausting process that at first will seem very artificial to you. However, there is no substitute for reading in this fashion if you wish to learn at anything but the superficial level. With practice, these questions will become automatic, will be asked and answered very rapidly, and from that point on you will always be learning instead of simply reading.

To get to the level of automatic questioning, I suggest that you work with one or more classmates, reading out loud a sentence at a time and discussing it thoroughly before proceeding to the next. You might find that active reading is fun after a while, as you begin to anticipate a point that the author is trying to make or as you discover implications that the author does not realize. As you become increasingly skilled in active reading, you may find that you have begun to generalize these skills to other parts of your life, such as listening to a friend or the news on television, your own writing, and nonverbal events in your life. If this generalization occurs, you are well on your way to becoming a person who learns from all aspects of your existence.

HOW TO SOLVE PROBLEMS LIKE A GENETICIST

Genetics is not a spectator sport; you cannot learn genetics without solving problems. Each problem should first be read in the same way that you read the textbook. Once you have read the problem, *write* the answers to the following questions:

1.   What question is being asked?

2.   What information is known?

3.   What information is missing?

4.   What information is extraneous?

5.   How will I symbolize the genes?

6.   What assumptions am I making?

7.   What are the possible hypotheses that will answer the question being asked?

Using this approach, the problems will literally solve themselves.

A serious threat to your ability to solve the problems in your text is misuse of this *Companion*. You can convince yourself far too easily that you understand a problem as you read the solution to it when, in fact, you do not understand it at all. Let me suggest the proper way to use this book:

1.   Read the section entitled "Important Terms and Concepts" before beginning to work the problems at the end of a chapter. If any term or concept does not cause you to recall what the text said about it, reread that section of the text.

2.   Work on a problem without reading the *Companion* until you are truly stuck.

3.   Read the explanation of the solution.

4.   Without consulting the *Companion*, immediately rework the problem.

5.   Two or three days later, work the problem without consulting the *Companion*. If you cannot do it at this point, you probably did not understand the problem earlier.

6.   If you cannot work the problem without consulting the *Companion*, repeat steps 2 to 4 once. If you cannot work the problem at that point, consult your teacher or a friend who can explain the problem to you.

7.   Throughout the problem-solving process consult the section entitled "Tips on Problem Solving" as needed. There is a limited number of types of problems. For each type of problem, there is a pattern to the method of solution. Each problem solved in this book has followed the pattern best suited for the problem. Learn to duplicate the patterns.

Once you have mastered all the problems from the text, take the Self-Test found at the end of each chapter. If you solve all of these problems correctly without referring to the answers supplied, you should be in good position to handle whatever your teacher may ask you in a test.

HOW TO LEARN GENETICS

In addition to all that has been outlined above, as a student you have the task of integrating what you learn from the textbook with the lectures that you attend. That is your task as a student.

In order to achieve that task, you need to work at it. Actively read the assigned chapter and try at least some of the problems before going to the class that deals with that chapter. Define for yourself what you understand and do not understand about the chapter material. Ask as many questions as is necessary in class to clarify any difficulties. Interrupt your teacher as often as is necessary when s/he says something that you do not understand. If your questions are framed in such a way and asked in such a manner that they demonstrate that you are struggling with this material and not simply harassing your teacher, all of your questions will be welcomed by your teacher. There is no such thing as a stupid question, except the question that is not asked.

A student frequently does not ask questions in class because the student thinks that s/he is the only one who could be so dumb as to not understand a specific point. The reality is that, if one student does not understand a point, most students in the class do not understand the point, and will be grateful that you have asked the question. Your teacher needs to know what you do not understand in order to do the best job of teaching possible. I urge you to engage with your teacher in active learning. Do yourself, all your classmates, and your teacher a favor by asking those questions that you are convinced are dumb. The first time, asking will be very difficult; it becomes easier with practice.

Once class is over, do not put away your notebook until the next class. Go home and review every note that you made in class. You might try having a second notebook for each class into which you write out your class notes more fully and add to them while the class is still fresh in your mind. After doing this, each time read all the previous notes that you have taken since the beginning of the course. Identify the material that you know thoroughly and the material that you still need to assimilate. Right then, as you are reminded of what you do not yet know, learn that material. If you go through this process after every class, you will not need to study at exam time.

The process of learning outlined above obviously cannot be completed in a "cram" session the night before a test or final exam. The attempt to learn genetics in that fashion is doomed to failure. The best approach is to study genetics almost every day, weekends included. Keep your sessions short, not more than two or three hours at a time. Pick a quiet place where you will not be interrupted or distracted. If you find your concentration wavering, take a short break. If you find that anxiety is interfering, do some physical exercise. Avoid caffeine, both while studying and, most importantly, before taking a test. If the night before a test you are forced to make a choice between a good night's sleep and trying to learn far too much material for the time available, choose sleep.

Many students will have some difficulty with the material and problems in Chapters 2 through 6. Thereafter, the material will be easier to conceptualize, and the problems will be easier to do. The reason for the difficulty with the earlier chapters is that they require a level of abstract thought not usually demanded in undergraduate courses. Beginning with Chapter 7, however, the material becomes more descriptive and, simultaneously, more consistent with the skills required for success in other biology courses. Be aware that you will have to work quite hard in dealing with this early material; also be aware that you are not alone in your difficulty.

Generations of students have struggled with genetics, and the vast majority have been successful in their struggle. Their reward has been that they have learned a new way to view the universe. It is my sincere hope that this will be your reward, too.

1

Genetics and the Organism

IMPORTANT TERMS AND CONCEPTS

Genetics is the study of the inheritance of traits by means of the examination of their variation.

Genes are the basic functional units of heredity. They are composed of DNA and contain information that determines specific traits.

Chromosomes consist of long DNA molecules complexed with protein. They contain many genes.

All life forms can be divided into **eukaryotes** and **prokaryotes**. Eukaryotes are organisms in which the genetic material is contained within a membrane-bound nucleus. Prokaryotes are organisms that do not have their genetic material contained within a membrane-bound nucleus. In both eukaryotes and prokaryotes, the **flow of information** is from DNA to RNA to protein.

Protein can be either structural or enzymatic. **Structural proteins** result in the physical forms of life. **Enzymatic proteins** result in the biochemical processes of life.

The life of any particular organism results from the interaction of its inherited material with the historical sequence of environments that it encounters. The **genotype** refers to the inherited genes in an organism. The **phenotype** refers to the physical appearance of an organism. The **norm of reaction** refers to the environment-phenotype relationship for a specific genotype. **Developmental noise** is the random variation that occurs in phenotype when both genotype and environment are held constant.

Genetic dissection is the process of identifying the specific heredi-
tary components of a biological system. This process is aided by the use
of **markers**, which are specific phenotypes produced by specific genotypes that allow the researcher to keep track of chromosomes, cells or
individuals.

SELF-TEST

✓ **1.** What does the abbreviation "DNA" mean?

20 **2.** How many different DNA molecules are there in an organism
that has ten pairs of chromosomes?

No **3.** Is the DNA in your father identical to the DNA in your mother?

No **4.** Is your DNA totally different from the DNA found in a dog? An
oak tree?

genes/form **5.** Distinguish between genotype and phenotype.

No **6.** Is there always a one-to-one relationship between genotype and
phenotype?

Both **7.** Which is more important to an organism, its genetic information
or the environment in which it develops?

No **8.** If two genetically identical organisms develop in identical environments, will they necessarily be identical for a specific trait?

No **9.** If two genetically different organisms develop in identical environments, will they necessarily be nonidentical for a specific trait?

No **10.** If two genetically different organisms develop in different environments, will they necessarily be nonidentical for a specific trait?

SOLUTIONS TO SELF-TEST

1. Deoxyribonucleic acid.

2. Because each chromosome contains one long DNA molecule,
there would be 10 X 2 = 20 DNA molecules in the organism.

3. No. Although your father and mother have genes that control the
same functions, not all the genes are identical. Because the genes are
composed of DNA, not all the DNA would be identical.

4. No. All organisms must solve similar problems in order to survive. As an example, the Krebs cycle occurs in humans, dogs, and trees. Because these metabolic changes take place in all three organisms, identical or very similar enzymes must exist in all three organisms. Because the information for the enzymes resides in the DNA, the DNA responsible for these enzymes must be identical or very similar.

5. Genotype is the inherited information, while phenotype is the end result of an interaction of that information with the environment.

6. No. For most traits there is a many-to-one relationship between genotype and phenotype.

7. Both are very important. The inherited material initially sets the limits for the organism, while the development of an organism in a specific environment determines where along the spectrum of the possible the organism will be. However, some genotypes are lethal in all environments and some environments are lethal for all genotypes.

8. No. Developmental noise will produce variation.

9. No. The response to the environment may produce the same phenotype from two different genotypes.

10. No. The response to differing environments may produce the same phenotype from two different genotypes.

2
Mendelian Analysis

IMPORTANT TERMS AND CONCEPTS

A **gene** controls one characteristic, or trait. **Alleles** are alternative forms of a gene. A good analogy is a coin. You can have pennies, nickels, and dimes, all "genes." You can have 1956, 1971, and 1992 pennies, all "alleles" of the penny "gene." Alleles determine alternate types (tall, short) for the gene (height) being studied.

A **pure line** is a strain that breeds true for the trait being studied. It is also called a **true breeding line.**

The **parental generation**, P, is the generation from which the first cross in a series is taken. Usually, but not always, the parents are true breeding.

The **first filial generation**, F_1, consists of the progeny from the parental generation.

The **second filial generation**, F_2, consists of progeny from the first filial generation.

Dominant refers to an allele that is expressed regardless of the other alleles present for the trait being studied. **Recessive** refers to an allele that is expressed only when it is the only type of allele present in an organism for the trait being studied.

A **heterozygous** line, or **hybrid** line, contains two different alleles for the trait being studied. The phenotype of the heterozygote indicates which allele is dominant.

A **homozygous** line contains identical alleles for the trait being studied. The line may be either homozygous recessive or homozygous dominant, depending upon which allele is present. It is a true breeding line.

Monohybrid refers to a single gene pair. F_1 monohybrid crosses lead to $1 : 2 : 1$ ratios.

Dihybrid refers to two gene pairs being studied simultaneously. F_1 dihybrid crosses result in a $9 : 3 : 3 : 1$ ratio.

Equal segregation of gene pairs refers to the separation of the two alleles of a gene into gametes, which contain only one allele each. This is the **first law of Mendel**.

Independent assortment of gene pairs refers to equal segregation of one allelic pair independently of another allelic pair. This is the **second law of Mendel**.

A **testcross** is a cross of a homozygous recessive organism with an organism of dominant appearance. It results in a $1 : 1$ ratio if the organism is heterozygous and a $1 : 0$ ratio if it is homozygous.

A **reciprocal cross** involves a pair of crosses that switch the trait being studied with the sex of the parent carrying that trait.

Continuous variation is seen in traits that exist on a spectrum, such as height and weight. **Discontinuous variation** is seen in traits that have discrete phenotypes, such as yellow versus brown and red versus blue.

Polymorphism, literally meaning "many forms," is the existence in a population of two or more common phenotypic variations for a trait. The different variations are called **morphs**.

Pedigree analysis is a tool for determining the genetic status of related individuals over several generations.

The **propositus** is the individual that first called attention to the family being studied.

WORKING WITH PROBABILITY

Probability is the number of times an event is expected to happen divided by the total number of times it could have happened.

"And" statement: indicates the need to multiply.

Example: the probability of a black female horse

= p(black horse) "and" p(female horse)

= p(black horse) $\times$ p(female horse)

Example: the probability of *AA Bb*

$$= p(A \text{ "and" } A) \text{ "and" } p(B \text{ "and" } b)$$

$$= p(A \times A) \times p(B \times b)$$

"Or" statement: indicates the need to add.

Example: the probability of a black or brown horse

$$= p(\text{black horse}) \text{ "or" } p(\text{brown horse})$$

$$= p(\text{black horse}) + p(\text{brown horse})$$

Example: the probability of *AA* or *Aa*

$$= p(A \text{ "and" } A) \text{ "or" } p(A \text{ "and" } a)$$

$$= p(A \times A) + p(A \times a)$$

"At least" statement: indicates the need to add.

Example: the probability of at least three out of five

$$= p(3 \text{ out of } 5) \text{ "or" } p(4 \text{ out of } 5) \text{ "or" } p(5 \text{ out of } 5)$$

$$= p(3 \text{ out of } 5) + p(4 \text{ out of } 5) + p(5 \text{ out of } 5)$$

Remember that the probability of at least three out of five = 1 – the probability of 0 or 1 or 2 out of 5.

Combinations statement: indicates the need to use the formula for combinations. This formula is

$$\frac{n!}{p! \, q!} \, (r)^p (s)^q$$

where *n* is the total number, *p* is the number of one kind, *q* is the number of the alternative, *r* is the probability of *p* occurring, and *s* is the probability of *q* occurring. The exclamation point indicates *factorial*. $5! = (5)(4)(3)(2)(1)$.

Example: If two heterozygous individuals have eight children, the probability of exactly two being homozygous recessive is

$$\frac{8!}{2! \, 6!} (1/4)^2 (3/4)^6 = \frac{8 \times 7 \times 6 \times 5 \times 4 \times 3 \times 2 \times 1}{2 \times 1 \times 6 \times 5 \times 4 \times 3 \times 2 \times 1} (1/4)^2 (3/4)^6$$

Be sure that you have thoroughly read the entire chapter before you attempt any of the problems.

SOLUTIONS TO PROBLEMS

1. Mendel's first law states that alleles segregate during meiosis. Mendel's second law states that genes independently assort during meiosis.

2. To determine whether the *Drosophila* is *AA* or *Aa*, a testcross should be done. By definition, this means using a fly that is *aa*. If the original fly is *AA*, all progeny will have the A phenotype. If the original fly is *Aa*, one half the progeny will have the A phenotype and one half will have the aa phenotype.

3. The progeny ratio is approximately 3 : 1, indicating a classic heterozygous-by-heterozygous mating. The parents must be *Bb* × *Bb*. Their black progeny must be *BB* and *Bb* in a 1 : 2 ratio, and their white progeny must be *bb*.

4. Begin by drawing a pedigree, letting the normal allele be *T* and the Tay-Sachs allele be *t*.

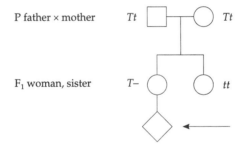

P father × mother   *Tt*   *Tt*

F₁ woman, sister   *T–*   *tt*

The woman's sister has to be *tt* because she had Tay-Sachs. Because Tay-Sachs is lethal, both parents cannot have the disorder; they are carriers. The original cross was *Tt* × *Tt*. The woman of concern here is either *TT* (probability of 1/3) or *Tt* (probability of 2/3).

The probability of her having a child with Tay-Sachs is
p(woman is *Tt*) × p(mate is *Tt*) × p(*tt* child, given both parents are *Tt*).

If she is a carrier and if she marries a man who is also a carrier, their unborn child has a probability of 1/4 of having Tay-Sachs. Thus, the final probability of having a child with Tay-Sachs is

p(woman is *Tt*) × p(*Tt* mate) × p(*tt* child)

=   2/3   ×   1   ×   1/4

= 2/12 = 1/6

with the man assumed to be a carrier. Each of her normal children has a 2/3 chance of being a carrier with this assumption.

If she is not a carrier or if she is a carrier and marries a non-carrier, all of her children will be normal. If one of the parents is a carrier, then normal children would have a 50% probability of being a carrier. If both parents are carriers, then 2/3 of the normal children would be carriers.

The woman should be informed of all the probabilities, including the probability that her mate will be a carrier, which will vary drastically with ethnic group, and she should be encouraged to have her carrier status checked initially. If she is a carrier, her mate and all her normal children should have their carrier status checked. Prior to testing, she should be told that her overall risk of having a Tay-Sachs child is slight unless she marries someone from an ethnic group with a high frequency of the allele.

5.   Each die has six sides, so the probability of any one side (number) is 1/6. To get specific red, green, and blue numbers involves "and" statements.

    a. $(1/6)(1/6)(1/6) = (1/6)^3$

    b. $(1/6)(1/6)(1/6) = (1/6)^3$

    c. $(1/6)(1/6)(1/6) = (1/6)^3$

    d. To get no sixes is the same as getting anything but sixes: $(1-1/6)(1-1/6)(1-1/6) = (5/6)^3$.

    e. There are three ways to get two sixes and one five:

6R, 6G, 5B	$(1/6)(1/6)(1/6)$
or	+
6R, 5G, 6B	$(1/6)(1/6)(1/6)$
or	+
5R, 6G, 6B	$(1/6)(1/6)(1/6)$
=	$3(1/6)^3$

    f. Here there are "and" and "or" statements:

       p(three sixes "or" three fives)

       $= p(6R$ "and" $6G$ "and" $6B$ "or" $5R$ "and" $5G$ "and" $5B)$

       $= (1/6)^3 + (1/6)^3 = 2(1/6)^3$

    g. There are six ways to fulfill this:

       $6(1/6)^3 = (1/6)^2$

    h. The easiest way to approach this problem is to consider each die separately:

The first die thrown can be any number. Therefore, the probability for it is 1.0.

The second die can be any number except the number obtained on the first die. Therefore, the probability of not duplicating the first die is $1.0 - p$(first die duplicated) $= 1.0 - 1/6 = 5/6$.

The third die can be any number except the numbers obtained on the first two dice. Therefore, the probability is $1.0 - p$(first two dice duplicated) $= 1.0 - 2/6 = 4/6$.

Therefore, the probability of all different dice is $(1.0)(5/6)(4/6) = 20/36 = 5/9$.

6. a.   Before beginning the specific problems, write the probabilities associated with each jar.

jar 1 $p(R) = 600/(600 + 400) = 0.6$

$p(W) = 400/(600 + 400) = 0.4$

jar 2 $p(B) = 900/(900 + 100) = 0.9$

$p(W) = 100/(900 + 100) = 0.1$

jar 3 $p(G) = 10/(10 + 990) = 0.01$

$p(W) = 990/(10 + 990) = 0.99$

1. $p(R, B, G) = (0.6)(0.9)(0.01) = 0.0054$

2. $p(W, W, W) = (0.4)(0.1)(0.99) = 0.0396$

3. Before plugging into the formula, you should realize that, while white can come from any jar, red and green must come from specific jars (jar 1 and jar 3). Therefore, white must come from jar 2:

$p(R, W, G) = (0.6)(0.1)(0.01) = 0.0006$

4. $p(R, W, W) = (0.6)(0.1)(0.99) = 0.0594$

5. There are three ways to satisfy this:

R, W, W   or   W, B, W   or   W, W, G

$= (0.6)(0.1)(0.99) + (0.4)(0.9)(0.99) + (0.4)(0.1)(0.01)$

$= 0.0594 + 0.3564 + 0.0004 = 0.4162$

6. At least one white is the same as 1 minus no whites:

p(at least 1 W) $= 1 - p$(no W) $= 1 - p(R, B, G)$

$= 1 - (0.6)(0.9)(0.01) = 1 - 0.0054 = 0.9946$

b. The cross is $Rr \times Rr$. The probability of red $(R-)$ is 3/4, and the probability of white (rr) is 1/4. Because only one white is needed, the only unacceptable result is all red.
In n trials, the probability of all red is $(3/4)^n$. Because the probability of failure must be 5 percent

$$(3/4)^n = 0.05$$

$$n = 10.41, \text{ or } 11 \text{ seeds.}$$

7. Charlie, his mate, or both, obviously were not pure-breeding, because his F_2 progeny were of two phenotypes. Let A = black and white, and a = red and white. If both parents were heterozygous, then red and white would have been expected in the F_1 generation. Red and white were not observed in the F_1 generation, so only one of the parents was heterozygous. The cross is

P $Aa \times AA$

F_1 $1\,Aa : 1\,AA$

Two F_1 heterozygotes (Aa) when crossed would give 1 AA (black and white) : 2 Aa (black and white) : 1 aa (red and white).

If the red and white F_2 progeny were from more than one mate of Charlie's, then the farmer acted correctly. However, if the F_2 progeny came only from one mate, the farmer may have acted too quickly.

8. You are told that normal parents have affected offspring. This is the pattern with recessive disorders.

9. To do this problem, you should first draw a pedigree. Next, you should realize that if you are given no information about an individual, you need to assume that the individual is phenotypically normal.

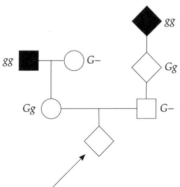

The woman must be Gg (G from mother, g from father), and the chance that she will pass g to her child is 1/2. The grandfather had to

pass the *g* allele to his child, who must be *Gg*. The chance that the fiance inherited the *g* allele from his parent is 1/2. The chance he will pass it to his child is 1/2. The final probability that the child will be galactosemic is the product of the three probabilities: $(1/2)(1/2)(1/2) = 1/8$.

10. Because the parents are heterozygous, both are *Aa*. Both twins could be albino or both twins could be normal ("and" "or" "and" = multiply add multiply). The probability of being normal (*A*–) is 3/4, and the probability of being albino (*aa*) is 1/4.

p(both normal) $+$ p(both albino)

$= p$(first normal) $\times p$(second normal) $+ p$(first albino)

$\times p$(second albino)

$=$ $(3/4)(3/4)$ $+$ $(1/4)(1/4)$

$=$ $9/16$ $+$ $1/16 = 5/8$.

11. The plants are approximately 3 blotched : 1 unblotched. This suggests that blotched is dominant to unblotched and that the original plant which was selfed was a heterozygote.

a. Let *A* = blotched, *a* = unblotched.

P   *Aa* (blotched) × *Aa* (blotched)

F_1 1 *AA* : 2 *Aa* : 1 *aa*

3 *A*– (blotched) : 1 *aa* (unblotched)

b. All unblotched plants should be pure-breeding in a testcross with an unblotched plant (*aa*) and one-third of the blotched plants should be pure-breeding.

12. In theory, it cannot be proved that an animal is not a carrier for a recessive allele. However, in an *A*– × *aa* cross, the more dominant phenotype progeny produced, the less likely it is that one parent is *Aa*. In such a cross one-half of the progeny would be *aa* and one-half would be *Aa* if the parent were *Aa*. With *n* dominant phenotype progeny, the probability that the parent is *Aa* is $(1/2)^n$.

13. The results suggest that winged (*A*–) is dominant to wingless (*aa*) (Cross 2 gives a 3 : 1 ratio). If that is correct, the crosses become:

		Number of progeny plants	
Pollination	Genotypes	Winged	Wingless
Winged (selfed)	$AA \times AA$	91	1*
Winged (selfed)	$Aa \times Aa$	90	30

(continued on next page)

Pollination	Genotypes	Number of progeny plants	
		Winged	Wingless
Wingless (selfed)	$aa \times aa$	4*	80
Winged × wingless	$AA \times aa$	161	0
Winged × wingless	$Aa \times aa$	29	31
Winged × wingless	$AA \times aa$	46	0
Winged × winged	$AA \times A-$	44	0
Winged × winged	$AA \times A-$	24	0

The five unusual plants are most likely due either to human error in classification or to contamination. Alternatively, they could result from environmental effects on development. For example, too little water may have prevented the seed pods from becoming winged even though they are genetically winged.

14. **a.** *Pedigree 1*: The best answer is recessive because the disorder skips generations and appears in a mating between two related individuals.

Pedigree 2: The best answer is dominant because it appears in each generation, roughly one-half of the progeny are affected, and affected individuals have an affected parent.

Pedigree 3: The best answer is dominant for the reasons stated for pedigree 2. Inbreeding, while present in the pedigree, does not allow an explanation of recessive because it cannot account for individuals in the second generation.

Pedigree 4: The best answer is recessive even though the disorder appears in each generation. Two unaffected individuals had one-fourth affected progeny, and the affected individuals in the third generation had an affected father and a mother who could be a carrier.

b. *Genotypes of pedigree 1*:

Generation 1: *AA, aa*

Generation 2: *Aa, Aa, Aa, A–, A–, Aa*

Generation 3: *Aa, Aa*

Generation 4: *aa*

Genotypes of pedigree 2:

Generation 1: *Aa, aa, Aa, aa*

Generation 2: *aa, aa, Aa, Aa, aa, aa, Aa, Aa, aa*

Generation 3: *aa, aa, aa, aa, aa, A–, A–, A–, Aa, aa*

Generation 4: *aa, aa, aa*

Genotypes of pedigree 3:

Generation 1: *Aa, aa*

Generation 2: *Aa, aa, aa, Aa*

Generation 3: *aa, Aa, aa, aa, Aa, aa*

Generation 4: *aa, Aa, Aa, Aa, aa, aa*

Genotypes of pedigree 4:

Generation 1: *aa, A–, Aa, Aa*

Generation 2: *Aa, Aa, Aa, aa, A–, aa, A–, A–, A–, A–, A–*

Generation 3: *Aa, aa, Aa, Aa, aa, Aa*

15.   The great-great grandmother (*) was *Tt*. At each generation, the probability that the *t* was received from the previous generation is 1/2. Therefore, the probability that the mating male and female in generation 5 received the *t* allele is $(1/2)^4$ for each. If they both received the *t* allele, then 1/4 of their children would be expected to have Tay-Sachs. The probability that a child of their union would have Tay-Sachs is

p(man received t) $\times$ p(woman received t)

$\times$ p(both passed t to child)

$=$ $(1/2)^4$ $\times$ $(1/2)^4$ $\times$ $(1/4)$

$=$ 1/16 $\times$ 1/16 $\times$ $1/4 = 1/1{,}024 = 0.000977$

16.   **a.**   The most likely possibility is that the disorder is recessive because skipping of generations is present and affected individuals do not have affected parents.

b.   The probability that the first child from individuals 1 and 2 will have the kidney disease is the probability that each has the gene times the probability that both pass it to their child. The father of individual 1 had to have received the gene from his mother. The chance that the father passed it to individual 1 is 1/2. Individual 2 had to have received the gene from her father. The final probability that the first child of individuals 1 and 2 will have the kidney disease is

p(1 received gene) $\times$ p(2 received gene)

$\times$ p(both passed gene to child)

$$= \quad (1/2) \quad \times \quad (1) \quad \times \quad (1/4) \quad = 1/8.$$

17. **a.** In order to draw this pedigree, you should realize that if an individual's status is not mentioned, then there is no way to assign a genotype to that person. The parents of the boy in question had a genotype that differed from his. Therefore, both parents were heterozygous and the boy, who is a non-roller, is homozygous recessive. Let *R* stand for the ability to roll the tongue and *r* stand for the inability to roll the tongue. The pedigree becomes

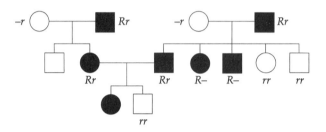

b. If the seven discordant pairs were not truly identical, that could account for the observation. If the seven discordant pairs were truly identical, that indicates that the ability to roll the tongue cannot be determined solely by one gene. Assuming the twins are identical, there must be either an environmental component to the expression of that gene or developmental noise (see Chapter 1) may play a role.

18. Let *C* stand for the normal allele and *c* stand for the allele that causes cystic fibrosis.

a.

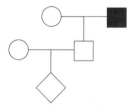

b. The man has a probability of 1.0 of having the *c* allele. His wife, who is from the general population, has a 1/50 chance of having the *c* allele. If both have the allele, then 1/4 of their children will have cystic fibrosis. The probability that their first child will have cystic fibrosis is

p(man has *c*) × p(woman has *c*) × p(both pass *c* to the child)

$$= \quad 1.0 \quad \times \quad 1/50 \quad \times \quad 1/4 \quad = 1/200 = 0.005$$

c. If the first child does have cystic fibrosis, then the woman is a carrier of the *c* allele. Both parents are *Cc*. The chance that the second child will be normal is the probability of a normal child in a heterozygous × heterozygous mating, or 3/4.

19. The inheritance pattern for red hair suggested by this pedigree is recessive.

20. *Taster by taster cross:* Tasters can be either *PP* or *Pp* and the genotypic status cannot be determined until a large number of progeny are observed. A failure to obtain a 3 : 1 ratio in the matings of two tasters would be expected because there are three types of matings:

	Children	
Mating	Genotypes	Phenotypes
PP × *PP*	all *PP*	all tasters
PP × *Pp*	1/2 *PP* : 1/2 *Pp*	1/2 tasters : 1/2 nontasters
Pp × *Pp*	1/4 *PP* : 1/2 *Pp* : 1/4 *pp*	3/4 tasters : 1/4 nontasters

Taster by nontaster cross: There are two types of matings that resulted in the observed progeny:

	Children	
Mating	Genotypes	Phenotypes
PP × *pp*	all *Pp*	all tasters
Pp × *pp*	1/2 *Pp* : 1/2 *pp*	1/2 tasters : 1/2 nontasters

Again, the failure to obtain either a 1 : 0 ratio or a 1 : 1 ratio would be expected because of the two mating types.

Nontaster by nontaster cross: There is only one mating that is nontaster by nontaster (*pp* × *pp*), so 100% of the progeny would be expected to be nontasters. Five of 223 children were classified as tasters. Some could be the result of mutation (unlikely), some could be the result of misclassification (likely), some could be the result of a second gene that affects the expression of the gene in question (possible), some could be the result of developmental noise (possible), and some could be due to illegitimacy (possible).

21. Use the following symbols:

Gene Function	Dominant Allele	Recessive Allele
Color	*R* = red	*r* = yellow
Loculed	*L* = two	*l* = many
Height	*H* = tall	*h* = dwarf

The starting plants are pure-breeding, so their genotypes are
red, two-loculed, dwarf: *RR LL hh*
and   yellow, many-loculed, tall: *rr ll HH*.

The farmer wants to produce a pure-breeding line that is yellow, two-loculed and tall, which would have the genotype *rr LL HH*.

The two pure-breeding starting lines will produce an F_1 that will be *Rr Ll Hh*. By doing an F_1 cross and selecting yellow, two-loculed and tall plants, the known genotype will be *rr L– H–*. The task then will be to do sequential testcrosses for both the *L–* and *H–* genes among these yellow, two-loculed and tall plants. Because the two genes in question are homozygous recessive in different plants, each plant that is yellow, two-loculed and tall will have to be testcrossed twice.

For each testcross, the plant will obviously be discarded if the testcross reveals a heterozygous state for the gene in question. If no recessive allele is detected, then the minimum number of progeny that must be examined to be 95% confident that the plant is homozygous is based on the frequency of the dominant phenotype, which is 3/4. In *n* progeny, the probability of obtaining all dominant progeny given that the plant is heterozygous is $(3/4)^n$. To be 95% confident of homozygosity, the following formula is used, where 5% is the probability that it is not homozygous:

$$(3/4)^n = 0.05$$

$n = 10.41$, or 11 dominant phenotype progeny must be obtained from each testcross to be 95% confident that the plant is homozygous.

22.   Let *A* represent achondroplasia and *a* represent normal height. Let *N* represent neurofibromatosis and *n* represent the normal allele. Because both conditions are extremely rare, the affected individuals are assumed to be heterozygous. The genes are also assumed to assort independently. The cross is

P   *Aa nn* × *aa Nn*

F_1 1 *Aa nn* : 1 *aa nn* : 1 *aa Nn* : 1 *Aa Nn*

      1 dwarf : 1 normal : 1 neurofibromatosis : 1 dwarf, neurofibromatosis

23.   **a.**   The ratio of dark : albino and short : long is 3 : 1. Therefore, each gene is heterozygous in the parents. The cross is *Cc Ss* × *Cc Ss*.

        b.   Because all progeny are dark, one of the parents is *CC*. The other is *C–*. The ratio of short : long is 1 : 1, a testcross. The cross is *C– Ss* × *C– ss*, with one of the parents *CC*. Assuming homozygosity, the cross is *CC Ss* × *CC ss*.

        c.   All progeny are short (*S–*), and the ratio of dark to albino is 1 : 1, indicating a testcross. Therefore, the cross is *Cc S–* × *cc*

$S-$, with one of the parents SS. Assuming homozygosity, the cross is $Cc\ SS \times cc\ SS$.

d. All progeny are albino (cc), and the ratio of short to long is 3 : 1, indicating a heterozygous × heterozygous cross. Therefore, the cross is $cc\ Ss \times cc\ Ss$.

e. The dark : albino ratio is 3 : 1, indicating a $Cc \times Cc$ cross. All animals are long (ss). The cross is $Cc\ ss \times Cc\ ss$.

f. All animals are dark, indicating at least one parent is homozygous for color. Short : long = 3 : 1, indicating $Ss \times Ss$. The cross is $C-\ Ss \times C-\ Ss$, with one parent CC. Assuming homozygosity, the cross is $CC\ Ss \times CC\ Ss$.

g. Dark : albino = 3 : 1. Short : long = 1 : 1, a testcross. The cross is $Cc\ Ss \times Cc\ ss$.

24. **a.** From Cross 3, purple is dominant to green. From Cross 4, cut is dominant to potato.

b. Let A/a stand for color and B/b stand for shape.

Cross 1: Immediately, the cross can be written $A-\ B- \times aa\ B-$. A 1 : 1 ratio for color indicates a testcross, and a 3 : 1 ratio for shape indicates a heterozygous cross. The cross is $Aa\ Bb \times aa\ Bb$.

Cross 2: Immediately the cross can be written $A-\ B- \times A-\ bb$. A 3 : 1 ratio for color and a 1 : 1 ratio for shape exists. The cross is $Aa\ Bb \times Aa\ bb$.

Cross 3: Because no green plants exist, the purple parent is homozygous. There is a 3 : 1 ratio for shape. The cross is $AA\ Bb \times aa\ Bb$.

Cross 4: No potato is seen, therefore cut is homozygous. There is a 1 : 1 ratio for color, a testcross. The cross is $Aa\ BB \times aa\ bb$.

Cross 5: A 1 : 1 : 1 : 1 ratio indicates a testcross for each gene. The cross is $Aa\ bb \times aa\ Bb$.

25. **a.** Look at each gene separately.

1. $A-\ B-\ C-\ D-\ E- = (1/2)(3/4)(1/2)(3/4)(1/2) = 9/128$

2. $aa\ B-\ cc\ D-\ ee = (1/2)(3/4)(1/2)(3/4)(1/2) = 9/128$

3. (question 1) + (question 2) $= 9/128 + 9/128 = 9/64$

4. $1 - $ (question 1) $- $ (question 2) $= 1 - 9/128 - 9/128 = 55/64$

    b.   1.   *Aa Bb Cc Dd Ee* $= (1/2)(1/2)(1/2)(1/2)(1/2) = 1/32$

          2.   *aa Bb cc Dd ee* $= (1/2)(1/2)(1/2)(1/2)(1/2) = 1/32$

          3.   (question 1) + (question 2) $= 1/32 + 1/32 = 1/16$

          4. $1 - $ (question 1) $- $ (question 2) $= 1 - 1/32 - 1/32 = 15/16$

    26.   The single yellow fly may be either recessive *yy* or may be yellow due to a diet of silver salts. Cross that fly with a known recessive yellow fly and raise half the larvae on a diet with no silver salts and half the larvae on a diet with silver salts. A true recessive will result in flies with yellow bodies on both diets, while a phenocopy that is genetically *Y*– will produce flies with brown or yellow bodies, depending on the diet.

    Phenocopies are caused by environmental factors. Many drugs used by pregnant women result in genetic defects that are phenocopies. One example is cleft lip and/or palate caused by Valium taken before the fetal face is completely formed. Retardation caused by the consumption of alcohol during pregnancy is another phenocopy effect.

TIPS ON PROBLEM SOLVING

    Ratios: A $1:2:1$ (or $3:1$) ratio indicates that one gene is involved (see Problem 3). A $9:3:3:1$ ratio, or some modification of it, indicates that two genes are involved (see Problem 23a). A testcross results in a $1:1$ ratio if the organism being tested is heterozygous and a $1:0$ ratio if it is homozygous (see Problem 2).

    Pedigrees: Normal parents have affected offspring in recessive disorders (see Problems 8, 9, 14). Normal parents have normal offspring and affected parents have affected offspring in dominant disorders (see Problems 14, 22). If phenotypically identical parents produce progeny with two phenotypes, the parents were both heterozygous (see Problems 14, 16, 17).

    Probability: When dealing with two or more independently assorting genes, consider each gene separately (see Problems 22, 23, 25).

SELF-TEST

    1.   In humans, when the hands are folded and the fingers are interlocked, placement of the left thumb on top is a dominant trait. Suppose that husband, wife, and one of their three children place their left thumb on top, while the two other children place their right thumb on top. What are the genotypes of all individuals?

2.   The ability to roll the tongue is dominant in humans. Among couples who are both heterozygous and have four children, what percentage of the families would be expected to show the expected phenotypic ratio?

3.   The following crosses were done in cats in order to determine the mode of inheritance of the tail. Evaluate each cross separately, in sequence, and then come to the best conclusion as to the mode of inheritance.

Cross	Parental Phenotype	Progeny Phenotype
1. cat 1 × cat 2	tailed × tailed	all tailed
2. cat 1 × cat 3	tailed × tailed	all tailed
3. cat 4 × cat 5	no tail × no tail	all no tail
4. cat 1 × cat 5	tailed × no tail	3 tailed, 3 no tail

4.   A woman gave birth to a child with Tay-Sachs disease, a lethal recessive disorder. What does that tell you about the genotypes of her parents? Her grandparents? Her great-grandparents?

5.   Genes D/d, E/e and F/f are independently assorting. If both parents are heterozygous for all genes, what is the probability of

   a.   an egg that is $D E F$?

   b.   a sperm that is $D e F$?

   c.   a child that is $DD Ee F$–?

   d.   a child that is D– E– ff?

6.   What are the hallmarks of a pedigree showing recessive inheritance? Dominant inheritance?

7.   If a woman is heterozygous for five different genes, how many different types of eggs can she produce with respect to those genes?

8.   You have a brother who has had several operations for a bone dysplasia that is known to be recessive. Your X rays show evidence of the disorder, but you never needed to have an operation. What are the risks to your children?

9.   A child is born with a disorder that is known to have both dominant and recessive forms. Also, a poor diet can cause the same disorder. How would you go about determining which form of the disorder the child has?

10.   A dog has the dominant phenotype $D-$. How can you determine if it is homozygous or heterozygous?

SOLUTIONS TO SELF-TEST

1.   Husband and wife: Rr. Child with left thumb on top: $R-$. Children with right thumb on top: rr.

2.   The expected phenotypic ratio is $3:1$. Some families would be $3:1$, but many would not be. The formula to use is

$$\frac{n!}{p!\,q!}\,(r)^p(s)^q$$

where n is the total number, p is the number of one kind, q is the number of the alternative, r is the probability of p occurring and s is the probability of q occurring. The exclamation point indicates factorial. $5! = (5)(4)(3)(2)(1)$.

$$(4!)(3/4)^3(1/4)^1/(3!)(1!) = 4(27/64)(1/4) = 27/64 = 42.2\%$$

In other words, only 42.2% of the families would actually have a $3:1$ ratio.

An alternative way to do the problem is to recognize that there are four different ways to achieve a family with a $3:1$ ratio:

First Child	Second Child	Third Child	Fourth Child	Probability
roller	roller	roller	nonroller	$(3/4)^3(1/4)$
				+
roller	roller	nonroller	roller	$(3/4)^3(1/4)$
				+
roller	nonroller	roller	roller	$(3/4)^3(1/4)$
				+
nonroller	roller	roller	roller	$(3/4)^3(1/4)$
				$4(3/4)^3(1/4)$

Again, the final probability of achieving exactly a $3:1$ ratio in many families is 42.2%.

3.

Cross	Conclusion
1	At least one of the parents is homozygous.
2	At least one of the parents is homozygous.

3   At least one of the parents is homozygous.

4   At least one of the parents is homozygous.

Nothing more than the above can be concluded from these crosses.

4.   At least one person in each generation must have been a carrier (heterozygous) for Tay-Sachs disease:

Parents: 1 in 2, at a minimum
Grandparents: 1 in 4, at a minimum
Great-grandparents: 1 in 8, at a minimum

5. **a.** $(1/2)(1/2)(1/2) = 1/8$

    b. $(1/2)(1/2)(1/2) = 1/8$

    c. $(1/4)(1/2)(3/4) = 3/32$

    d. $(3/4)(3/4)(1/4) = 9/64$

6.   *Recessive*: Affected people may have normal parents; unaffected people may have an affected child; two affected people have only affected children; among the people who are genetically related, one-fourth may be affected.

Dominant: Affected people have at least one affected parent; two unaffected people have unaffected children; among the people who are genetically related, one-half may be affected.

7.   For each gene there are two alternatives. Therefore, there are 2^5 different eggs that she may produce.

8.   Not all people who have the genotype for a disorder necessarily have the phenotype associated with it. You have some aspects of the phenotype at the X-ray level, which means that you also have the genotype for the disorder. However, unless you marry someone who is a carrier, your children should be symptom-free, although one-half would be expected to be carriers.

9.   Assuming that testing cannot distinguish among the three possible causes, the only way to pinpoint the cause is to do a complete family history that would include questions about diet. Most likely, the exact form of the disorder will not be determined.

10.   A testcross with *dd* will result in all *D–* progeny if the dog is *DD* and in 1 *D–* : 1 *dd* if the dog is heterozygous *Dd*.

A SYSTEMATIC APPROACH TO PROBLEM SOLVING

Now that you have struggled with a number of genetics problems, it may be worthwhile to make some generalizations about problem solving beyond what has been presented for each chapter so far.

The first task always is to determine exactly what information has been presented and what is being asked. Frequently, it is necessary to rewrite the problem or to symbolize the presented information in some way.

The second task is to formulate and test hypotheses. If the results generated by a hypothesis contradict some aspect of the problem, then the hypothesis is rejected. If the hypothesis generates data compatible with the problem, then it is retained.

A systematic approach is the only safe approach in working genetics problems. Shortcuts in thought processes usually lead to an incorrect answer.

Consider the following two types of problems.

1.   When analyzing pedigrees, there are usually only four possibilities (hypotheses) to be considered: autosomal dominant, autosomal recessive, X-linked dominant, and X-linked recessive. The criteria for each should be checked against the data. Additional factors that should be kept in mind are epistasis, penetrance, expressivity, age of onset, incorrect diagnosis in earlier generations, adultery, adoptions that are not mentioned, and inaccurate information in general. All of these factors can be expected in real life, although few will be encountered in the problems presented here.

2.   When studying matings, frequently the first task is to decide whether you are dealing with one gene, two genes, or more than two genes (hypotheses). The location of the gene(s) may or may not be important. If location is important, then there are two hypotheses: autosomal and X-linked. If there are two or more genes, then you may have to decide on linkage relationships between them. There are two hypotheses: unlinked and linked.

If ratios are presented, then $1 : 2 : 1$ (or some modification signaling dominance) indicates one gene, $9 : 3 : 3 : 1$ (or some modification reflecting epistasis) indicates two genes, and $27 : 9 : 9 : 9 : 3 : 3 : 3 : 1$ (or some modification signaling epistasis) indicates three genes. If ratios are presented that bear no relationship to the above, such as $35 : 35 : 15 : 15$, then you are dealing with two linked genes (see Chapter 5 for a discussion of linkage).

If phenotypes rather than ratios are emphasized in the problem, then a cross of two mutants that results in wild type indicates the involvement of two genes rather than alleles of the same gene. Both mutants are recessive to wild type. A correlation of sex with phenotype indicates X-linkage for the gene mutant in the female parent, while a lack of correlation indicates autosomal location.

If the problem involves X-linkage, frequently the only way to solve it is to focus on the male progeny.

Once you determine the number of genes being followed and their location, the problem essentially solves itself if you make a systematic listing of genotype and phenotype.

Sometimes, the final portion of a problem will give additional information that requires you to adjust all the work that you have done up to that point. As an example, in Problem 37 of Chapter 4, parts a and b led you to assume that you were working with two genes. In part c, data incompatible with this assumption were presented. Your initial assumption of two genes was correct for the information given in the first two parts; it was not a mistake.

Other than a lack of systematic thought, the greatest mistake that a student can make is to label a rejected hypothesis an error. This decreases self-confidence and increases anxiety, with the result that real mistakes will likely follow. The beginner needs to keep in mind that science progresses by the rejection of hypotheses. When a hypothesis is rejected, something concrete is known: the proposed hypothesis does not explain the results. An unrejected hypothesis may be right or it may be wrong, and there is no way to know without further experimentation.

A very generalized flowchart for problem solving would look like this:

1.   Determine what information is being presented and what is being asked.

2.   Formulate all possible hypotheses.

3.   Check the consequences of each hypothesis against the data (the given information).

4.   Reject all hypotheses that are incompatible with the data. Retain all hypotheses that are compatible with the data.

5.   If no hypothesis is compatible with the data, return to step 1.

3

Chromosome Theory of Inheritance

IMPORTANT TERMS AND CONCEPTS

The **chromosome theory of heredity** means that genes are located on chromosomes and that the behavior of genes during mitosis and meiosis parallels the behavior of chromosomes during mitosis and meiosis.

Mitosis is the orderly distribution of one chromatid from each chromosome to each of two daughter cells. The chromosome number remains constant between cell generations. The stages of the mitotic cycle are interphase, prophase, metaphase, anaphase, and telophase. Interphase is divided into three stages: G1, S, and G2. G1 is the "gap" before chromosome replication. "S" is the stage of chromosome replication and DNA synthesis. G2 is the stage after chromosome replication.

Meiosis consists of two sequential cell divisions. Usually meiosis I (reductional division) is the orderly distribution of one chromosome from each chromosome pair to each of two daughter cells. The chromosome number is reduced by half. The stage between meiosis I and II is called interkinesis. Usually meiosis II (equational division) is the orderly distribution of one chromatid from each chromosome to each of two daughter cells. In form, meiosis II is identical to mitosis. The chromosome number remains constant between cell generations. Both meiotic divisions are subdivided into a number of stages.

The **nuclear spindle** is a protein structure that aids in proper chromosome movement during mitosis and meiosis.

Homologs (also spelled **homologues**) are two morphologically identical chromosomes that carry genes for the same functions. One comes from each parent.

Synapsis is the pairing of homologous chromosomes prior to thefirst meiotic division. The process occurs with the aid of the **synaptonemal complex**, a protein structure.

A **chiasma** is the chromosomal structure that is assumed to be the visible proof of the molecular event of crossing-over.

A **genome** (usually $1n$) consists of one set of unique chromosomes. The number of chromosomes per genome varies with the species.

A **diploid** ($2n$) cell or organism contains two homologous genomes, one from each parent.

A **haploid** ($1n$) cell or organism has one genome.

The number of sets of genomes present in an organism varies with the species, as does which sex is the heterogametic sex (if sexual differentiation exists). Some organisms are mostly diploid, some mostly haploid, and some alternate between haploid and diploid. Other organisms may routinely have more than two genomes (see Chapter 9). In all species that have meiosis, the laws of Mendel apply.

A **heteromorphic pair** is a pair of sex chromosomes that are nonidentical in shape and/or size and presumably have only partial homology. Genes present only on the X or Y chromosome in the heterogametic sex are called **hemizygous.**

The **heterogametic** sex has two nonidentical sex chromosomes (XY males in humans). The **homogametic** sex has two identical sex chromosomes (XX females in humans).

X-linkage refers to genes located on the X chromosome.

Y-linkage refers to genes located on the Y chromosome.

Autosomes are the paired (in diploids) nonsex chromosomes of both sexes.

Pseudoautosomal refers to the behavior of genes located on both the X and Y chromosomes.

X-inactivation occurs during early development of all mammals. It involves most of one of the two X chromosomes in females and is detectable by the presence of the **Barr body** during interphase. Because the highly condensed Barr body is genetically inactive, and because inactivation is random with respect to which chromosome is inactivated in each cell, females have two functional cell lines for each heterozygous gene on the X chromosome. Females are therefore **mosaics.**

Wild type refers to the most frequent allelic form of a gene found in natural (or laboratory) populations. It is indicated by a superscript + in the *Drosophila* system of symbolism. Deviations from the wild type are used to name the gene. Dominant deviations from wild type use an uppercase letter while recessive deviations use a lowercase letter. Thus curly, a dominant deviation, is *Cy*, and the wild-type form of the gene is *Cy⁺*. The white-eye allele, a recessive deviation from wild type, is *w*, and the wild-type allele of that gene is *w⁺*.

Be sure that you have thoroughly read the entire chapter before you attempt any of the problems.

SOLUTIONS TO PROBLEMS

1.   *i.*   In mitosis the chromosome number remains unchanged, but in meiosis the chromosome number is halved.

    ii.   In mitosis sister chromatids separate from each other, but in meiosis both homologous chromosomes and sister chromatids separate from each other.

    iii. Mitosis leads to two cells; meiosis leads to four cells.

    iv. Homologous pairing occurs only in meiosis.

    v.   Recombination is much more frequent in meiosis than in mitosis.

2.   Because mitosis does not involve the separation of allelic alternatives, the daughter cells will both be *Aa Bb Cc*.

3.   P   *ad⁻ a* × *ad⁺ ∝*

    Transient diploid *ad⁺/ad⁻ a/∝*

        F_1 1 *ad⁺ a*, white

            1 *ad⁻ a*, purple

            1 *ad⁺ ∝*, white

            1 *ad⁻ ∝*, purple

4.   P   *s⁺/s⁺* × *s/Y*

        F_1 1 *s⁺/s*   normal female

            1 *s⁺/Y*   normal male

        F_2 1 *s⁺/s⁺*   normal female

$1\ s^+/s$ normal female

$1\ s^+/Y$ normal male

$1\ s/Y$ small male

In the cross $s^+/s \times s/Y$, the progeny will be

$1\ s^+/s$ normal female

$1\ s/s$ small female

$1\ s^+/Y$ normal male

$1\ s/Y$ small male

5.

	Mitosis	Meiosis
fern	sporophyte	prothallus
	gametophyte	
moss	sporophyte	archegonia
	gametophyte	antheridia
flowering plant	sporophyte	flowers
	gametophyte	
pine tree	sporophyte	pinecones
	gametophyte	
mushroom	sporophyte	hyphae
	gametophyte	
frog	somatic cells	gonads
butterfly	somatic cells	gonads
snail	somatic cells	gonads

6.   This problem is tricky because the answers depend on how a cell is defined. In general, geneticists consider the transition from one cell to two cells to occur with the onset of anaphase in both mitosis and meiosis even though cytoplasmic division occurs at a later stage.

    a. 46 physically separate chromosomes, each with 2 chromatids = 92 chromatids

    b. 46 physically separate chromosomes, each with 2 chromatids = 92 chromatids

    c. 46 physically separate chromosomes in each of 2 about-to-be-formed cells, each with 1 chromatid = 92 chromatids

  d. 23 physically separate chromosomes in each of 2 about-to-be-
      formed cells, each with 2 chromatids = 46 chromatids

  e. 23 physically separate chromosomes in each of 2 about-to-be-
      formed cells, each with 1 chromatid = 46 chromatids

7. e. chromosome pairing.

8. His children will have to inherit the satellite 4 (probability = 1/2),
the abnormally staining 7 (probability = 1/2), and the Y chromosome
(probability = 1/2). To get all three, the probability is $(1/2)(1/2)(1/2) = 1/8$.

9. The parental set of centromeres can match either parent, which
means there are two ways to satisfy the problem. For any one pair, the
probability of a centromere from one parent going into a specific gamete
is 1/2. For n pairs, the probability of all the centromeres being from one
parent is $(1/2)^n$. Therefore, the total probability of having a haploid complement of centromeres from either parent is $2(1/2)^n = (1/2)^{n-1}$.

10. a. Your mother gives you 23 chromosomes, one-half of all that
         she has and one-half of all that you have. Therefore, you have
         one-half of all your genes in common with your mother.

     b. For any heterozygous gene (Aa) in your mother,

You	Brother
A	A
A	a
a	A
a	a

Thus, there are two of four combinations between you and you brother
that will be a match. The same holds for any heterozygous gene in your
father. Therefore, you and your brother will have one-half of your genes
in common for each gene that is heterozygous in your parents. You and
your brother will have identical alleles from your parents for each gene
that is homozygous in your parents. The degree of homozygosity in a
parent is unknown. For this reason, the final answer can be stated only
for heterozygosity in the parents, and homozygosity must be ignored.

11. First assume that the cross is autosomal and that the male is the
heterogametic sex:

    P $G-$ (graceful female) $\times$ gg (gruesome male)

F_1 1 *Gg* graceful female

       1 *g–* ? female

       1 *Gg* graceful male

       1 *g–* ? male

This cross does not meet the observation, so it must be wrong. The cross also cannot be *G– × gY* (X-linked), because graceful females will result.

  Next assume that the female is the heterogametic sex:

P   *GO* (graceful female) × *gg* (gruesome male)

F_1 1 *gO* gruesome female

       1 *Gg* graceful male

Notice that this outcome matches the observed results. Therefore, in the schmoo the female is the heterogametic sex. The *O* can be a female-deter-mining chromosome or no chromosome.

12.   The disease cannot be autosomal because there is a sexual split in the progeny. It cannot be X-linked recessive for two reasons: (1) males get their Y from their fathers and couldn't have the disease, and (2) females get a normal X from their mother, who is unlikely to be a carrier. If the mother *is* a carrier, it is highly unlikely she would pass the gene to all of her daughters and none of her sons. The daughters will show any dominant X-linked gene that their father has because he must pass it to them. He cannot pass an X chromosome to his sons. The answer is **d.**, X-linked dominant.

13.   Let *H* = hypophosphatemia and *h* = normal. The cross is *HY × hh*, yielding *Hh* (females) and *hY* (males). The answer is **e.**, 0.

14.   *If* the historical record is accurate, the data suggest Y-linkage. Another explanation is an autosomal gene that is dominant in males and recessive in females. This has been observed for other genes in both humans and other species.

15.   You should draw pedigrees for the following problems.

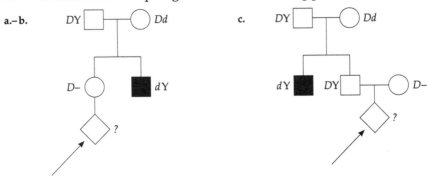

a.–b.   DY □──○ Dd   c.   DY □──○ Dd

a. The probability that the woman inherited the *d* allele from her mother is 1/2. The probability that she passes it to her child is 1/2. The probability that the child is male is 1/2. The total probability of the woman having an affected child is $(1/2)(1/2)(1/2) = 1/8$.

b. Your maternal grandmother had to be a carrier, *Dd*. The probability that your mother received the allele is 1/2. The probability that your mother passed it to you is 1/2. The total probability is $(1/2)(1/2) = 1/4$.

c. Because your father does not have the disease, you cannot inherit the allele from him. The probability is 0.

16. a. Because neither parent shows it, the disease must be recessive. Because of the sexual split in the progeny, it is most likely X-linked. If it were autosomal, all three parents would have to carry it, which is rather unlikely.

    b. P *AY, Aa, AY*

        F_1 *AY, A–, aY, A–, AY, aY, aY, A–, aY, A–*

17. You should draw the pedigree before beginning.

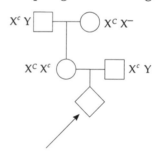

a. X^CX^c, X^cX^c

b. p(colorblind) p(male) $= (1/2)(1/2) = 1/4$.

c. The girls will be 1 normal (X^CX^c) : 1 colorblind (X^cX^c)

d. The cross is $X^CX^c \times X^cY$, yielding 1 normal : 1 colorblind for both sexes.

18. a. This problem involves X-inactivation. Let B = black and b = orange.

Female	Males
$X^BX^B = BB =$ black	$X^BY = BY =$ black

(continued on next page)

$X^bX^b = bb =$ orange $\qquad$ $X^bY = bY =$ orange

$X^BX^b = Bb =$ tortoiseshell

b. P $\quad X^bX^b$ (orange) $\times X^BY$ (black) $\qquad$ or $\quad bb \times BY$

$\quad$ F$_1$ $\quad X^BX^b$ tortoiseshell female $\qquad$ or $\quad Bb$

$\qquad\quad X^bY$ orange male $\qquad\qquad$ or $\quad bY$

c. P $\quad X^BX^B$ (black) $\times X^bY$ (orange) $\qquad$ or $\quad BB \times bY$

$\quad$ F$_1$ $\quad X^BX^b$ tortoiseshell female $\qquad$ or $\quad Bb$

$\qquad\quad X^BY$ black male $\qquad\qquad$ or $\quad BY$

d. Because the males are black or orange, the mother had to have been tortoiseshell. One-half the daughters are black, indicating homozygosity, which means that their father was black.

e. Males were orange or black, indicating that the mothers were tortoiseshell. Orange females, indicating homozygosity, mean that the father was orange.

19. **e.** 1/4

20. **a.** X-linked recessive

b. *Generation 1:* $X^+/Y, X^+/X^x$

Generation 2: $X^+-, X^x/Y, X^+/Y, X^+-, X^+/X^x, X^+/Y$

Generation 3: $X^+, X^+/Y, X^+/X^x, X^+/X^x, X^+/Y, X^+-, X^x/Y, X^+/Y, X^+-$

c. The first couple has no chance of an affected child because the son received his Y chromosome from his father. The second couple has a 50 percent chance of having affected sons and no chance of having affected daughters. The third couple has no chance of having an affected child.

21. **a.** autosomal recessive: excluded by unaffected female in third generation.

b. autosomal dominant: consistent.

c. X-linked recessive: excluded by affected female with unaffected father.

d. X-linked dominant: excluded by unaffected female in third generation.

e. Y-linked: excluded by affected females.

22. **a.** Cross 6, bent × bent, leads to some normal progeny, indicating that bent is dominant.

   b. The sexual differences in phenotype in cross 6 indicate that it is X-linked.

   c. Let B = bent and b = normal.

	Parents		Progeny	
Cross	Female	Male	Female	Male
1	bb	BY	Bb	bY
2	Bb	bY	Bb, bb	BY, bY
3	BB	bY	Bb	BY
4	bb	bY	bb	bY
5	BB	BY	BB	BY
6	Bb	BY	BB, Bb	BY, bY

23. Start this problem by writing the crosses and results so that all the details are clear.

   P   brown, short female × red, long male

   F$_1$ red, long females

   red, short males

These results tell you that long is dominant to short and that the chromosome carrying the gene is X-linked, because males differ from females in their genotype with regard to wing length. The results also tell you that eye color is autosomal, because males do not differ in phenotype from females with regard to eye color, and that red is dominant to brown. Let B = red, b = brown, S = long, and s = short. The cross can be rewritten as follows:

   P $b/b\ s/s \times B/B\ S/Y$

   F$_1$ $1/2\ B/b\ S/s$ females

   $1/2\ B/b\ s/Y$ males

   F$_1$ gametes

   female: $1/4\ BS : 1/4\ Bs : 1/4\ bS : 1/4\ bs$

   male: $1/4\ Bs : 1/4\ bs : 1/4\ BY : 1/4\ bY$

F$_2$ females

    1/16 B/B S/s red, long

    1/16 B/B s/s red, short

    2/16 B/b S/s red, long

    2/16 B/b s/s red, short

    1/16 b/b S/s brown, long

    1/16 b/b s/s brown, short

F$_2$ males

    1/16 B/B S/Y red, long

    1/16 B/sB s/Y red, short

    2/16 B/b S/Y red, long

    2/16 B/b s/Y red, short

    1/16 b/b S/Y brown, long

    1/16 b/b s/Y brown, short

The final phenotypic ratio is

3/8 red, long	1/8 brown, short
3/8 red, short	1/8 brown, long

24. Notice that F$_2$ males differ in phenotype from the females in the first cross. The sexual difference in the F$_2$ suggests that the gene is sex-linked. The first cross also indicates that the wild-type large spots are dominant over the lacticolor small spots. Let A = wild type and a = lacti.

Cross 1: If the male is assumed to be the hemizygous sex, then it soon becomes clear that the assumption is incorrect because the predictions do not match what was observed:

P aa female × AY male

F$_1$ Aa wild-type females

      aY lacti males

Therefore, assume that the female is the hemizygous sex. Let Z stand for the sex-determining chromosome in females. The cross becomes:

P aZ female × AA male

F$_2$ 1/2 AZ wild-type females $A-$ wild-type males

       1/2 aZ lacti females

Cross 2:

P AZ female × aa male

F$_1$ aZ lacti females

    Aa wild-type males

F$_2$ $1/2\ AZ$ wild-type females $1/2\ Aa$ wild-type males

    $1/2\ aZ$ lacti females $1/2\ aa$ lacti males

25.   On the basis of phenotype, the woman appears to have two different cell lines for G6PD activity in her red blood cells. If G = normal enzyme activity and g = reduced enzyme activity and malaria resistance, then the woman appears to have $G–$ and gg cells. This can most easily be explained by X-inactivation in the woman's cells. Assume that she is Gg. In approximately one-half of her cells the G allele will be inactivated, leaving only a functional g allele. Those cells will be resistant to the malaria parasite. In the other one-half of her cells the g allele will be inactivated. Those cells will have a functional G allele and will be susceptible to the parasite.

26.   The suggestion is that the woman was a carrier for testicular feminization. Testicular feminization is an X-linked recessive disorder that renders individuals unresponsive to androgens. Chromosomal males with the disorder exhibit an almost idealized feminine appearance, with large breasts, little to no body hair, extremely smooth skin; they are sterile. Females usually show no effect in the heterozygous state.

The gene for testicular feminization is on the X chromosome, and therefore would be subjected to inactivation an expected 50 percent of the time. If testicular feminization is responsible for the woman's unusual phenotype, then the allele that results in this disorder in males would be functioning in approximately 50 percent of her cells. Those cells would be unresponsive to androgens, which would account for the increased breast size and the lack of pubic hair. That these symptoms are confined to one side of her body suggests that she had an unusual midline split as to which X chromosome was inactivated. Her right side expressed the testicular feminization allele, while her left side expressed the normal allele. The menstrual irregularities are completely compatible with her being a carrier for testicular feminization.

If she were a carrier, then 50 percent of her sons would be expected to suffer from testicular feminization. Her brothers would also have a 50 percent risk of having the disorder. Also, her daughters would be expected to have a 50 percent chance of being carriers, which could lead to this disorder in 50 percent of her grandsons. In other words, the pedigree is completely compatible with the suggestion that she was a carrier for testicular feminization:

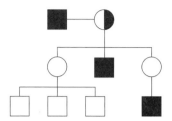

27. **a.** Note that only males are affected. For rare traits, this is what is expected for an X-linked recessive disorder.

   b. The mothers of all affected sons must be heterozygous for the disorder. In addition, the daughters of all affected men must be heterozygous. Finally, barring mutation, individual I2 must have been heterozygous.

28. Note that only males are affected but that affected males have affected sons. This suggests that the disorder is caused by an autosomal dominant with expression limited to males.

TIPS ON PROBLEM SOLVING

Problem 11 clearly illustrates the process of successive generation of hypotheses, which are then tested against the data.

X-linkage or autosomal: if the male phenotype is different from the female phenotype, X-linkage is involved for the allele carried by the female (see Problems 15, 27).

Inheritance patterns: There are only seven possible inheritance patterns for a gene (see Problem 21). Usually only numbers 1–4 will be encountered:

1. autosomal dominant

2. autosomal recessive

3. X-linked dominant

4. X-linked recessive

5. autosomal with expression limited to one sex

6. Y-linked

7. X and Y linked (pseudoautosomal)

SELF-TEST

1. When does application of Mendel's first law occur?

2. When does application of Mendel's second law occur?

3. How many DNA molecules would there be per cell in a mature sperm from an organism in which $2n = 18$?

4. How many chromatids per cell would there be in the first polar body of a mammal with $2n = 24$?

5. In a haploid organism in which $1n = 15$, how many chromosomes would there be in a cell beginning meiosis I?

6. Outline a decision-making flowchart for deciding on the mode of inheritance from data in a human pedigree.

7. In some organisms, the male is the homogametic sex. For a recessive sex chromosome–linked disorder, which sex would be affected at a higher rate?

8. Two heterozygotes for independently assorting genes A/a and B/b mate. Among their offspring, there are only two phenotypic classes, $A- B-$ and $aa\ bb$, in a 9 : 7 ratio. How can you account for this?

9. If a person is $Dd\ E/Y$, what gametes will he produce?

10. Genes D/d, E/e and F/f are independent. What will be the progeny and their ratios in a mating of the following individuals: $Dd\ EE\ Ff \times Dd\ ee\ FY$?

SOLUTIONS TO SELF-TEST

1. The first law states that alleles segregate from each other, which occurs at the onset of anaphase I.

2. The second law states that genes independently assort, which occurs at the onset of anaphase I.

3. If $2n = 18$, a mature sperm would have nine chromosomes, each with one chromatid. There would be one DNA molecule per chromosome, or nine DNA molecules.

4. The first polar body in mammals contains $1n$ of chromosomes, each with two chromatids. If $2n = 24$, $1n = 12$. Therefore, there would be 24 chromatids in the polar body.

5. To be entering meiosis I, fertilization or fusion must have occurred, so there would be 30 chromosomes.

6. There are two decisions that need to be made in most situations: (1) whether the disorder is dominant or recessive and (2) whether it is X-linked or autosomal. The decisions can be made in either order, but it is often easier to decide between X-linked and autosomal first.

1. Is the disorder X-linked or autosomal?

   a. What is the sex ratio among affected individuals? If equal, then may be autosomal. If clearly skewed, X-linked.

   b. Is there male-to-male transmission? If yes, then autosomal. If no, may be X-linked.

2. If the disorder is X-linked:

   a. If females are affected at a greater rate than males, the disorder is dominant.

   b. If males are affected at a greater rate than females, the disorder is recessive.

3. If the disorder is autosomal:

   a. Do affected individuals have affected parents? If yes, possibly dominant. If no, recessive.

   b. Do normal parents have affected offspring? If yes, recessive. If no, dominant.

There are three other possibilities: Y linkage, autosomal with expression limited to one sex, and pseudoautosomal inheritance. However, they are so rare that they normally will not be encountered.

7. females

8. The two genes somehow affect the expression of each other. $A–B–$ is one phenotypic class; all other gene combinations constitute the other phenotypic class.

9. *DE, dE, DY, dY*

10.

1/16 *DD Ee FF*	1/8 *Dd Ee FF*	1/16 *dd Ee FF*
1/16 *DD Ee FY*	1/8 *Dd Ee FY*	1/16 dd Ee FY
1/16 *DD Ee Ff*	1/8 *Dd Ee Ff*	1/16 dd Ee Ff
1/16 *DD Ee fY*	1/8 *Dd Ee fY*	1/16 *dd Ee fY*

4
Extensions of Mendelian Analysis

IMPORTANT TERMS AND CONCEPTS

Incomplete dominance produces in the heterozygote a phenotype intermediate between those of the two homozygotes. A $1:2:1$ ratio is observed. Examples are flower color (red and white $\rightarrow$ pink) and enzyme activity (high and low $\rightarrow$ medium).

Codominance is revealed when the heterozygote possesses the phenotype of both homozygotes. A $1:2:1$ ratio is observed. Examples are hemoglobin variants (Hb^A and $Hb^S \rightarrow Hb^A + Hb^S$) and phosphoglucomutase variants (PGM-1 and PGM-2 $\rightarrow$ PGM-1 + PGM-2), as determined by electrophoresis.

For allelic interactions, what you determine to be the mode of interaction depends quite frequently on the manner in which the trait is observed. Consider the heterozygote Hb^AHb^S. If you look at the red blood cells under normal conditions, you conclude that Hb^A is dominant to Hb^S. Under conditions of low oxygen tension the cells sickle, leading to the opposite conclusion. At the level of electrophoresis of the globin proteins, however, the conclusion is codominance.

Multiple alleles lead to single-gene-pair ratios ($1:1$, $3:1$, $1:2:1$).

Multiple genes lead to ratios indicating two genes ($9:3:3:1$) or three genes ($27:9:9:9:3:3:3:1$), or some modification of the ratios, in heterozygote × heterozygote crosses.

Recessive lethal genes cause a distortion in the expected ratio. An example is a $2:1$ ratio in a heterozygote × heterozygote cross.

Epistasis is the alteration of expression of one gene by the expression of another gene. Distortions of expected ratios are observed ($12 : 4$, $9 : 7$, $9 : 6 : 1$, etc.).

Modifier genes modify the expression of other genes, for example genes for light and dark color. They are detected in heterozygote × heterozygote crosses by a $9 : 3 : 3 : 1$ ratio.

Complementary genes work together to produce a phenotype. Heterozygote × heterozygote crosses usually yield a $9 : 7$ ratio.

Suppression occurs when one gene blocks the expression of another. In F_1 crosses, the ratios can be $13 : 3$, $12 : 4$, or some other variant of the expected ratio.

Penetrance is a populational term and is defined as the percentage of individuals of a given genotype that express the phenotype associated with the genotype. A lack of penetrance in an individual is due to epistatic relationships between genes. The environment may also be a factor.

Expressivity is the extent to which a phenotype is expressed in an individual. The range is from minimal to full, depending upon the effects of epistatic genes and environmental factors.

Pleiotropy is the phenomenon of multiple effects from one gene. This results in a syndrome (a collection of symptoms associated with a particular disorder).

Dominance occurs within genes, between alleles, whereas epistasis occurs between genes.

Be sure that you have thoroughly read the entire chapter before you attempt any of the problems.

SOLUTIONS TO PROBLEMS

1. The woman must be *AO*, so the mating is *AO* × *AB*. Their children will be

Genotype	Phenotype
1 *AA*	A
1 *AB*	AB
1 *AO*	A
1 *BO*	B

2.   You are told that the cross of two erminette fowls results in 22 erminette, 14 black, and 12 pure white. Two facts are important: (1) the parents consist of only one phenotype, yet the offspring have three phenotypes; and (2) the progeny appear in an approximate ratio of $1:2:1$. These facts should tell you immediately that you are dealing with a heterozygous × heterozygous cross involving one gene and that the erminette phenotype must be the heterozygous phenotype.

When the heterozygote shows a different phenotype than either of the two homozygotes, the heterozygous phenotype results from incomplete dominance or codominance. Because two of the three phenotypes contain black, either fully or in an occasional feather, you might classify the erminette as an instance of incomplete dominance because it is intermediate between fully black and fully white. Alternatively, because the erminette has both black and white feathers, you might classify the phenotype as codominant. Your decision will rest on whether you look at the whole animal (incomplete dominance) or at individual feathers (codominance). This is yet another instance where what you conclude is determined by how you observe.

To test the hypothesis that the erminette phenotype is a heterozygous phenotype, you could cross an erminette with either, or both, of the homozygotes. You should observe a $1:1$ ratio in the progeny of both crosses.

3.   a.   The original cross and results were

P long, white × round, red

F_1 oval purple

F_2 9 long, red	19 oval, red	8 round, white
15 long, purple	32 oval, purple	16 round, purple
8 long, white	16 oval, white	9 round, red
32 long	67 oval	32 round

The data show that, when the results are rearranged by shape, a $1:2:1$ ratio is observed for color within each shape category. Likewise, when the data are rearranged by color, a $1:2:1$ ratio is observed for shape within each color category:

9 long, red	15 long, purple	8 round, white
19 oval, red	32 oval, purple	16 oval, white
9 round, red	16 round, purple	8 long, white
37 red	63 purple	32 white

A $1:2:1$ ratio is observed when there is a heterozygous × heterozygous cross. Therefore, the original cross was a dihybrid cross. Both oval and purple must represent an incomplete dominant phenotype. Let L = long, L' = round, R = red and R' = white. The cross becomes

P $LL\ R'R' \times L'L'\ RR$

F_1 $LL'\ RR' \times LL'\ RR'$

F_2

$1/4\ LL$ —
- $1/4\ RR$ = $1/16$ long, red
- $1/2\ RR'$ = $1/8$ long, purple
- $1/4\ R'R'$ = $1/16$ long, white

$1/2\ LL'$ —
- $1/4\ RR$ = $1/8$ oval, red
- $1/2\ RR'$ = $1/4$ oval, purple
- $1/4\ R'R'$ = $1/8$ oval, white

$1/4\ L'L'$ —
- $1/4\ RR$ = $1/16$ round, red
- $1/2\ RR'$ = $1/8$ round, purple
- $1/4\ R'R'$ = $1/16$ round, white

b. A long, purple × oval, purple cross is as follows:

P $LL\ RR' \times LL'\ RR'$

F_1

$1/2\ LL$ —
- $1/4\ RR$ = $1/8$ long, red
- $1/2\ RR'$ = $1/4$ long, purple
- $1/4\ R'R'$ = $1/8$ long, white

$1/2\ LL'$ —
- $1/4\ RR$ = $1/8$ oval, red
- $1/2\ RR'$ = $1/4$ oval, purple
- $1/4\ R'R'$ = $1/8$ oval, white

4.   The easy way to solve this problem is to note that the Himalayan phenotype is observed only in homozygotes. Because one parent does not have the Himalayan allele, it will be impossible to obtain progeny that are homozygous for it. The answer is **e.**, 0 percent.

The more scholarly approach to this problem is to look at the progeny and their ratio before concluding that Himalayan will not be observed. The progeny are

1 C^+C^{ch} full color   1 $C^{ch}C^{ch}$ chinchilla

1 C^+C^h full color   1 $C^{ch}C^h$ chinchilla

5.   **a.**   You could begin this problem using one of several assumptions. Only one will be right, but there is no way to know in advance which that will be. The correct assumption is that there is one gene, with multiple alleles.

	Parents	Progeny	Conclusion
Cross 1:	*ba* × *ba* →	3 *b*– : 1 *aa*	black is dominant to albino
Cross 2:	*bs* × *aa* →	1 *ba* : 1 *sa*	black is dominant to sepia
Cross 3:	*ca* × *ca* →	3 *c*– : 1 *aa*	cream is dominant to albino
Cross 4:	*sa* × *ca* →	1 *ca* : 2 *s*– : 1 *aa*	sepia is dominant to albino
Cross 5:	*bc* × *aa* →	1 *ba* : 1 *ca*	black is dominant to cream
Cross 6:	*bs* × *c*– →	1 *b*– : 1 *s*–	black is dominant to sepia
Cross 7:	*bs* × *s*– →	1 *b*– : 1 *s*–	black is dominant to cream
Cross 8:	*bc* × *sc* →	2 *b*– : 1 *sc* : 1 *cc*	sepia is dominant to cream
Cross 9:	*sc* × *sc* →	3 *s*– : 1 *cc*	sepia is dominant to cream
Cross 10:	*ca* × *aa* →	1 *ca* : 1 *aa*	cream is dominant to albino

The order of dominance is $b > s > c > a$.

   b.   The cross between parents is *bs* × *bc*. The progeny are

1 *bb* black   1 *bc* black

1 *bs* black   1 *sc* sepia

6.   Both codominance (=) and classical dominance (>) are present in the multiple allelic series for blood type: $A = B$, $A > O$, $B > O$.

	Parents' Phenotype	Parents' Possible Genotypes	Parents' Possible Children
a.	AB × O	*AB* × *OO*	*AO, BO*
b.	A × O	*AA* or *AO* × *OO*	*AO, OO*
c.	A × AB	*AA* or *AO* × *AB*	*AA, AB, AO, BO*
d.	O × O	*OO* × *OO*	*OO*

The children are

Phenotype	Possible Genotypes
1. O	OO
2. A	AA, AO
3. B	BB, BO
4. AB	AB

Using the assumption that each set of parents had to have had one child, the following combinations are the only ones that will work as a solution.

Parents	Child
a. AB × O	3. B
b. A × O	2. A
c. A × AB	4. AB
d. O × O	1. O

7. M and N are codominant alleles. The rhesus group is determined by classically dominant alleles. The ABO alleles are mixed codominance and classical dominance (see Problem 6).

Person	Blood Group			Obligate	Paternal	Donation
Husband	O	M	Rh$^+$	O	M	R or r
Wife's lover	AB	MN	Rh$^-$	A or B	M or N	r
Wife	A	N	Rh$^+$	-	-	-
Child 1	O	MN	Rh$^+$	O	M	R or r
Child 2	A	N	Rh$^+$	A or O	N	R or r
Child 3	A	MN	Rh$^-$	A or O	M	r

The wife is $AO\ NN\ Rr$. Only the husband could donate O to child 1. Only the lover could donate A and N to child 2. Both the husband and the lover could have donated the necessary alleles to child 3.

8. The key to solving this problem is in the statement that breeders cannot develop a pure-breeding stock and that a cross of two platinum foxes results in some normal progeny. Platinum must be dominant to normal color and heterozygous (Aa). An 82 : 38 ratio is very close to a 2 : 1. Because a 1 : 2 : 1 ratio is expected in a heterozygous cross, one genotype is nonviable. It must be the AA, homozygous platinum, genotype that is nonviable, because the homozygous recessive genotype is normal color (aa). Therefore, the platinum allele is a pleiotropic allele that

governs coat color in the heterozygous state and is a recessive lethal in the homozygous state.

9. **a.** Because Pelger crossed with normal results in two phenotypes in a $1:1$ ratio, either Pelger or normal is heterozygous (Aa) and the other is homozygous (aa) recessive. The problem states that normal is true breeding, or, aa. Pelger must be Aa.

   b. The cross of two Pelger rabbits results in three phenotypes. This means that the Pelger anomaly is dominant to normal. This cross is $Aa \times Aa$, with an expected ratio of $1:2:1$. Because the normal must be aa, the extremely abnormal progeny must be AA. There were only 39 extremely abnormal progeny because the others died before birth.

   c. The Pelger allele is pleiotropic. In the heterozygous state it is dominant for nuclear segmentation of white blood cells. In the homozygous state it is a recessive lethal.
   You could look for the nonsurviving fetuses in utero. Because the hypothesis of embryonic death of the homozygous dominant predicts a one-fourth reduction in litter size, you could also do an extensive statistical analysis of litter size, comparing normal × normal with Pelger × Pelger.

   d. By analogy with rabbits, the absence of a homozygous Pelger anomaly in humans can be explained as recessive lethality. Alternatively, because 1 in 1000 births results in a Pelger anomaly, a heterozygous × heterozygous mating would be expected in only 1 of 1 million ($1/1000 \times 1/1000$) matings, and only 1 in 4 of the progeny would be expected to be homozygous. Thus, the homozygous Pelger anomaly is expected in only 1 of 4 million births. This is extremely rare and might not be recognized.

   e. By analogy with rabbits, among the children of a man and a woman with the Pelger anomaly two-thirds of the surviving progeny would be expected to show the Pelger anomaly and one-third would be expected to be normal. The child who is homozygous for the Pelger allele would be expected to have severe skeletal defects if he survived until birth.

10. **a.** The sex ratio is expected to be $1:1$ but this was not observed. Approximately one-half of the males are missing.

   b. If the normal-looking female were heterozygous for an X-linked recessive allele that was lethal in either the homozygous or the hemizygous state, then all the female progeny and one-half of the male progeny would survive.

c. In order to test this explanation, assume that the original cross was $Aa \times AY$. One-half of the females from this cross should be heterozygous and one-half should be homozygous. These F_1 females could be crossed individually with normal males and the sex ratio of the progeny could be determined for each cross.

11. Note that a cross of the short-bristled female with a normal male results in two phenotypes with regard to bristles and an abnormal sex ratio of 2 females : 1 male. Furthermore, all the males are normal, while the females are normal and short in equal numbers. Whenever the sexes differ with respect to phenotype among the progeny, an X-linked gene is involved. Because only the normal phenotype is observed in males, the short-bristled phenotype must be heterozygous, and the allele must be a recessive lethal. Thus the first cross was $Aa \times aY$.

Long-bristled females (aa) were crossed with long-bristled males (aY). All their progeny would be expected to be long-bristled (aa or aY).

Short-bristled females (Aa) were crossed with long-bristled males (aY). The progeny expected are

1 Aa short-bristled females   1 aY long-bristled males

1 aa long-bristled females   1 AY nonviable

12. In order to do this problem, you need first to restate the information provided. The following two genes are independently assorting:

hh = hairy ss = no effect

Hh = hairless Ss suppresses Hh, giving hairy

HH = lethal SS = lethal

a. The cross is $Hh\ Ss \times Hh\ Ss$. Because this is a typical dihybrid cross, the expected ratio is $9:3:3:1$. However, the problem cannot be worked in this simple fashion because of the epistatic relationship of these two genes. Therefore, the following approach should be used.

For the H gene, you expect $1/4\ HH : 1/2\ Hh : 1/4\ hh$. For the S gene, you expect $1/4\ SS : 1/2\ Ss : 1/4\ ss$. To get the final ratios, multiple the frequency of the first genotype by the frequency of the second genotype.

$1/4\ HH$————— all progeny die regardless of the S gene

$2/4\ Hh$ ⟨
　　　　——$1/4\ SS$ = $2/16\ Hh\ SS$ die
　　　　——$1/2\ Ss$ = $4/16\ Hh\ Ss$ hairy
　　　　——$1/4\ ss$ = $2/16\ Hh\ ss$ hairless

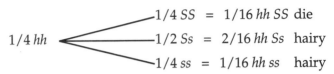

Of the 9 living progeny, the ratio of hairy to hairless is 7 : 2.

b. This cross is *Hh ss* × *Hh Ss*. A 1 : 2 : 1 ratio is expected for the *H* gene and a 1 : 1 ratio is expected for the *S* gene.

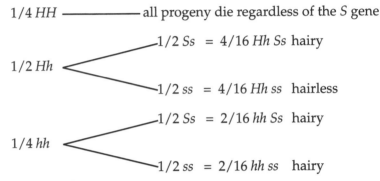

Of the 12 living progeny, the ratio of hairy to hairless is 2 : 1.

13. Note that the F$_2$ are in a 9 : 6 : 1 ratio. This indicates a dihybrid cross in which *A– bb* has the same appearance as *aa B–*. Let the disc phenotype be the result of *A– B–* and the long phenotype be the result of *aa bb*. The crosses are

    P   *AA BB* (disc) × *aa bb* (long)

    F$_1$ *Aa Bb* (disc)

    F$_2$ 9 *A– B–* disc

          3 *aa B–* sphere

          3 *A– bb* sphere

          1 *aa bb*   long

14. The suggestion from the data is that the two albino lines had defects in two different genes. When the extracts from the two lines were placed in the same test tube, they were capable of producing color because the gene product of one line was capable of compensating for the absence of a gene product from the second line.

a. The most obvious control is to cross the two pure-breeding lines. The cross would be *AA bb* × *aa BB*. The progeny will be *Aa Bb* and all should be reddish purple. Alternatively, grind up leaves from each line separately and see if they become red.

b. The most likely explanation is that the red pigment is produced by the action of at least two different gene products, for example:

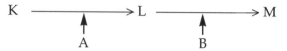

c. The genotypes of the two lines should be *AA bb* and *aa BB*.

d. The F_1 would all be *Aa Bb*, colored. The F_2 would be

9 *A– B–*   colored

3 *A– bb*   albino

3 *aa B–*   albino

1 *aa bb*   albino

15. a. This is yet another example where one phenotype in the parents gives rise to three phenotypes in the offspring. The frizzle fowl must be heterozygous with incomplete dominance. The cross is

P   *Aa × Aa*

F_1 1 *AA* : 2 *Aa* : 1 *aa*

The frizzle is *Aa*, with normal and wooly being homozygotes.

b. In order to produce only frizzle fowl, all crosses should involve a normal × woolly.

16. a. The second generation indicates that Marfan's syndrome is caused by a dominant autosomal allele.

b. The pedigree exhibits pleiotropy and variable expressivity. Reduced penetrance is not evident.

c. The pleiotropy indicates that a gene product that exists in a number of different organs is defective. The variable expressivity is due to epistasis by one or more other genes.

17. The data indicate that white is dominant to solid purple. Note that the F_2 are in a 12 : 3 : 1 ratio. In order to achieve such a ratio, epistasis must be involved.

a. Because a modified 9 : 3 : 3 : 1 ratio was obtained in the F_2, the F_1 had to be a double heterozygote. Solid purple occurred at one-third the rate of white, which means that it will be in the form of either *D– ee* or *dd E–*. In order to achieve a double heterozygote in the F_1, the original white parent also has to be either *D– ee* or *dd E–*.

Arbitrarily assume that the original cross was *DD ee* (white) × *dd EE* (purple). The F$_1$ would all be *Dd Ee*. The F$_2$ would be

9 *D– E–*	white, by definition
3 *dd E–*	purple, by definition
3 *D– ee*	white, by logical deduction
1 *dd ee*	spotted purple, by logical deduction

Under these assumptions, *D* blocks the expression of both *E* and *e*. The *d* allele has no effect on the expression of *E* and *e*. *E* results in solid purple, while *e* results in spotted purple. It would also be correct, of course, to assume the opposite set of epistatic relationships (*E* blocks the expression of *D* or *d*, *D* results in solid purple, and *d* results in spotted purple).

b. The cross is white × solid purple. While the solid purple genotype must be *dd E–*, as defined in part a, the white genotype can be one of several possibilities. Note that the progeny phenotypes are in a 1 : 2 : 1 ratio and that one of the phenotypes, spotted, must be *dd ee*. In order to achieve such an outcome, the purple genotype must be *dd Ee*. The white genotype of the parent must contain both a *D* and a *d* allele in order to produce both white (*D–*) and spotted plants (*dd*). At this point, the cross has been deduced to be *Dd – –* (white) × *dd Ee* (purple).

If the white plant is *EE*, the progeny will be

1/2 *Dd E–*	white
1/2 *dd E–*	solid purple

This was not observed. If the white plant is *Ee*, the progeny will be

3/8 *Dd E–*	white
1/8 *Dd ee*	white
3/8 *dd E–*	solid purple
1/8 *dd ee*	spotted purple

The phenotypes were observed, but in a different ratio. If the white plant is *ee*, the progeny will be

1/4 *Dd Ee*	white
1/4 *Dd ee*	white

1/4 $dd\ Ee$ solid purple

1/4 $dd\ ee$ spotted purple

This was observed in the progeny. Therefore, the parents were $Dd\ ee$ (white) × $dd\ Ee$ (purple).

18. **a. and b.** Crosses 1–3 show a 3 : 1 ratio, indicating that brown, black and yellow are all alleles of one gene. Crosses 4–6 show a modified 9 : 3 : 3 : 1 ratio, indicating that at least two genes are involved. Those crosses also indicate that the presence of color is dominant to its absence. Furthermore, epistasis must be involved for there to be a modified 9 : 3 : 3 : 1 ratio.

By looking at the F_1 of crosses 1–3, the following allelic dominance relationships can be seen easily: black > brown > yellow. Arbitrarily assign the following genotypes for homozygotes: $B^l B^l$ = black, $B^r B^r$ = brown, $B^y B^y$ = yellow.

By looking at the F_2 of crosses 4–6, a white phenotype is composed of two categories: the double homozygote and one class of the mixed homozygote-heterozygote. Let lack of color be caused by cc. Color will therefore be $C-$.

Cross	Parents	F_1	F_2
1.	$B^r B^r\ CC$ × $B^y B^y\ CC$	$B^r B^y\ CC$	3 $B^r- CC$:1 $B^y B^y\ CC$
2.	$B^l B^l\ CC$ × $B^r B^r\ CC$	$B^l B^r\ CC$	3$B^l - CC$:1 $B^r B^r\ CC$
3.	$B^l B^l\ CC$ × $B^y B^y\ CC$	$B^l B^y\ CC$	3 $B^l- CC$:1 $B^y B^y\ CC$
4.	$B^l B^l\ cc$ × $B^y B^y\ CC$	$B^l B^y\ Cc$	9 $B^l- C-$: 3 $B^y B^y\ C-$:3 $B^l- cc$: 1 $B^y B^y\ cc$
5.	$B^l B^l\ cc$ × $B^r B^r\ CC$	$B^l B^r\ Cc$	9 $B^l- C-$: 3 $B^r B^r\ C-$:3 $B^l- cc$: 1 $B^r B^r\ cc$
6.	$B^l B^l\ CC$ × $B^y B^y\ cc$	$B^l B^y\ Cc$	9 $B^l- C-$: 3 $B^y B^y\ C-$:3 $B^l- cc$: 1 $B^y B^y\ cc$

19.   Whenever a cross involving two deviants from normal results in a normal phenotype, more than one gene is involved in producing the phenotype, the normal is dominant to the deviation, and the two parents are abnormal for different genes. Thus, one parent could be $aa\ BB$, and the other parent could be $AA\ bb$. All offspring would be $Aa\ Bb$ (normal). The doubly heterozygous offspring have one copy of a functional allele for each gene, whereas each of the two parents is lacking a functional allele for one of the genes.

20.   **a.** To solve this problem you will have to use a trial-and-error approach.

The first decision regards the number of genes involved. Cross 2 tells you that there are at least two genes because white × white yields a new phenotype. Cross 5, however, indicates that there are at least three genes involved because a 1 : 7 ratio is not observed with two genes.

Look at cross 1. The two lines cannot compensate for each other, suggesting a shared homozygous defective gene.

Compare crosses 2 and 3. Lines 1 and 3 can compensate for each other's defects but lines 2 and 3 cannot. This suggests that line 2 shares a defective homozygous gene with line 3 and that line 1 is normal for the defective gene seen in line 3 but not in line 2.

At this point, you must arbitrarily make some assumptions and test them against the results. Let the three genes involved be A/a, B/b and D/d. You could assume, for instance, that lines 1 and 2 share a defect in gene A/a, and that lines 2 and 3 share a defect in B/b. However, if line 3 can compensate for line 1 but not for line 2, there must be an additional defect in line 2. Thus far, we have determined the genotypes of the lines to be

line 1:   *aa   BB*   ??

line 2:   *aa   bb   dd*

line 3:   *AA bb   DD*

Because lines 1 and 2 cannot produce color, line 1 must be *aa BB dd*. Now the crosses can be explained.

Cross 1: *aa BB dd* × *aa bb dd* →	all *aa Bb dd*	white
Cross 2: *aa BB dd* × *AA bb DD*→	all *Aa Bb Dd*	red
Cross 3: *aa bb dd* × *AA bb DD*→	all *Aa bb Dd*	white
Cross 4: *Aa Bb Dd* × *aa BB dd* →	1/8 *Aa Bb Dd*	red
	1/8 *Aa Bb dd*	white
	1/8 *aa Bb Dd*	white
	1/8 *aa Bb dd*	white
	1/8 *Aa BB Dd*	red
	1/8 *Aa BB dd*	white
	1/8 *aa BB Dd*	white
	1/8 *aa BB dd*	white
Cross 5: *Aa Bb Dd* × *aa bb dd* →	1/8 *Aa Bb Dd*	red
	1/8 *Aa Bb dd*	white

	1/8 *Aa bb Dd*	white
	1/8 *Aa bb dd*	white
	1/8 *aa Bb Dd*	white
	1/8 *aa Bb dd*	white
	1/8 *aa bb Dd*	white
	1/8 *aa bb dd*	white
Cross 6: *Aa Bb Dd × AA bb DD* →	1/8 *AA Bb Dd*	red
	1/8 *Aa Bb Dd*	red
	1/8 *AA Bb DD*	red
	1/8 *Aa Bb DD*	red
	1/8 *AA bb DD*	white
	1/8 *Aa bb DD*	white
	1/8 *AA bb Dd*	white
	1/8 *Aa bb Dd*	white

    b. The cross is *Aa Bb Dd × Aa bb Dd*. The red progeny will have to be *A– B– D–*, which equals $(3/4)(1/2)(3/4) = 9/32$.

21.   The first step in each cross is to write as much of the genotype as possible from the phenotype.

Cross 1: A– B– × aa bb   →   1 *A– B–* : 2 ?- ?- : 1 *aa bb*

Because the double recessive appears, the blue parent must be *Aa Bb*. The two purple then must be *Aa bb* and *aa Bb*.

Cross 2:   ?? ?? × ?? ??   →   1 *A– B–* : 2 ?? ?? : 1 *aa bb*

The two parents must be, in either order, *Aa bb* and *aa Bb*. The two purple progeny must be the same. The blue progeny are *Aa Bb*.

Cross 3:   *A– B– × A– B–* →   3 *A– B–* : 1 ?? ??

The only conclusions possible here are that one parent is either *AA* or *BB* and the other parent is *Bb* if the first is *AA* or *Aa* if the first is *BB*.

Cross 4:   *A– B– ×* ?? ??   →   3 *A– B–* : 4 ?? ?? : 1 *aa bb*

The purple parent can be either *Aa bb* or *aa Bb* for this answer. Assume the purple parent is *Aa bb*. The blue parent must be *Aa Bb*. The progeny are

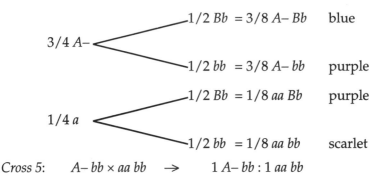

$1/2\ Bb\ = 3/8\ A\!-Bb$ blue

$3/4\ A\!-$

$1/2\ bb\ = 3/8\ A\!-bb$ purple

$1/2\ Bb\ = 1/8\ aa\ Bb$ purple

$1/4\ a$

$1/2\ bb\ = 1/8\ aa\ bb$ scarlet

Cross 5: $A\!-bb \times aa\ bb$ $\rightarrow$ $1\ A\!-bb : 1\ aa\ bb$

As written this is a testcross for gene A/a. The purple parent and progeny are $Aa\ bb$. Alternatively, the purple parent and progeny could be $aa\ Bb$.

22. The F_1 progeny of cross 1 indicate that sun-red is dominant to pink. The F_2 progeny, which are approximately in a 3 : 1 ratio, support this. The same pattern is seen in crosses 2 and 3, with sun-red dominant to orange and orange dominant to pink. Thus, we have a multiple allelic series with sun-red > orange > pink. In all three crosses, the parents must be homozygous.

If c^{sr} = sun-red, c^o = orange, and c^p = pink, then the crosses and the results are

	Parents	F_1	F_2
Cross 1.	$c^{sr}c^{sr} \times c^p c^p$	$c^{sr}c^p$	$3\ c^{sr}\!- : 1\ c^p c^p$
Cross 2.	$c^o c^o \times c^{sr}c^{sr}$	$c^{sr}c^o$	$3\ c^{sr}\!- : 1\ c^o c^o$
Cross 3.	$c^o c^o \times c^p c^p$	$c^o c^p$	$3\ c^o\!- : 1\ c^p c^p$

Cross 4 presents a new situation. The color of the F_1 differs from that of either parent, suggesting that two separate genes are involved. An alternative explanation is either codominance or incomplete dominance. If either codominance or incomplete dominance is involved, then the F_2 will appear in a 1 : 2 : 1 ratio. If two genes are involved, then a 9 : 3 : 3 : 1 ratio, or some variant of it, will be observed. The progeny actually are in a 9 : 4 : 3 ratio. This means that two genes are involved and that there is epistasis. Furthermore, for three phenotypes to be present in the F_2, the two F_1 parents must have been heterozygous.

Let a stand for the scarlet gene and A for its colorless allele, and assume that there is a dominant allele, C, that blocks the expression of the gene that we have been studying to this point.

Cross 4:   P $c^o c^o\ AA \times CC\ aa$

$F_1\ Cc^o\ Aa$

F$_2$ 9 C– A– yellow

    3 C– aa scarlet

    3 $c^o c^o$ A– orange

    1 $c^o c^o$ aa orange (epistasis, with c^o blocking the expression of aa).

23. a. P   *AA* (agouti) × *aa* (nonagouti)

    gametes *A* and *a*

    F$_1$ *Aa* (agouti)

    gametes *A* and *a*

    F$_2$ 1 *AA* (agouti) : 2 *Aa* (agouti) : 1 *aa* (nonagouti)

b. P   *BB* (wild type) × *bb* (cinnamon)

    gametes *B* and *b*

    F$_1$ *Bb* (wild type)

    gametes *B* and *b*

    F$_2$ 1 *BB* (wild type) : 2 *Bb* (wild type) : 1 bb (cinnamon)

c. P   *AA bb* (cinnamon or brown agouti) × *aa BB* (black nonagouti)

    gametes *Ab* and *aB*

    F$_1$ *Aa Bb* (wild type or black agouti)

d. 9 *A– B–* black agouti

    3 *aa B–* black nonagouti

    3 *A–* bb cinnamon

    1 aa *bb* chocolate

e. P   *AA bb* (cinnamon) × *aa BB* (black nonagouti)

    gametes *Ab* and *aB*

    F$_1$ *Aa Bb* (wild type):

    gametes *AB, Ab, aB,* and *ab*

    F$_2$ 9 *A– B–* wild type

            1 *AA BB*

            2 *Aa BB*

            2 *AA Bb*

           4 *Aa Bb*

       3 *aa B–* black nonagouti:

           1 *aa BB*

           2 *aa Bb*

       3 *A– bb* cinnamon:

           1 *AA bb*

           2 *Aa bb*

           1 *aa bb* chocolate

f. P   *Aa Bb* × *AA bb*   *Aa Bb* × *aa BB*

       (wild type) (cinnamon)   (wild type) (black nonagouti)

     F_1 1 *AA Bb* wild type   1 *Aa BB* wild type

            1 *Aa Bb* wild type   1 *Aa Bb* wild type

            1 *AA bb* cinnamon   1 *aa BB* black nonagouti

            1 *Aa bb* cinnamon   1 *aa Bb* black nonagouti

g. P   *Aa Bb* × *aa bb*

       (wild type) (chocolate)

     F_1 1 *Aa Bb* wild type

            1 *Aa bb* cinnamon

            1 *aa Bb* black nonagouti

            1 *aa bb* chocolate

h. To be albino, the mice must be *cc*, but the genotype with regard to the *A/a* and *B/b* genes can be determined only by realizing that the wild type is *AA BB* and looking at the F_2 progeny.

Cross 1: P   *cc ?? ??* × *CC AA BB*

        F_1 *Cc A– B–*

        F_2 87 wild type   *C– A– B–*

             32 cinnamon   *C– A– bb*

             39 albino   *cc ?? ??*

    For cinnamon to appear in the F_2, the F_1 parents must be *Bb*. Because the wild type is *BB*, the albino parent must have been bb. Now the F_1 parent can be written *Cc A– Bb*. With such a cross, one-fourth of the progeny would be expected to be albino (*cc*), which is what is observed. Three-fourths of the remaining progeny would be black, either agouti or nonagouti, and one-fourth would be either cinnamon, if agouti, or chocolate, if nonagouti. Because chocolate is not observed, the F_1 parent must not carry the allele for nonagouti. Therefore, the F_1 parent is *AA* and the original albino must have been *cc AA bb*.

Cross 2: P   *cc ?? ?? × CC AA BB*

　　　　F_1 *Cc A– B–*

　　　　F_2 62 wild type   *C– A– B–*

　　　　　　 18 albino   *cc ?? ??*

This is a 3 : 1 ratio, indicating that only one gene is heterozygous in the F_1. That gene must be *Cc*. Therefore, the albino parent must be *cc AA BB*.

Cross 3: P   *cc ?? ?? × CC AA BB*

　　　　F_1 *Cc A– B–*

　　　　F_2 96 wild type   *C– A– B–*

　　　　　　 30 black   *C– aa B–*

　　　　　　 41 albino   *cc ?? ??*

For a black nonagouti phenotype to appear in the F_2, the F_1 must have been heterozygous for the A/a gene. Therefore, its genotype can be written *Cc Aa B–* and the albino parent must be *cc aa ??*. Among the colored F_2 a 3 : 1 ratio is observed, indicating that only one of the two genes is heterozygous in the F_1. Therefore, the F_1 must be *Cc Aa BB* and the albino parent must be *cc aa BB*.

Cross 4: P   *cc ?? ?? × CC AA BB*

　　　　F_1 *Cc A– B–*

　　　　F_2 287 wild type   *C– A– B–*

　　　　　　　 86 black   *C– aa B–*

　　　　　　　 92 cinnamon   *C– A– bb*

　　　　　　　 29 chocolate   *C– aa bb*

　　　　　　 164 albino   *C– ?? ??*

To get chocolate F_2 progeny the F_1 parent must be heterozygous for all genes and the albino parent must be *cc aa bb*.

24. To solve this problem, first restate the information:

      A– yellow   *A*– *R*– gray

      R– black   *aa rr* white

The cross is gray × yellow, or *A*– *R*– × *A*– *rr*. The F_1 progeny are

      3/8 yellow   1/8 black

      3/8 gray   1/8 white

To achieve white, both parents must carry an *r* and an *a* allele. Now the cross can be rewritten as *Aa Rr* × *Aa rr*.

25. **a.** P single-combed × walnut-combed

         (*rr pp*)   (*RR PP*)

   F_1 *Rr Pp*   walnut

   F_2 9 *R*– *P*– walnut

       3 *rr P*– pea

       3 *R*– *pp* rose

       1 *rr pp*   single

   b. P walnut-combed × rose-combed

         (*R*– *P*–)   (*R*– *pp*)

   F_1 3/8 *R*– *pp*   rose

       3/8 *R*– *P*–   walnut

       1/8 *rr P*–   pea

       1/8 *rr pp*   single

The 3 *R*– : 1 *rr* ratio indicates that the parents were heterozygous for the *R/r* gene. The 1 *P*– : 1 *pp* ratio indicates a testcross for this gene. Therefore, the parents were *Rr Pp* and *Rr pp*.

   c. P walnut-combed × rose-combed

         (*R*– *P*–)   (*R*– *pp*)

   F_1 walnut

          (*R*– *P*–)

To get this result, one of the parents must be homozygous R, but both need not be, and the walnut parent must be homozygous PP.

d. $RR\ PP,\ Rr\ PP,\ RR\ Pp,\ Rr\ Pp$

26. Notice that the F_1 shows a difference in phenotype correlated with sex. At least one of the two genes is X-linked. The F_2 ratio suggests independent assortment between the two genes. Because purple is present in the F_1, the F_2 white-eyed male must have at least one P allele. The presence of white eyes in the F_2 suggests that the F_1 was heterozygous for pigment production, which means that the male also must carry the a allele. A start on the parental genotypes can now be made:

P $AA\ pp \times a-P-$, where "$-$" could be either a Y chromosome or a second allele.

The question now is, which gene is X-linked? If the A/a gene is X-linked, the cross is

P $AA\ pp \times a/Y\ PP$

F_1 $Aa\ Pp \times A/Y\ Pp$

All F_2 females will inherit the A allele from their father. Under this circumstance, no white-eyed females would be observed. Therefore, the A/a gene cannot be X-linked. The cross is

P $AA\ pp \times aa\ P/Y$

F_1 $Aa\ Pp$ purple-eyed females

   $Aa\ p/Y$ red-eyed males

F_2	females		males	
	$3/8\ A\!-Pp$	purple	$3/8\ A\!-P/Y$	purple
	$3/8\ A\!-pp$	red	$3/8\ A\!-p/Y$	red
	$1/8\ aa\ Pp$	white	$1/8\ aa\ P/Y$	white
	$1/8\ aa\ pp$	white	$1/8\ aa\ p/Y$	white

27. The results indicate that two genes are involved (modified $9:3:3:1$ ratio), with white blocking the expression of color by the other gene. The ratio of white : color is $3:1$, indicating that the F_1 is heterozygous (Ww). Among colored dogs, the ratio is 3 black : 1 brown, indicating that black is dominant to brown and the F_1 is heterozygous (Bb). The original brown dog is $ww\ bb$ and the original white dog is $WW\ BB$. The F_1 progeny are $Ww\ Bb$ and the F_2 progeny are

9 *W– B–*	white	3 *ww B–*	black
3 *W– bb*	white	1 *ww bb*	brown

28.

Cross	Results	Conclusion
A– C– R– × *aa cc RR*	50% colored	Colored or white will depend on the *A* and *C* genes. Because half the seeds are colored, one of the two genes is heterozygous.
A– C– R– × *aa CC rr*	25% colored	Color depends on *A* and *R* in this cross. If only one gene were heterozygous, 50% would be colored. Therefore, both *A* and *R* are heterozygous. The seed is *Aa CC Rr*.
A– C– R– × *AA cc rr*	50% colored	This supports the above conclusion.

29. a. The *AA CC RR prpr* parent produces pigment that is not converted to purple. The phenotype is red. The *aa cc rr PrPr* does not produce pigment. The phenotype is yellow.

b. The F_1 will be *Aa Cc Rr Prpr*, which will produce pigment. The pigment will be converted to purple.

c. The difficult way to determine the phenotypic ratios is to do a branch diagram, yielding the following results.

81/256 *A– C– R– Pr–*	purple		9/256 *aa C– R– Pr–*	yellow
27/256 *A– C– R– prpr*	red		9/256 *aa C– R– prpr*	yellow
27/256 *A– C– rr Pr–*	yellow		9/256 *aa C– rr Pr–*	yellow
9/256 *A– C– rr prp*	yellow		3/256 *aa C– rr prpr*	yellow
27/256 *A– cc R– Pr–*	yellow		27/256 *aa cc R– Pr–*	yellow
9/256 *A– cc R– prpr*	yellow		3/256 *aa cc R– prpr*	yellow
9/256 *A– cc rr Pr–*	yellow		3/256 *aa cc rr Pr–*	yellow
3/256 *A– cc rr prpr*	yellow		1/256 *aa cc rr prpr*	yellow

The final phenotypic ratio is 81 purple : 27 red : 148 yellow.

The easier method of determining phenotypic ratios is to recognize that four genes are involved in a heterozygous ×

heterozygous cross. Purple requires a dominant allele for each gene. The probability of all dominant alleles is $(3/4)^4 = 81/256$. Red results from all dominant alleles except for the Pr/pr gene. The probability of that outcome is $(3/4)^3(1/4) = 27/256$. The remainder of the outcomes will produce no pigment, resulting in yellow. The probability is $256 - 81 - 27 = 148$.

d. The cross is $Aa\ Cc\ Rr\ Prpr \times aa\ cc\ rr\ prpr$. Again, either a branch diagram or the easier method can be used. The final probabilities are

purple $= (1/2)^4 = 1/16$

red $= (1/2)^3(1/2) = 1/16$

yellow $= 1 - 1/16 - 1/16 = 14/16$

30. a. The cross is

P $td\ su$ (wild type) $\times td^+\ su^+$ (wild type)

F$_1$ 1 $td\ su$ wild type

   1 $td\ su^+$ requires tryptophan

   1 $td^+\ su^+$ wild type

   1 $td^+\ su$ wild type

b. 1 tryptophan-dependent : 3 tryptophan-independent

31. a. This type of epistasis is called suppression.

b. I. $Bb\ Ee,\ Bb\ Ee$

II. $bb\ Ee,\ Bb\ Ee,\ --ee$, $bb\ E-,\ Bb\ E-,\ bb\ Ee$

III. $Bb\ E-,\ b-ee,\ bb\ E-,\ Bb\ E-,\ bb\ E-,\ Bb\ E-,\ b-ee$

32. P $AA\ BB\ CC\ DD\ SS \times aa\ bb\ cc\ dd\ ss$

F$_1$ $Aa\ Bb\ Cc\ Dd\ Ss$

F_2

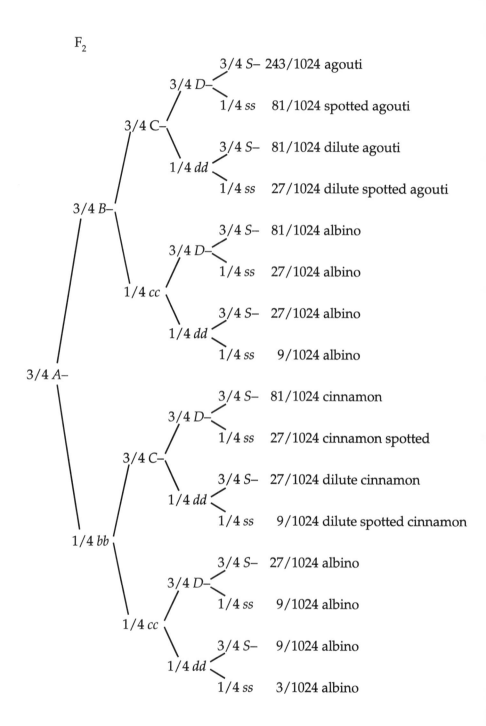

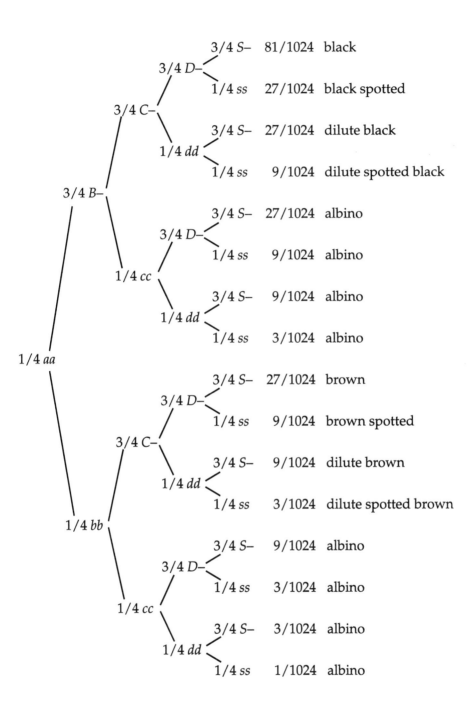

33.   **a. and b.**   The two starting lines are *ii DD MM WW* and *II dd mm ww*, and you are seeking *ii dd mm ww* . There are many ways to proceed, one of which follows below.

I   *ii DD MM WW* × *II dd mm ww*

II   *Ii Dd Mm Ww* × *Ii Dd Mm Ww*

III select *ii dd mm ww*, which has a probability of $(1/4)^4 = 1/256$.

c. and d.   In the first cross, all progeny chickens will be of the desired genotype. Therefore, the only problems are to be sure that progeny of both sexes are obtained for the second cross, which is relatively easy, and that enough females are obtained to make the time required for the desired genotype to appear feasible. Because chickens lay one to two eggs a day, the more females who are egg-laying, the faster the desired genotype will be obtained. In addition, it will be necessary to obtain a male and a female of the desired genotype in order to establish a pure breeding line.

Assume that each female will lay two eggs a day, that money is no problem and that excess males cause no problems. By hatching 200 eggs from the first cross, approximately 100 females will be available for the second cross. These 100 females will produce 200 eggs each day. Thus, in one week a total of 1,400 eggs will be produced. Of these 1,400 eggs, there will be approximately 700 of each sex. At a probability of 1/256, the desired genotype should be achieved 2.7 times for each sex within that first week.

34.   Pedigrees like this are quite common. They indicate lack of penetrance due to epistasis or environmental effects. Individual A must have the dominant autosomal gene.

35.   In cross 1, the following can be written immediately:

P   *M– D– ww* (dark reddish) × *mm ?? ??* (white with
yellowish spots)

F_1 1/2   *M– D– ww*   dark reddish

1/2   *M– dd ww*   light reddish

All progeny are colored, indicating that no W allele is present in the parents. Because the progeny are in a 1 : 1 ratio, only one of the genes in the parents is heterozygous. Also, the light reddish progeny, *dd*, indicates which gene that is. Therefore, the genotypes must be

P   *MM Dd ww* × *mm dd ww*

F$_1$ 1 *Mm Dd ww* : 1 *Mm dd ww*

In cross 2, the following can be written immediately:

P   *mm ?? ??* (white with yellowish spots) × *M– dd ww*

(light reddish)

F$_1$ 1/2   *M– ?? W–* white with reddish spots

1/4   *M– D– ww* dark reddish

1/4   *M– dd ww* light reddish

For light and dark plants to appear in a 1 : 1 ratio among the colored plants, one of the parents must be heterozygous *Dd*. The ratio of white to colored is 1 : 1, a testcross, so one of the parents is heterozygous *Ww*. All plants are reddish, indicating that one parent is homozygous *MM*. Therefore, the genotypes are

P   *mm Dd Ww* × *MM dd ww*

F$_1$ 1/2   *Mm Dd* (or *dd*) *Ww*

1/4   *Mm Dd ww*

1/4   *Mm dd ww*

Note that two genotypes were determined for white plants with yellowish spots in the two crosses: *mm dd ww* and *mm Dd ww*. Both are correct. Because the plants do not make pigment, the enhancer (*D–* or *dd*) gene is irrelevant to the phenotype.

36. a.   This is a dihybrid cross with only one phenotype in the F$_2$ being colored. The ratio of white to red indicates that the double recessive is not the colored phenotype. Instead, the general formula for color is represented by X– *yy*.

Let line 1 be *AA BB* and line 2 be *aa bb*. The F$_1$ is *Aa Bb*. Assume that *A* blocks color in line 1 and *bb* blocks color in line 2. The F$_1$ will be white because of the presence of *A*. The F$_2$ are

9 *A– B–*   white because of *A*

3 *A– bb*   white because of *A*

3 *aa B–*   red

1 *aa bb*   white because of *bb*

b.   *Cross 1: AA BB* × *Aa Bb* →   all *A– B–* white

Cross 2: aa bb × Aa Bb   →   1/4   *Aa Bb*   white

1/4   *Aa bb*   white

1/4   *aa bb*   white

1/4   *aa Bb*   red

37.   **a.**   Note that blue is always present, indicating *EE* (blue) in both parents. Because of the ratios that are observed neither *C* nor *D* is varying. In this case, the gene pairs that are involved are *A/a* and *B/b*. The F_1 is *Aa Bb* and the F_2 is

9 *A– B–*   blue + red, or purple

3 *A– bb*   blue + yellow, or green

3 *aa B–*   blue + white$_2$, or blue

1 *aa bb*   blue + white$_2$, or blue

     b.   Blue is not always present, indicating *Ee* in the F_1. Because green never appears, the F_1 must be *BB CC DD*. The F_1 is *Aa Ee*, and the F_2 is

9 *A– E–*   red + blue, or purple

3 *A– ee*   red + white$_1$, or red

3 *aa E–*   white$_2$ + blue, or blue

1 *aa ee*   white$_2$ + white$_1$, or white

     c.   Blue is always present, indicating that the F_1 is *EE*. No green appears, indicating that the F_1 is *BB*. The two genes involved are *A/a* and *D/d*. The F_2 is

9 *A– D–* blue + red + white$_4$, or purple

3 *A– dd*   blue + red, or purple

3 *aa D–*   blue + white$_2$ + white$_4$, or blue

1 *aa dd*   white$_2$ + blue + red, or purple

     d.   The presence of yellow indicates *bb ee* in the F_2. Therefore, the F_1 is *Bb Ee* and the F_2 is

9 *B– E–*   red + blue, or purple

3 *B– ee*   red + white$_1$, or red

3 *bb E–*   yellow + blue, or green

1 *bb ee*   yellow + white$_1$, or yellow

38. **a.** Begin by noting that cross 1 suggests that one gene is involved and that single is dominant to double. Cross 2 supports this conclusion. Now note that in crosses 3 and 4, a 1 : 1 ratio is seen in the progeny, suggesting that superdouble is an allele of both single and double. Superdouble must be heterozygous, however, and it must be dominant to both single and double. Because the heterozygous superdouble yields both single and double when crossed with the appropriate plant, it cannot be heterozygous for the dominant single allele. Therefore, it must be heterozygous for the recessive double allele. A multiple allelic series has been detected: superdouble > single > double.

For now, assume that only one gene is involved and attempt to rationalize the crosses with the assumptions made above.

Cross	Parents	Progeny	Conclusion
1	$A^S A^S \times A^D A^D$	$A^S A^D$	A^S is dominant to A^D
2	$A^S A^D \times A^S A^D$	$3 A^S - : 1 A^D A^D$	supports conclusion from cross 1
3	$A^D A^D \times A^{Sd} A^D$	$1 A^{Sd} A^D : 1 A^D A^D$	A^{Sd} is dominant to A^D
4	$A^S A^S \times A^{Sd} A^D$	$1 A^{Sd} A^S : 1 A^S A^D$	A^{Sd} is dominant to A^D
5	$A^D A^D \times A^{Sd} A^S$	$1 A^{Sd} A^D : 1 A^D A^S$	supports conclusion of heterozygous superdouble
6	$A^D A^D \times A^S A^D$	$1 A^D A^D : 1 A^D A^S$	supports conclusion of heterozygous superdouble

b. While this explanation does rationalize all of the crosses, it does not take into account either the female sterility or the origin of the superdouble plant from a double-flowered variety.

A number of genetic mechanisms could be proposed to explain the origin of superdouble from the double-flowered variety. Most of the mechanisms will be discussed in later chapters and so will not be mentioned here. However, it can safely be assumed at this point that, whatever the mechanism, it was aberrant enough to block the formation of the complex structure of the female flower from forming properly. Because of female sterility, no homozygote for superdouble can be observed.

39. **a.** All of the crosses suggest two independently assorting genes. However, that does not mean that there are a total of only two genes governing eye color. In fact, there are four genes controlling eye color that are being studied here. Let

> aa = defect in the yellow 1 line
>
> bb = defect in the yellow 2 line
>
> dd = defect in the brown line
>
> ee = defect in the orange line

The genotypes of each line are as follows

> yellow 1: *aa BB DD EE*
>
> yellow 2: *AA bb DD EE*
>
> brown: *AA BB dd EE*
>
> orange: *AA BB DD ee*

b.

P   *aa BB DD EE* × *AA bb DD EE*   yellow 1 × yellow 2

F_1 *Aa Bb Dd Ee*   red

F_2 9 *A– B– DD EE*   red

3 *aa B– DD EE*   yellow

3 *A– bb DD EE*   yellow

1 *aa bb DD EE*   yellow

P   *aa BB DD EE* × *AA BB dd EE*   yellow 1 × brown

F_1 *Aa BB Dd EE*   red

F_2 9 *A– BB D– EE*   red

3 *aa BB D– EE*   yellow

3 *A– BB dd EE*   brown

1 *aa BB dd EE*   yellow

P   *aa BB DD EE* × *AA BB DD ee*   yellow 1 × orange

F_1 *Aa BB DD Ee*   red

F_2 9 *A– BB DD E–*   red

3 *aa BB DD E–*   yellow

3 *A– BB DD ee*   orange

1 *aa BB DD ee*   orange

P   *AA bb DD EE* × *AA BB dd EE*   yellow 2 × brown

F_1 *AA Bb Dd EE*   red

   9 *AA B– D– EE*   red

   3 *AA bb D– EE*   yellow

   3 *AA B– dd EE*   brown

   1 *AA bb dd EE*   yellow

P   *AA bb DD EE × AA BB DD ee*   yellow 2 × orange

F_1 *AA Bb DD Ee*   red

   9 *AA B– DD E–*   red

   3 *AA bb DD E–*   yellow

   3 *AA B– DD ee*   orange

   1 *AA bb DD ee*   yellow

P   *AA BB dd EE × AA BB DD ee*   brown × orange

F_1 *AA BB Dd Ee*   red

F_2 9 *AA BB D– E–*   red

   3 *AA BB dd E–*   brown

   3 *AA BB D– ee*   orange

   1 *AA BB dd ee*   orange

c. When constructing a biochemical pathway, remember that the earliest gene that is defective in a pathway will determine the phenotype of a doubly defective genotype. Look at the following double-recessive homozygotes from the crosses. Notice that the double defect *dd ee* has the same phenotype as the defect *aa ee*. This suggests that the *E/e* gene functions earlier than do the *A/a* and *D/d* genes. Using this logic, the following table can be constructed:

Genotype	Phenotype	Conclusion
aa BB DD ee	orange	*E/e* functions before *A/a*
AA BB dd ee	orange	*E/e* functions before *D/d*
aa bb DD EE	yellow	*B/b* functions before *A/a*
AA bb DD ee	yellow	*B/b* functions before *E/e*
aa BB dd EE	yellow	*A/a* functions before *D/d*
AA bb dd EE	yellow	*B/b* functions before *D/d*

The genes function in the following sequence: *B, E, A, D*.
The metabolic path is:

$$yellow_2 \rightarrow orange \rightarrow yellow_1 \rightarrow brown \rightarrow red$$
$$\uparrow \qquad \uparrow \qquad \uparrow \qquad \uparrow$$
$$B \qquad E \qquad A \qquad D$$

40. **a.** A trihybrid cross would give a 63 : 1 ratio. Therefore, there are three R loci segregating in this cross.

b. P $R_1R_1 \; R_2R_2 \; R_3R_3 \times r_1r_1 \; r_2r_2 \; r_3r_3$

F_1 $R_1r_1 \; R_2r_2 \; R_3r_3$

F_2 27 $R_1- \; R_2- \; R_3-$ red

   9 $R_1- \; R_2- \; r_3r_3$ red

   9 $R_1- \; r_2r_2 \; R_3-$ red

   9 $r_1r_1 \; R_2- \; R_3-$ red

   3 $R_1- \; r_2r_2 \; r_3r_3$ red

   3 $r_1r_1 \; R_2- \; r_3r_3$ red

   3 $r_1r_1 \; r_2r_2 \; R_3-$ red

   1 $r_1r_1 \; r_2r_2 \; r_3r_3$ white

c. **1.** In order to obtain a 1 : 1 ratio, only one of the genes can be heterozygous. A representative cross would be $R_1r_1 \; r_2r_2 \; r_3r_3 \times r_1r_1 \; r_2r_2 \; r_3r_3$.

2. In order to obtain a 3 red : 1 white ratio, two alleles must be segregating and they cannot be within the same gene. A representative cross would be $R_1r_1 \; R_2r_2 \; r_3r_3 \times r_1r_1 \; r_2r_2 \; r_3r_3$.

3. In order to obtain a 7 red : 1 white ratio, three alleles must be segregating and they cannot be within the same gene. The cross would be $R_1r_1 \; R_2r_2 \; R_3r_3 \times r_1r_1 \; r_2r_2 \; r_3r_3$.

d. The formula is $1 - (1/2)^N$, where N = the number of loci that are segregating in the representative crosses above. In F_1 crosses, the formula is $1 - (1/2)^{2N}$, where N is the number of loci.

41. **a. and b.** The disorder is governed by an autosomal recessive allele and there are two genes that result in deaf-mutism.

I. *Aa BB × Aa BB, AA Bb × AA Bb*

II. Individuals 1, 3−6 : *A− BB*

Individuals 9, 10, 12–15 : *AA B–*

Individuals 2, 7 : *aa BB*

Individuals 8, 11 : *AA bb*

III. All *Aa Bb*

42.   a.   The first impression from the pedigree is that the gene causing blue sclera and brittle bones is pleiotropic with variable expressivity. If two genes were involved, it would be highly unlikely that all people with brittle bones also had blue sclera.

     b.   The allele appears to be an autosomal dominant.

     c.   Both incomplete penetrance and variable expressivity are demonstrated in the pedigree. Individuals II-4, II-16, III-2 and III-14 have descendants with the disorder although they do not themselves express the disorder. Therefore, 4/20 people have the gene, but it is not penetrant in them. That is an 80% penetrance. Of the 16 individuals who have the allele expressed in their phenotype, 9 do not have brittle bones. Usually, expressivity is put in terms of none, variable and highly variable, rather than expressed as percentages.

43.   a. and b.   Assuming that both the Brown and the Van Scoy lines were homozygous, the parental cross suggests that hygienic behavior is recessive to nonhygienic. The F_1 cross yielded a 1 : 2 : 1 ratio, suggesting a single gene. A consideration of the specific behavior, however, initially causes some puzzlement.

     If the behavior is classified as either hygienic or nonhygienic, with removal of dead pupae as the criterion for hygienic behavior, nonhygienic behavior is dominant to hygienic behavior. This supports the conclusion from the parental cross.

     If the removal of dead pupae from uncapped compartments is the criterion for hygienic behavior, then hygienic behavior is classically dominant to nonhygienic behavior.

     The suggestion from all these data is that there may be two genes acting epistatically. One involves uncapping and one involves removal of dead pupae. If this is true, uncapping and removal of dead pupae, two behaviors that normally go together in the Brown line, have been separated in the F_2 progeny. Those bees that lack uncapping behavior are still able to express removal of dead pupae if environmental conditions are such that they do not need to uncap a compartment first.

Let: U = no uncapping, u = capping, R = no removal,
r = removal
P $uurr$ × $UURR$
(Brown)   (Van Scoy)
F_1 $UuRr$ × $uurr$
F_2

nonhygienic $\begin{bmatrix} 1/4 \ UuRr & & 1/4 \ uuRr & \text{uncapping} \\ 1/4 \ Uurr\text{–removal} & 1/4 \ uurr & \text{hygienic} \end{bmatrix}$

TIPS ON PROBLEM SOLVING

Whenever a cross involving two deviants from normal results in a normal phenotype, more than one gene is involved in producing the phenotype, the normal is dominant to the deviation, and the two parents are abnormal for different genes (see Problem 39).

Whenever the sexes differ with respect to phenotype among the progeny, an X-linked gene is involved (see Problem 10).

If two deviants from normal are crossed and the males are wild type, two genes are involved, the deviation is recessive and the gene that is deviant in the female is autosomal. (see Problem 19).

If the F_1 phenotype differs from that of either parent, two separate genes may be involved. An alternative explanation is either codominance or incomplete dominance. If either codominance or incomplete dominance is involved, then the F_2 progeny will appear in a 1 : 2 : 1 ratio. If two genes are involved, then a 9 : 3 : 3 : 1 ratio, or some variant of it, will be observed (see Problems 2 and 3).

Multiple alleles show a 1 : 2 : 1 ratio or some modification of that ratio. Multiple genes show a 9 : 3 : 3 : 1 ratio or some modification of that ratio (see Problems 2 and 3).

SELF-TEST

1. Discuss the difference between dominance and epistasis.

2. What are the factors that lead to a lack of penetrance?

3. What are the factors that lead to variable expressivity?

4. How can you distinguish between multiple alleles and multiple genes affecting a characteristic?

5. What is the maximum number of phenotypes that can be observed when the gene in question is multiply allelic?

6. In a pedigree, how can you distinguish between recessiveness and a lack of penetrance of a dominant disorder?

7. You have two pure-breeding lines of *Drosophila*, lines A and B, which have scarlet eyes. Answer the following questions in sequence.

   a. A cross of line-A females with line-B males yields all wild-type offspring. What can you conclude?

   b. The reciprocal cross yields wild type females and scarlet-eyed males. What can you conclude?

   c. When you cross F_1 females from part a with F_1 males from part b, what phenotypic ratio is observed?

8. In species X, both *AA* and *aa* individuals die. Another independent gene, *BB*, blocks the lethality of only the *AA* genotype. Otherwise, it has no effect. What genotypic ratio among the viable progeny would be observed in a cross of *Aa Bb* with *Aa BB*?

9. What genotypic ratio is observed in a testcross of a triple hybrid?

10. Consider the dihybrid cross *Aa Bb* × *Aa Bb*. Among 16-offspring matings, what is the percentage that would be expected to have exactly 9 *A–B–*?

11. Discuss the following pedigree, where the symbols are as indicated:

a.-d. Matings of Individual #5

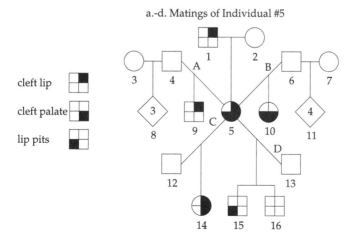

cleft lip

cleft palate

lip pits

SOLUTIONS TO SELF-TEST

1. Dominance refers to relationships between alleles, and epistasis refers to relationships between genes.

2. A lack of penetrance can be due either to the environment or to the expression of other genes.

3. Variable expressivity can be due either to the environment or to the expression of other genes.

4. Multiple alleles show a $1:2:1$ ratio or some modification of that ratio. Multiple genes show a $9:3:3:1$ ratio or some modification of that ratio.

5. For any specific cross, the maximum number of phenotypes is four.

6. It is often quite difficult to distinguish between recessiveness and a lack of penetrance of a dominant disorder. In practice, those disorders that have low penetrance are often ascribed to the interaction of multiple genes (epistasis), and risk values are based upon empiric observations rather than upon Mendelian ratios. The same is true of recessive disorders.

7. **a.** Two genes govern eye color. The defects are both recessive. The defect in line A is autosomal.

   b. The defect in line B is X-linked. The two crosses can be represented as

   Cross 1:   P   *dd EE* × *DD eY*

   F$_1$ *Dd Ee* females

   Dd EY males

   Cross 2:   P   *dd EY* × *DD ee*

   F$_1$ *Dd Ee* females

   Dd eY males

   c. The cross is

   P   *Dd Ee* × *Dd eY*

   F$_1$ females

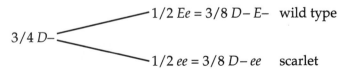

3/4 D–

1/2 *Ee* = 3/8 *D– E–*   wild type

1/2 *ee* = 3/8 *D– ee*   scarlet

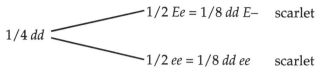

$1/2\ Ee = 1/8\ dd\ E-$ scarlet

$1/4\ dd$

$1/2\ ee = 1/8\ dd\ ee$ scarlet

3 wild type : 5 scarlet

F_1 males

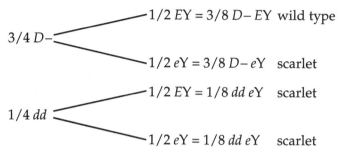

$1/2\ EY = 3/8\ D-\ EY$ wild type

$3/4\ D-$

$1/2\ eY = 3/8\ D-\ eY$ scarlet

$1/2\ EY = 1/8\ dd\ eY$ scarlet

$1/4\ dd$

$1/2\ eY = 1/8\ dd\ eY$ scarlet

3 wild type : 5 scarlet

8.   P $Aa\ Bb \times Aa\ BB$

F_1

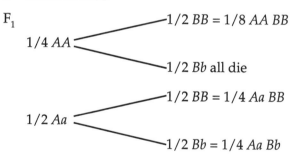

$1/2\ BB = 1/8\ AA\ BB$

$1/4\ AA$

$1/2\ Bb$ all die

$1/2\ BB = 1/4\ Aa\ BB$

$1/2\ Aa$

$1/2\ Bb = 1/4\ Aa\ Bb$

$1/4\ aa$ all die

Because only 5/8 of the progeny survive, the genotypic ratio of the viable progeny is

     $1/5\ AA\ BB$

     $2/5\ Aa\ BB$

     $2/5\ Aa\ Bb$

9.   The cross is $Aa\ Bb\ Dd \times aa\ bb\ dd$. The gametes from the second parent, $a\ b\ d$, and from the first parent are

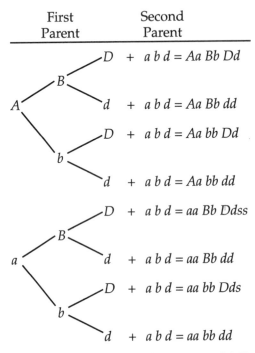

First Parent	Second Parent

D + a b d = Aa Bb Dd

d + a b d = Aa Bb dd

D + a b d = Aa bb Dd

d + a b d = Aa bb dd

D + a b d = aa Bb Ddss

d + a b d = aa Bb dd

D + a b d = aa bb Dds

d + a b d = aa bb dd

All gametes occur at a frequency of 1/8.

10. The formula to use is

$$\frac{n!}{p!\,q!}\,(r)^p(s)^q$$

where n is the total number, p is the number of one kind, q is the number of the alternative, r is the probability of p occurring and s is the probability of q occurring. The exclamation point indicates factorial. $5! = 5 \times 4 \times 3 \times 2 \times 1$.

The probability of A– B– is $(3/4)(3/4) = 9/16$. The probability of all other outcomes is $1 - (3/4)(3/4) = 7/16$. The answer is $16!(9/16)^9(7/16)^7/(9!)(7!)$.

11. Disturbance in the formation of the lip and palate is dominant and most likely autosomal. A pleiotropic gene leads to the specific symptoms of the cleft lip and palate syndrome, showing reduced penetrance and variable expressivity.

5

Linkage I: Basic Eukaryotic Chromosome Mapping

IMPORTANT TERMS AND CONCEPTS

Recombination is the process that generates gametes with gene combinations different from that seen in the parental source. Recombination can be **interchromosomal**, involving genes on nonhomologous chromosomes, or **intrachromosomal**, involving homologous chromosomes.

If the recombination is interchromosomal, an equal frequency of all gamete types results. If the recombination is intrachromosomal, the frequency of gamete types depends on the physical distance between the genes being studied. Genes that are located more than 50 map units from each other are said to be **unlinked**; all gametes occur in equal frequency. Genes that are 50 map units or fewer apart are said to be **linked**; the frequency of parental-type gametes will be greater than 50 percent and the frequency of recombinant-type gametes will be less than 50 percent.

Recombination of linked genes results from a physical exchange of genetic material between homologous chromosomes. The **chiasmata** seen in meiosis I are considered to be the cytological evidence of **crossing-over**, the process that leads to recombination. The percentage of recombination is used as a measure of the physical distance between two genes. It is calculated by the following formula:

$$\frac{(100\%)(\text{number of recombinant progeny})}{\text{total number of progeny}} = \text{number of map units (m.u.)}$$

Linkage maps are formed by combining the results from a series of crosses.

A **three-point testcross** can be done to determine the relative location of three genes simultaneously. To do a three-point testcross, a triple-recessive parent is mated with a triple-heterozygous parent. The contribution of the testcross parent is ignored. This is because the testcross parent must contribute the three recessive alleles to each of the progeny.

The **gene order** in a three-point testcross is determined by comparing the parental-type progeny, which will be most frequent, with the **double-crossover** progeny, which will be the least frequent. The gene that has switched with respect to the other two genes in this comparison must be located between them:

parentals: $D\,a\,R, d\,A\,r$

double crossovers: $d\,a\,R,\ D\,A\,r$

The order is $A\,D\,R$; the parental chromosomes are $a\,D\,R/A\,d\,r$.

Map units in a three-point testcross are determined by identifying progeny that result from a crossover in each region. In the example above, single crossovers in the $A-D$ region would be $a\,d\,r$ and $A\,D\,R$. Single crossovers in the $D-R$ region would be $a\,D\,r$ and $A\,d\,R$. Because double-crossover progeny result from a crossover in both regions, their frequency is added to the frequency of single crossovers for each region. The formula for calculating the distance between two genes is

$$\frac{(100\%)(\text{number of single crossovers} + \text{number of double crossovers})}{\text{total number of progeny}}$$

= number of map units

The double-crossover progeny would be $a\,d\,R$ and $A\,D\,r$ in the above example.

The expected types and numbers of progeny can be determined from a linkage map. To determine the expected number of double crossovers, multiply the total number of progeny by the map units in both regions. To determine the expected number of single crossovers, multiply the total number of progeny by the map units in that region and subtract the number of double crossovers from the total.

Interference (I) occurs when a crossover in one region affects the frequency of a crossover in a second region. It is defined as

$$1 - \frac{\text{observed double crossovers}}{\text{expected double crossovers}}$$

If interference exists, it needs to be calculated from data when deter-mining map distances or used to adjust frequencies when calculating the expected progeny types from a linkage map. In the latter situation, the value of I will be given. To calculate the observed number of double crossovers, use the following formula:

observed double crossovers = $(1 - I)$(expected double crossovers)

Use the **chi square** (χ^2) test to decide whether observations are com-patible with the hypothesis that generated the expected values.

Be sure that you have thoroughly read the entire chapter before you attempt any of the problems.

SOLUTIONS TO PROBLEMS

For the following, CO is used to designate single recombinants and DCO is used to designate double recombinants.

1.   The $Aa\ Bb$ progeny are parentals. An expected 90 percent of the progeny are parentals, and they are of two types: $Aa\ Bb$ and $aa\ bb$. Therefore, 45 percent of the progeny will be $Aa\ Bb$.

2.   P $A\,d/A\,d \times a\,D/a\,D$

   F_1 $A\,d/a\,D$

   F_2 1 $A\,d/A\,d$

         2 $A\,d/a\,D$

         1 $a\,D/a\,D$

3.   P $R\,S/r\,s \times R\,S/r\,s$

      gametes $1/2\,(1-0.35)$ $R\,S$

            $1/2\,(1-0.35)$ $r\,s$

            $1/2\,(0.35)$ $R\,s$

            $1/2\,(0.35)$ $r\,S$

   F_2 0.1056 $R\,S/R\,S$ 0.1138 $r\,s/r\,S$

      0.1056 $r\,s/r\,s$ 0.1138 $r\,s/R\,s$

      0.2113 $R\,S/r\,s$ 0.0306 $R\,s/R\,s$

      0.1138 $R\,S/r\,S$ 0.0306 $r\,S/r\,S$

      0.1138 $R\,S/R\,s$ 0.0613 $R\,s/r\,S$

4. The cross is *Ee Ff* × *ee ff*. If independent assortment exists, the progeny should be in a $1:1:1:1$ ratio, which is not observed. Therefore, there is linkage. *E f* and *e F* are recombinants equaling one-third of the progeny. The two genes are 33.3 map units (m.u.) apart.

5. Because only parental types were recovered, the two genes must be quite close to each other, making recombination quite rare.

6. Parental types are the most frequent: 442 *Aa Bb* and 458 *aa bb*. Because one parent was *aa bb*, contributing only *a b* to the offspring, the parental types can be rewritten as 442 *A B/a b* and 458 *a b/a b*. Thus, the female parent was *A B/a b*. The two recombinant types are 46 *A b/a b* and 54 *a B/a b*. The frequency of recombination between two genes is

$$\frac{100\%(\text{total number of recombinants}}{\text{total number of progeny}}$$

$$=\frac{100\%(46+54\ )}{(442+458+46+54)}=\frac{100\%(100)}{1000}=10\text{ m.u.}$$

7. **a.** The F_1 is *Aa Bb*, which is crossed to *aa bb*. Among the progeny, $(1/2)(1/2)=1/4$ will be *aa bb*.

b. The F_1 is *AB/ab*, which is crossed to *ab/ab*. One half of the progeny will be *ab/ab*.

c. The cross is the same as in part b. The *ab/ab* progeny are a parental type. Parentals occur at a rate of 90%, which means that 45% will be *ab/ab*.

d. The cross is the same as in part b. The *ab/ab* progeny are a parental type. Parentals occur at a rate of 76%, which means that 38% will be *ab/ab*.

8. Meiosis is occurring in an organism that is *C d/c D*, producing haploid spores ultimately. The parental types are *C d* and *c D*, in equal frequency. The recombinant types are *C D* and *c d*, in equal frequency. Eight map units means 8 percent recombinants. Thus, *C D* and *c d* will each be present at a frequency of 4 percent, and *C d* and *c D* will each be present at a frequency of $(100\%-8\%)/2=46\%$.

a. 4 percent; **b.** 4 percent; **c.** 46 percent; **d.** 8 percent

9. To solve this problem, you must realize that

1. One chiasma involves two of the four chromatids in a homologous pair. Therefore, 16 percent of the meioses having a chiasma will lead to 8 percent recombinants.

2. One-half of the recombinants will be *B r* and one-half will be *b R*. The answer is b, 4 percent.

10. **a.** Gene pairs A/a, B/b, and C/c are linked, and D/d shows no recombination with A/a. This is determined by looking at only the two genes you are trying to make a decision about.

Are A/a and B/b linked?

$$A\ B\ =\ 140 + 305 = 445$$
$$a\ b\ =\ 145 + 310 = 455$$
$$a\ B\ =\ 42 + 6 = 48$$
$$A\ b\ =\ 43 + 9 = 52$$

The two genes are 10 m.u. apart.

Are A/a and D/d linked?

$$A\ D\ =\ 0$$
$$a\ d\ =\ 0$$
$$A\ d\ =\ 43 + 140 + 9 + 305 = 497$$
$$a\ D\ =\ 42 + 145 + 6 + 310 = 503$$

The two genes show no recombination = 0 m.u.

Are B/b and D/d linked?

$$B\ D\ =\ 42 + 6 = 48$$
$$b\ d\ =\ 43 + 9 = 52$$
$$B\ d\ =\ 140 + 305 = 445$$
$$b\ D\ =\ 145 + 310 = 455$$

The two genes are 10 m.u. apart.

Are C/c and D/d linked?

$$C\ D\ =\ 42 + 310 = 350$$
$$c\ d\ =\ 43 + 305 = 348$$
$$C\ d\ =\ 140 + 9 = 149$$
$$c\ D\ =\ 145 + 6 = 151$$

The two genes are 30 m.u. apart.

All four genes are linked.

b. and c.   Because A/a and D/d show no recombination, first rewrite the progeny omitting D and d (or omitting A and a).

a B C	42
A b c	43
A B C	140
a b c	145
a B c	6
A b C	9
A B c	305
a b C	310
	1000

Note that the progeny now look like those of a typical three-point testcross, with *A B c* and *a b C* the parental types (most frequent) and *a B c* and *A b C* the double recombinants (least frequent). The gene order is *B/b A/a C/c*. This is determined by comparing double recombinants with the parentals; the gene that "switches" in reference with the other two is the gene in the center (*B A c → B a c, b a C → b A C*).

Next, rewrite the progeny again, this time putting the genes in the proper order, and classify the progeny.

B a C	42	CO A–B
b A c	43	CO A–B
B A C	140	CO A–C
b a c	145	CO A–C
B a c	6	DCO
b A C	9	DCO
B A c	305	parental
b a C	310	parental

To construct the map of these genes, use the following formula:

$$\text{distance between two genes} = \frac{100\% \, (\text{number of single CO} + \text{number of DCO})}{\text{total number of progeny}}$$

For the *A/a* to *B/b* distance:

$$\frac{100\% \, (42 + 43 + 6 + 9)}{1000} = \frac{100\% (100)}{1000} = 10 \text{ m.u.}$$

For the A/a to C/c distance:

$$\frac{100\% \, (140 + 145 + 6 + 9)}{1000} = \frac{100\% \, (300)}{1000} = 30 \text{ m.u.}$$

The map is

$$\underset{B}{\vert} \underset{10 \text{ m.u.}}{\quad\quad} \underset{A}{\vert} \underset{30 \text{ m.u.}}{\quad\quad} \underset{C}{\vert}$$

Now it is time to deal with the D/d alleles. Notice that only two combinations were observed with A/a: $A \, d$ and $a \, D$. The parental chromosomes actually were B (A,d) c/b (a,D) C, where the parentheses indicate that the order of the genes within is unknown.

d. Interference $= 1 - [(\text{observed DCO})/(\text{expected DCO})]$

$= 1 - \{(6 + 9)/[(0.10)(0.30)(1000)]\}$

$= 1 - (15/30) = 0.5$

11. a. Males must be heterozygous for both genes, and the two must be closely linked: $M \, F/m \, f$.

b. $m \, f/m \, f$

c. Sex is determined by the male contribution. The two parental gametes are $M \, F$, determining maleness $(M \, F/m \, f)$, and $m \, f$, determining femaleness $(m \, f/m \, f)$. Occasional recombination would yield $M \, f$, determining a hermaphrodite $(M \, f/m \, f)$, and $m \, F$, determining total sterility $(m \, F/m \, f)$.

d. recombination in the male yielding $M f$

e. Hermaphrodites are rare because the genes are tightly linked.

12. The verbal description indicates the following cross and result:

P $N- A- \times nn \, OO$

F_1 $Nn \, AO \times Nn \, AO$

The results indicate linkage, so the cross and results must be rewritten:

P $N \, A/?? \times n \, O/n \, O$

F_1 $N \, A/n \, O \times N \, A/n \, O$

F_2 66% $N- A-$

    16% $n \, O/n \, O$

     9% $nn \, A-$

     9% $N \, O/? \, O$

Only one genotype is fully known: 16% $n\,O/n\,O$, a combination of two parental gametes. The frequency of two parental gametes coming together is the frequency of the first times the frequency of the second. Therefore, the frequency of each $n\,O$ gamete is the square root of 0.16, or 0.4. Within an organism the two parental gametes occur in equal frequency. Therefore, the frequency of $N\,A$ is also 0.4. The parental total is 0.8, leaving 0.2 for all recombinants. Therefore, $N\,O$ and $n\,A$ occur at a frequency of 0.1 each. The two genes are 20 m.u. apart.

13. The original cross was

$$P \quad PL/PL \;\times\; pl/pl$$

$$F_1 \quad PL/pl \;\times\; PL/pl$$

Before proceeding, recognize that crossing-over can occur in both parents and that some crossovers cannot be detected by phenotype. The gametes from each plant are as follows:

    parental types: $P\,L, p\,l$

    recombinants: $P\,l, p\,L$

The F_2 is as follows:

PL/PL	purple, long	pl/pL	red, long
PL/pl	purple, long	pl/pl	red, round
PL/Pl	purple, long	Pl/pL	purple, long
PL/pL	purple, long	Pl/Pl	purple, round
Pl/pl	purple, round	pL/pL	red, long

Of these ten different genotypes, only red, round can be identified unambiguously. It consists of two parental-type gametes and occurs at a frequency of 14.4 percent. The probability of such a genotype can be calculated by multiplying the probability of a gamete from the first parent times the probability of the same gamete from the second parent. Thus, the square root of 14.4 percent will yield the frequency of this one type of parental gamete, or 37.99 percent. Because parental types occur with equal frequency, the parentals are 75.98 percent and the recombinants are 24.02 percent. Therefore, there are approximately 24 m.u. between the two genes.

A more precise calculation involves the use of an advanced statistical technique known as the method of maximum likelihood.

14. $P \quad abc/abc \quad\times\; a^+b^+c^+/a^+b^+c^+$

    $F_1 \quad abc/a^+b^+c^+ \quad\times\; abc/a^+b^+c^+$

F_2 1364 $a^+- b^+- c^+-$

365   $a\ b\ c/a\ b\ c$

87   $aa\ bb\ c^+-$

84   $a^+- b^+- cc$

47   $aa\ b^+- c^+-$

44   $a^+- bb\ cc$

5   $aa\ b^+- cc$

4   $a^+- bb\ c^+-$

Remember that recombination does not occur in the male *Drosophila*.

a. Because you cannot distinguish between $a\ b\ c/a^+\ b^+\ c^+$ and $a^+\ b^+\ c^+/a^+\ b^+\ c^+$, use the frequency of $a\ b\ c/a\ b\ c$ to estimate the frequency of $a^+\ b^+\ c^+$ (parental) gametes from the female.

parentals   730 (2×365)

CO a–b: 91 $(a + +, + b\ c = 47 + 44)$

CO b–c: 171 $(a\ b +, + + c = 87 + 84)$

DCO: 9 $(a + c, + b + = 5 + 4)$

——

1001

a–b: $100\%(91 + 9)/1001 = 10$ m.u.

b–c: $100\%(171 + 9)/1001 = 18$ m.u.

b. Coefficient of coincidence = (observed DCO)/(expected DCO)

$= 9/[(0.1)(0.18)(1001)]$

$= 9/18 = 0.5$

15. a. By comparing the two most frequent classes (parentals: *an br⁺ f⁺*, *an⁺ br f*) to the least frequent classes (DCO: *an⁺ br f⁺*, *an br⁺ f*), the gene order can be determined. The gene in the middle switches with respect to the other two (the order is *an f br*). Now the crosses can be written fully.

P   *an f⁺ br⁺/an f⁺ br⁺* × *an⁺ f br/an⁺ f br*

F_1 *an⁺ f br/an f⁺ br⁺* × *an f br/an f br*

F_2 355 *an f br/an f⁺ br⁺*   parental

339 *an f br/an⁺ f br*   parental

88   $an\ f\ br/an^+\ f^+\ br^+$ CO an–f

55   $an\ f\ br/an\ f\ br$ CO an–f

21   $an\ f\ br/an^+\ f\ br^+$ CO f–br

17   $an\ f\ br/an\ f^+\ br$ CO f–br

2   $an\ f\ br/an^+\ f^+\ br$ DCO

2   $an\ f\ br/an\ f\ br^+$ DCO

b. an–f: 100% (88 + 55 + 2 + 2)/879 = 16.72 m.u.

f–br: 100% (21 + 17 + 2 + 2)/879 = 4.78 m.u.

$$\underset{\text{16.72 m.u.}}{\overset{an}{\rule{0pt}{0pt}}}\quad\underset{\text{4.78 m.u.}}{\overset{f}{\rule{0pt}{0pt}}}\quad\overset{br}{\rule{0pt}{0pt}}$$

c.   Interference = 1 – [(observed DCO)/(expected DCO)]

= 1 – {4/[(0.1672)(0.0478)(879)]}

= 1 – 0.569 = 0.431

16.   By comparing the most frequent classes (parental: + v lg, b + +) with the least frequent classes (DCO: + + +, b v lg) the gene order can be determined. The gene in the middle switches with respect to the other two, yielding the following sequence: v b lg. Now the cross can be written

P $v\ b^+\ lg/v^+\ b\ lg^+ \times v\ b\ lg/v\ b\ lg$

F_1 305 $v\ b\ lg/v\ b^+\ lg$ parental

275   $v\ b\ lg/v^+\ b\ lg^+$ parental

128   $v\ b\ lg/v^+\ b\ lg$ CO b–lg

112   $v\ b\ lg/v\ b^+\ lg^+$ CO b–lg

74   $v\ b\ lg/v^+\ b^+\ lg$ CO v–b

66   $v\ b\ lg/v\ b\ lg^+$ CO v–b

22   $v\ b\ lg/v^+\ b^+\ lg^+$ DCO

18   $v\ b\ lg/\ v\ b\ lg$ DCO

v–b: 100%(74 + 66 + 22 + 18)/1000 = 18.0 m.u.

b–lg: 100%(128 + 112 + 22 + 18)/1000 = 28.0 m.u.

c.c. = (observed DCO)/(expected DCO)

= (22 + 18)/[(0.28)(0.18)(1000)] = 0.79

17.   Let F = fat, L = long tail, and Fl = flagella. The gene sequence is $F\ L\ Fl$ (compare most frequent to least frequent). The cross is

P F L Fl / f l fl × f l fl/f l fl

F_1 398 F L Fl / f l fl parental

   370 f l fl / f l fl parental

    72 F L fl / f l fl CO L–Fl

    67 f l Fl / f l fl CO L–Fl

    44 f L FL / fl fl CO F–L

    35 F l fl / f l fl CO F–L

     9 f L fl / f l fl DCO

     5 F l Fl / f l fl DCO

L–Fl: $100\%(72 + 67 + 9 + 5)/1000 = 15.3$ m.u.

F–L: $100\%(44 + 35 + 9 + 5)/1000 = 9.3$ m.u.

$$\begin{array}{ccc} F & L & Fl \\ \vert \quad\text{9.3 m.u.}\quad & \vert \quad\text{15.3 m.u.}\quad & \vert \end{array}$$

18. **a–b.** The data indicate that the progeny males have a different phenotype than the females. Therefore, all the genes are on the X chromosome. The two most frequent phenotypes in the males indicate the genotypes of the X chromosomes in the female, and the two least frequent phenotypes in the males indicate the gene order. Data from only the males are used to determine map distances. The cross is

P $x z y^+/x^+ z^+ y \times x^+ z^+ y^+/Y$

F_1 males

    430   $x z y^+/Y$ parental

    441   $x^+ z^+ y/Y$ parental

     39   $x z y/Y$ CO z–y

     30   $x^+ z^+ y^+/Y$ CO z–y

     32   $x^+ z y^+/Y$ CO x–z

     27   $x z^+ y/Y$ CO x–z

      1   $x^+ z y/Y$ DCO

      0   $x z^+ y^+/Y$ DCO

c. z–y: $100\%(39 + 30 + 1)/1000 = 7.0$ m.u.

   x–z: $100\%(32 + 27 + 1)/1000 = 6.0$ m.u.

c.c. = (observed DCO)/(expected DCO)

= $1/[(0.06)(0.07)(1000)] = 0.238$

19.   Recall that the parentals are most frequent and the double crossovers are least frequent. Also recall that to determine gene sequence you need to compare parentals to double crossovers: the gene in the center switches with regard to outside markers. Therefore, the gene sequence is

   1.   *b a c*

   2.   *b a c*

   3.   *b a c*

   4.   *a c b*

   5.   *a c b*

20.   The gene order is *a c b d*.

Recombination between *a* and *c* occurs at a frequency of

$100\%(139 + 3 + 121 + 2)/(669 + 139 + 3 + 121 + 2 + 2,280+ 653 + 2,215)$

$= 100\%(265/6,082) = 4.36\%$.

Recombination between *b* and *c* occurs at a frequency of

$100\%(669 + 3 + 2 + 653)/(669 + 139 + 3 + 121 + 2 + 2,280 + 653 + 2,215)$

$= 100\%(1,327/6,082) = 21.82\%$.

Recombination between *b* and *c* occurs at a frequency of

$100\%(8 + 14 + 153 + 141)/(8 + 441 + 90 + 376 + 14 + 153 + 64 + 141)$

$= 100\%(316/1,287) = 24.55\%$.

The conflict between the two calculated distances between *b* and *c* is expected because each set of data would not be expected to yield exactly identical results.

Recombination between *b* and *d* occurs at a frequency of

$100\%(8 + 90 + 14 + 64)/(8 + 441 + 90 + 376 + 14 + 153 + 64 + 141)$

$= 100\%(176/1,287) = 13.68\%$.

The general map is

$$\overset{a}{\vdash} \text{13.7 m.u.} \overset{c}{\vdash} \text{21.8 – 24.6 m.u.} \overset{b}{\vdash} \text{4.4 m.u.} \overset{d}{\vdash}$$

21.   a.   The hypothesis is that the genes are not linked. Therefore, a $1 : 1 : 1 : 1$ ratio is expected.

b. χ^2 is

$(54-50)^2/50 + (47-50)^2/50 + (52-50)^2/50 + (47-50)^2/50$

$= 0.32 + 0.18 + 0.08 + 0.18 = 0.76.$

c. With 3 degrees of freedom, the p value is between 0.50 and 0.90.

d. Between 50% and 90% of the time values this extreme from the prediction would be obtained by chance alone.

e. Accept the initial hypothesis.

f. Because the χ^2 value was insignificant, the two genes are assorting independently. The genotypes of all individuals are

P dp^+dp^+ ee × $dpdp$ e^+e^+

F_1 dp^+dp e^+e

tester $dpdp$ ee

progeny long, ebony dp^+dp ee

long, gray dp^+dp e^+e

short, gray $dpdp$ e^+e

short, ebony $dpdp$ ee

22. The cross was *asp gal rad⁺ aro⁺* × *asp⁺ gal⁺ rad aro*.

a. The first task is to decide if there is any linkage among the four genes. Arrange the results according to frequencies:

0.136	0.064	0.034	0.016
asp gal + +	*asp gal* + *rad*	*asp gal aro* +	*asp gal aro rad*
+ + *aro rad*	*asp* + + +	*asp* + *aro rad*	*asp* + *aro* +
asp + + *rad*	+ *gal aro rad*	+ *gal* + +	+ *gal* + *rad*
+ *gal aro* +	+ + *aro* +	+ + + *rad*	+ + + +

If all four genes were independently assorting, then all the classes would occur at an equal frequency. This is not observed. Therefore, there is some linkage among these genes.

The two parental classes are present in the highest frequency, as are two other classes: *asp* + + *rad* and + *gal aro* +. Note that *asp* and *gal* are assorting independently of each other, which means that they are unlinked. Also note that *aro* and *rad* are assorting independently of each other and are, therefore, unlinked. Finally, note that *gal* and *rad* are not assorting independently and *asp* and *rad* are not assorting independently. There are two linkage groups and the original cross was

gal rad⁺ asp aro⁺ × gal⁺ rad asp⁺ aro.

Reclassify the data with regard to the *gal-rad* linkage.

Parentals				Recombinants				
0.136	*asp gal*	+	+	0.064	*asp gal*	+	*rad*
0.136	+	+	*aro rad*	0.064	*asp*	+	+	+
0.136	*asp*	+	+ *rad*	0.064	+	*gal aro rad*
0.136	+	*gal aro*	+	0.064	+	+ *aro*	+
0.034	*asp gal aro*	+	0.016	*asp gal aro rad*
0.034	*asp*	+ *aro rad*	0.016	*asp*	+ *aro*	+
0.034	+ *gal*	+	+	0.016	+ *gal*	+ *rad*
0.034	+	+	+ *rad*	0.016	+	+	+	+
0.680				0.320				

The frequency of recombination between *gal* and *rad* is 32%.

Reclassify the data with regard to the *aro-asp* linkage.

Parentals				Recombinants				
0.136	*asp gal*	+	+	0.034	*asp gal aro*	+
0.136	+	+ *aro rad*	0.034	*asp*	+ *aro rad*
0.136	*asp*	+	+ *rad*	0.034	+ *gal*	+	+
0.136	+ *gal aro*	+	0.034	+	+	+ *rad*
0.064	*asp gal*	+ *rad*	0.016	*asp gal aro rad*
0.064	*asp*	+	+	+	0.016	*asp*	+ *aro*	+
0.064	+ *gal aro rad*	0.016	+ *gal*	+ *rad*
0.064	+	+ *aro*	+	0.016	+	+	+	+
0.80				0.200				

The frequency of recombination between *aro* and *asp* is 20%.

b. The map of the four genes is

$$\underset{gal}{\vert} \quad \underset{32 \text{ m.u.}}{} \quad \overset{rad}{\vert} \quad \overset{aro}{\vert} \quad \underset{20 \text{ m.u.}}{} \quad \overset{asp}{\vert}$$

23. **a. and b.**   The wild type is dominant for both traits. First, notice that the F_2 offspring differ with regard to sex. At least one of the genes is X-linked. Second, notice that the two genes are not assorting independently. This means that both genes are on the X chromosome. The cross was

P $GA/GA \times g\,a/Y$

F_1 $GA/g\,a$ females and GA/Y males

F_2 females	males
45% GA/GA	45% GA/Y
45% $g\,a/GA$	45% $g\,a/Y$
5% $g\,A/GA$	5% $g\,A/Y$
5% $G\,a/GA$	5% $G\,a/Y$

24. **a.**

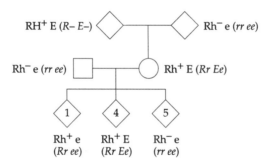

b. yes

c. dominant

d. As drawn, the pedigree indicates independent assortment. However, the data also support linkage, with the $R\,e/r\,e$ individual representing a crossover. The distance between the two genes would be $100\%(1/10) = 10$ m.u. There is no way to choose between the alternatives without more data.

25. The cross is

P $PAR/PAR \times p\,a\,r/p\,a\,r$

F_1 $PAR/p\,a\,r \times p\,a\,r/p\,a\,r$, a three-point testcross

a. number of parentals is

1 – (single CO individuals – DCO individuals)

= 1 – {[0.15 + 0.20 – 2(0.15)(0.20)] – [(0.15)(0.20)]}

= 0.68.

Because one-half of the parentals are Earth alleles and one-half are Vulcan, the frequency of children with all three Vulcanian characteristics is 1/2(0.68) = 0.34.

b. same as above, 0.34.

c. The frequency will be one-half the DCOs, or 1/2(0.15)(0.20) = 0.015.

d. The frequency will be

1/2 p(CO P–A) p(no CO A–R) = 1/2(0.15)(0.80) = 0.06.

26. a. To obtain a plant that is *a b c/a b c* from selfing of *A b c/a B C*, both gametes must be derived from a single crossover between *A* and *B*. The frequency of the *a b c* gamete is

1/2 p(CO A–B) p(no CO B–C) = 1/2(0.20)(0.70) = 0.07

Therefore, the frequency of the homozygous plant will be $(0.07)^2 = 0.0049$.

b. The cross is *A b c/a B C* × *a b c/a b c*. The progeny are

A b c/a b c, parental: (1/2)[1 –(CO A–B) – (CO B–C) + DCO](1000)

= (1/2){1 – 0.20 – 0.30 + [(0.20)(0.30)]}(1000)

= 280

a B C/a b c, parental: (1/2)[1 – (CO A–B) – (CO B–C) + DCO](1000)

= (1/2){1 – 0.20 – 0.30 + [(0.20)(0.30)]}(1,000)

= 280

A B C/a b c, CO A–B: (1/2)[(CO A–B) – DCO](1000)

= (1/2){0.20 – [(0.20)(0.30)]}(1000) = 70

a b c/a b c, CO A–B: (1/2)[(CO A–B) – DCO](1000)

= (1/2){0.20 – [(0.20)(0.30)]}(1000) = 70

A b C/a b c, CO B–C: (1/2)[(CO B–C) – DCO](1000)

= (1/2){0.30 – [(0.20)(0.30)]}(1000) = 120

$a\,B\,c/a\,b\,c$, CO $B–C$: $\quad$ $(1/2)[(CO\ B–C) – DCO](1000)$

$\quad = \quad (1/2)\{0.30 – [(0.20)(0.30)]\}(1000) = 120$

$A\,B\,c/a\,b\,c$, DCO: $\quad$ $(1/2)(DCO)(1000)$

$\quad = \quad (1/2)(0.20)(0.30)(1000) = 30$

$a\,b\,C/a\,b\,c$, DCO: $\quad$ $(1/2)(DCO)(1000)$

$\quad = \quad (1/2)(0.20)(0.30)(1000) = 30$

c. Interference $\quad = 1 – (\text{observed DCO})/(\text{expected DCO})$

$0.2 = 1 – (\text{observed DCO})/(0.20)(0.30)$

observed DCO $= (0.20)(0.30) – (0.20)(0.20)(0.30) = 0.048$

Of 1000 progeny, 48 will be DCO. The progeny are

$A\,b\,c/a\,b\,c$, parental: $\quad$ $(1/2)[1 – (CO\ A–B) – (CO\ B–C) + DCO](1000)$

$\quad = \quad (1/2)(1 – 0.20 – 0.30 + 0.048)(1000) = 274$

$a\,B\,C/a\,b\,c$, parental: $\quad$ $(1/2)[1 – (CO\ A–B) – (CO\ B–C) + DCO](1000)$

$\quad = \quad (1/2)(1 – 0.20 – 0.30 + 0.048)(1000) = 274$

$A\,B\,C/a\,b\,c$, CO $A–B$: $\quad$ $(1/2)[(CO\ A–B) – DCO](1000)$

$\quad = \quad (1/2)(0.20 – 0.048)(1000) = 76$

$a\,b\,c/a\,b\,c$, CO $A–B$: $\quad$ $(1/2)[(CO\ A–B) – DCO](1000)$

$\quad = \quad (1/2)(0.20 – 0.048)(1000) = 76$

$A\,b\,C/a\,b\,c$, CO $B–C$: $\quad$ $(1/2)[(CO\ B–C) – DCO](1000)$

$\quad = \quad (1/2)(0.30 – 0.048)(1000) = 126$

$a\,B\,c/a\,b\,c$, CO $B–C$: $\quad$ $(1/2)[(CO\ B–C) – DCO](1000)$

$\quad = \quad (1/2)(0.30 – 0.048)(1000) = 126$

$A\,B\,c/a\,b\,c$, DCO: $\quad$ $(1/2)(DCO)(1000)$

$\quad = \quad (1/2)(48) = 24$

$a\,b\,C/a\,b\,c$, DCO: $\quad$ $(1/2)(DCO)(1000)$

$\quad = \quad (1/2)(48) = 24$

27. Assume there is no linkage. The genotypes should occur with equal frequency, which is the expected value. In each case, there are four genotypes ($n = 4$), which means there are 3 degrees of freedom ($n – 1 = 3$).

$$\chi^2 = \Sigma\,(\text{observed} – \text{expected})^2/\text{expected}$$

1. $\chi^2 = \dfrac{(310-300)^2 + (315-300)^2 + (287-300)^2 + (288-300)^2}{30}$

$= \dfrac{100 + 225 + 169 + 144)}{30} = 2.1266$

$P > 0.50$, nonsignificant. Therefore, the hypothesis of no linkage cannot be rejected.

2. $\chi^2 = \dfrac{36-30)^2 + (38-30)^2 + (23-30)^2 + (23-30)^2}{30}$

$= \dfrac{36 + 64 + 49 + 49}{30} = 6.6$

$P > 0.10$, nonsignificant. The hypothesis of no linkage cannot be rejected.

3. $\chi^2 = \dfrac{(360-300)^2 + (380-300)^2 + (230-300)^2 + (230-300)^2}{300}$

$= \dfrac{3600 + 6400 + 4900 + 4900}{300} = 66.0$

$P < 0.005$, significant. The hypothesis of no linkage must be rejected.

4. $\chi^2 = \dfrac{(74-60)^2 + (72-60)^2 + (50-60)^2 + (44-60)^2}{60}$

$= \dfrac{196 + 144 + 100 + 256}{60} = 11.60$

$P < 0.01$, significant. The hypothesis of no linkage must be rejected.

28. The data approximate a $9:3:3:1$ ratio, which suggests two genes. Let A = resistance to rust 24, a = susceptibility to rust 24, B = resistance to rust 22, b = susceptibility to rust 22.

a. P   *AA bb* (770B) × *aa BB* (Bombay)

   F_1 *Aa Bb* × *Aa Bb*

F_2 184 $A–B–$

58    $A–bb$

63    $aa\ B–$

15    $aa\ bb$

320

b. Expect:

(320)(9/16) = 180 $A–B–$

(320)(3/16) =   60 $A–bb$

(320)(3/16) =   60 $aa\ B–$

(320)(1/16) =   20 $aa\ bb$

$$\chi^2 = \frac{(184-180)^2}{180} + \frac{(58-60)^2}{60} + \frac{(63-60)^2}{60} + \frac{(15-20)^2}{20}$$

$$= \frac{16}{180} + \frac{4}{60} + \frac{9}{60} + \frac{25}{20} = 1.555$$

P (3 df) > 0.58, nonsignificant. A P value is the probability that the result would be observed by chance alone. Therefore, the hypothesis of two independently assorting genes cannot be rejected.

29. a. Both disorders must be recessive to yield the patterns of inheritance that are observed. Notice that only males are affected, strongly suggesting X-linkage for both disorders. In the first pedigree there is a 100% correlation between the presence or absence of both disorders, indicating close linkage. In the second pedigree, the presence and absence of both disorders are inversely correlated, again indicating linkage. In the first pedigree, the two defective alleles must be *cis* within the heterozygous females to show 100% linkage in the affected males, while in the second pedigree the two defective alleles must be *trans* within the heterozygous female.

b. and c.   Let *a* stand for the allele giving rise to steroid sulfatase deficiency (vertical bar) and *b* stand for the allele giving rise to ornithine transcarbamylase deficiency (horizontal bar). Crossing-over cannot be detected without attaching genotypes to the pedigrees. When this is done, it can be seen that crossing-over need not have to occur in either of the pedigrees to give rise to the observations.

First Pedigree

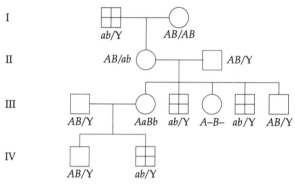

Second Pedigree

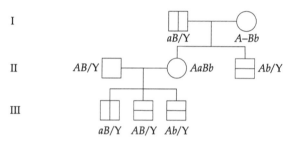

30. a. Blue sclerotics appears to be an autosomal dominant disorder. Hemophilia appears to be an X-linked recessive disorder.

   b. If the individuals in the pedigree are numbered as generations I through IV and the individuals in each generation are numbered clockwise, starting from the top right-hand portion of the pedigree, their genotypes are:

   I: *bb Hh, Bb HY*

   II: *Bb HY, Bb HY, bb HY, Bb H–, bb HY, Bb Hh, Bb H–, bb H–*

   III: *bb H–, Bb H–, bb hY, bb HY, Bb HY, Bb H–, Bb HY, Bb hY, Bb H–, bb HY, Bb H– bb HY, Bb H–, Bb HY, Bb hY, bb HY, bb HY, bb H–, bb HY, bb HY, Bb H–, Bb HY, Bb hY*

   IV: *bb H–, Bb H–, Bb H–, bb Hh, bb Hh, bb HY, bb HH, bb HY, bb Hh, bb H–, bb H–, bb HY, bb HY, bb H–, bb HY, bb HY, Bb HY, bb HY, bb HH, bb HY, bb HY, bb HH, bb H–, bb H–, bb H–, bb HY, bb HY, bb HY, bb Hh, Bb H–, Bb HY, bb HY, Bb HY, bb H–*

   c. There is no evidence of linkage between these two disorders.

Because of the modes of inheritance for these two genes, no linkage would be expected.

d. The two genes exhibit independent assortment.

e. No individual could be considered intrachromosomally recombinant. However, a number show interchromosomal recombination: all individuals in generation III that have both disorders.

31. a. Note that only males are affected by both disorders. This suggests that both are X-linked recessive disorders.

b. Individual II-2 must have inherited both disorders in a *trans* configuration. Therefore, individual III-2 represents recombination.

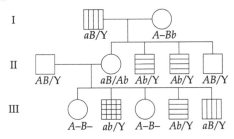

c. Because the genes are on the X chromosome, this is intrachromosomal recombination. However, the progeny size is too small to give a reliable estimate of crossing-over.

32. If h = hemophilia and b = colorblindness, the genotypes for individuals in the pedigree can be written as

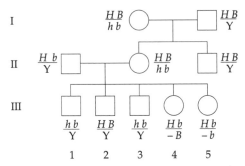

The mother of the two women in question would produce the following gametes:

0.45 $H B$ 0.05 $H b$

0.45 $h b$ 0.05 $h B$

Woman III-4 can be either $H\,b/H\,B$ (0.45 chance) or $H\,b/h\,B$ (0.05 chance), because she received B from her mother. If she is $H\,b/h\,B$ [$0.05/(0.45 + 0.05) = 0.10$ chance], she will produce the parental and recombinant gametes with the same probabilities as her mother. Thus, her child has a 45 percent chance of receiving $h\,B$, a 5 percent chance of receiving $h\,b$, and a 50 percent chance of receiving a Y from his father. The probability that her child will be a hemophiliac son is $(0.1)(0.50)(0.5) = 0.025 = 2.5$ percent.

Woman III-5 can be either $H\,b/H\,b$ (0.05 chance) or $H\,b/h\,b$ (0.45 chance), because she received b from her mother. If she is $H\,b/h\,b$ [$0.45/(0.45 + 0.05) = 0.90$ chance], she has a 50 percent chance of passing h to her child, and there is a 50 percent chance that the child will be male. The probability that she will have a son with hemophilia is $(0.9)(0.5)(0.5) = 0.225 = 22.5$ percent.

33. a. Cross 1 reduces to

P   *AA BB DD* × *aa bb dd*

F_1 $A\,B\,D/a\,b\,d$ × $a\,b\,d/a\,b\,d$, correct order

F_2			
	A B D	316	parental
	a b d	314	parental
	A B d	31	CO B–D
	a b D	39	CO B–D
	A b d	130	CO A–B
	a B D	140	CO A–B
	A b D	17	DCO
	a B d	13	DCO

A–B: $100\%(130 + 140 + 17 + 13)/1000 = 30$ m.u.

B–D: $100\%(31 + 39 + 17 + 13)/1000 = 10$ m.u.

Cross 2 reduces to

P   *AA CC EE* × *aa cc ee*

F_1 $A\,C\,E/a\,c\,e$ × $a\,c\,e/a\,c\,e$, correct order

F_2			
	A C E	243	parental
	a c e	237	parental
	A c e	62	CO A–C
	a C E	58	CO A–C

$A\ C\ e$	155	CO C–E
$a\ c\ E$	165	CO C–E
$a\ C\ e$	46	DCO
$A\ c\ E$	34	DCO

A–C: 100% $(62 + 58 + 46 + 34)/1000 = 20$ m.u.

C–E: 100% $(155 + 165 + 46 + 34)/1000 = 40$ m.u.

The map can be put together in one way that accommodates all the data:

$$E \overset{}{\underset{40\text{ m.u.}}{|}} \quad C \overset{}{\underset{20\text{ m.u.}}{|}} \quad A \overset{}{\underset{30\text{ m.u.}}{|}} \quad B \overset{}{\underset{10\text{ m.u.}}{|}} \quad D \,|$$

b. Interference (I) = 1 – [(observed DCO)/(expected DCO)]

For cross 1: I = 1 – {30/[(0.30)(0.10)(1000)]}

= 1 – 1 = 0, no interference.

For cross 2: I = 1 – {80/[(0.20)(0.40)(1000)]}

= 1 – 1 = 0, no interference.

TIPS ON PROBLEM SOLVING

In a three-point testcross, the gene order is determined by comparing the parental type progeny, which will be most frequent, with the double-crossover progeny, which will be least frequent. The gene that has switched with respect to the other two genes in this comparison must be located between them:

parentals: $D\ a\ R,\ d\ A\ r$

double crossovers: $d\ a\ R,\ D\ A\ r$

The order is $A\ D\ R$; the parental chromosomes are $a\ D\ R/A\ d\ r$ (see Problem 10).

In three-point testcrosses, if the data indicate that the progeny males have a different phenotype than the females, the genes are on the X chromosome. The two most frequent phenotypes in the males indicate the genotypes of the X chromosomes in the female, and the two least frequent phenotypes in the males indicate the gene order (see Problem 18). To estimate the frequency of crossing-over, utilize the data from the males only (see Problem 18).

If, in a three-point cross, the data indicate that the genes are autosomal, it is frequently necessary to focus on the homozygous recessive progeny exclusively (see Problem 14). Also, if the cross is not a testcross, it may be necessary to use the homozygote recessive frequency to estimate the frequency of crossing-over (see Problem 12).

SELF-TEST

1. Given the following map, what are the recombinant genotypes and their frequency from the cross $M\,n/m\,N \times m\,n/m\,n$?

$$\overset{M}{\underset{}{\vdash}} \quad 16 \text{ m.u.} \quad \overset{N}{\underset{}{\dashv}}$$

2. There is 24 percent crossing-over in humans between two autosomal genes, L and M. In 250 primary oocytes, how many would be expected to have a chiasma between these two genes?

3. In *Drosophila*, a cross was made between two homozygous lines, A and B. Line A females carried a mutant allele that resulted in rough eye texture. They were crossed with line B males, who had a mutant allele for a different gene that resulted in rough eye texture. The F_1 progeny were wild-type females and males with a rough eye texture. The F_2 progeny were

females		males	
50%	wild type	13%	wild type
50%	rough	87%	rough

Analyze these data.

4. Consider the following F_2 progeny.

0.41	Dd Ee	0.045	dd Ee
0.2025	dd EE	0.045	Dd ee
0.2025	DD ee	0.0025	DD EE
0.045	Dd EE	0.0025	dd ee
0.045	DD Ee		

Are the genes linked? If linked, by how many m.u.? What were the parental chromosomes?

5. A testcross resulted in the following progeny. Construct a gene map from the data. What is the interference value?

375	Aa Bb dd	90	Aa Bb Dd
380	aa bb Dd	85	aa bb dd
26	aa Bb Dd	8	aa Bb dd
30	Aa bb dd	6	Aa bb Dd

6. You are given the following map and the information that inter-ference is 0.4. What is the change in the number of double-crossover progeny due to interference?

L $\qquad$ 10 m.u. $\qquad$ M $\qquad$ 5 m.u. $\qquad$ N

7. In rats, a mutant recessive allele, k, results in kinky hairs. Another mutant recessive allele, t, results in a short, stubby tail. The two genes are 30 m.u. apart. What are the progeny phenotypes from two het-erozygous parents, in coupling?

SOLUTIONS TO SELF-TEST

1. The recombinants will be $M N/m\ n$ and $m\ n/m\ n$. Each will occur at a rate of $1/2(0.16) = 8\%$ percent.

2. Although each recombination event gives rise to two recombi-nants and two parentals, this occurs after the primary oocyte stage. Therefore, the frequency of crossing-over is simply $(0.24)(250) = 60$ oocytes with a chiasma.

3. The F_1 progeny indicate that the defect in the female line (line A) is X-linked. If the line B defect is autosomal, it would result in indepen-dent assortment in the F_2 male progeny. This was not observed. Therefore, both genes are X-linked.

Call the defect in line A rr and the defect in line B ss. The cross is

P $r S/r S \times R s/Y$

F_1 $r S/R s \times r S/Y$

F_2 males

   $r S/Y$ rough

   $R s/Y$ rough

   $r s/Y$ rough

   $R S/Y$ wild type

The $R\ S/Y$ genotype occurred in 13 percent of the population, which represents half of the recombinants. Therefore, the two genes are 26 m.u. apart.

4.   If the genes are not linked, then a $9:3:3:1$ ratio would occur. The observed ratio is

        0.5025 $D-E-$ 0.2475 $D-ee$

        0.2475 $dd\ E-$ 0.0025 $dd\ ee$

This ratio is very far from the expected ratio, assuming independent assortment. Therefore, the genes are linked.

The parental chromosomes can be determined from the least frequent classes, which represent crossovers. If crossovers are $DD\ EE$ and $dd\ ee$, the F_1 chromosomes must be $D\ e/d\ E$. Assuming that the parentals were homozygous, the original cross must have been $DD\ ee \times dd\ EE$.

The two least frequent classes each represent the fusion of recombinant gametes. The probability of such a fusion is the probability of a recombinant gamete times the probability of a recombinant gamete. Therefore, the probability of a recombinant gamete is the square root of either genotypic class, or 0.05. Because each recombinant gamete has a reciprocal gamete occurring at the same frequency, the total frequency of recombination is $(2)(0.05) = 0.10$. Therefore, the genes are 10 m.u. apart.

5.   The gene order is $B\ A\ D$, and the two parental chromosomes are $B\ A\ d/b\ a\ d$.

      $B–A$: $100\%(26 + 30 + 8 + 6)/1000 = 7$ m.u.

      $A–D$: $100\%(90 + 85 + 8 + 6)/1000 = 18.9$ m.u.

      $I = 1 - \{(8 + 6)/[(0.07)(0.189)(1000)]\} = 1 - 1.06 = -0.06$.

6.   The observed and expected number of double crossovers, without interference, is $(0.1)(0.05) = 0.005$.

With interference of 0.4, the observed number of double crossovers is

      $I = 1 - [(\text{observed DCO})/(\text{expected DCO})]$

      observed DCO $=$ expected DCO $- [I\ (\text{expected DCO})]$

                $= 0.005 - [(0.4)(0.005)]$

                $= 0.003$

The change in the number of double crossovers is 0.002.

7.   P $K\ T/k\ t \times K\ T/k\ t$

To work this problem, first determine the gametic frequencies:

0.35 *K T*   0.15 *K t*

0.35 *k t*   0.15 *k T*

The frequency of the progeny will be

Phenotype	Genotypes	Frequency
kinky	*kk TT, kk Tt*	$(0.15)(0.15) + 2(0.35)(0.15) = 0.1275$
short tail	*KK tt, Kk tt*	$(0.15)(0.15) + 2(0.35)(0.15) = 0.1275$
kinky, short tail	*kk tt*	$(0.35)(0.35) = 0.1225$
wild type	*K– T–*	$1 - 0.1275 - 0.1275 - 0.1225 = 0.6225$

6

Linkage II: Special Eukaryotic Chromosome Mapping Techniques

IMPORTANT TERMS AND CONCEPTS

Multiple crossovers in larger intervals result in an underestimate of map distance between two genes. The relationship between real map distance and the **recombinant frequency**, RF, is not linear. The **mapping function** provides a closer approximation of the real relationship. The **Poisson distribution** describes the frequency of 0, 1, 2, . . . n crossovers, given the average number of crossovers. The general expression is

$$f(i) = e^{-m}m^i/i!$$

where e is the base of natural logarithms, m is the mean number of events, and i is an integer that ranges from 0 to n.

Meiotic events in diploid organisms are studied by means of an estimation based on the observation of random meiotic products. An indirect calculation of the recombinant frequency is conducted using the Poisson distribution. In contrast, the four products of a single meiotic event can be studied directly through **tetrad analysis** in certain haploid organisms. This allows for a direct calculation of the recombinant frequency, again using the Poisson distribution.

Linear tetrad analysis is frequently conducted using *Neurospora*. Recall that meiosis, followed immediately by mitosis, results in eight meiotic products.

A monohybrid cross in which no crossing-over occurs between the gene studied and the centromere results in **first-division segregation** (M_I) of alleles and a 4 : 4 pattern of the progeny.

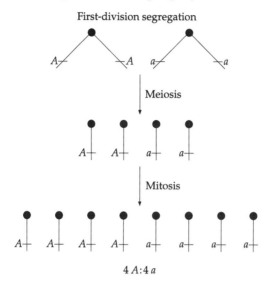

First-division segregation

4 A:4 a

Any deviation from this pattern is the result of **second-division segregation** (M_{II}) of alleles and signals crossing-over. One example of a second-division segregation pattern is

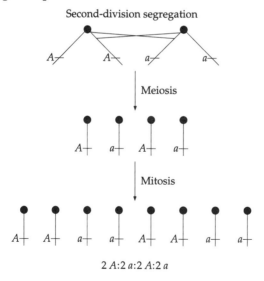

Second-division segregation

2 A:2 a:2 A:2 a

Because each crossover produces two recombinant and two nonrecombinant products, the frequency of recombinant asci must be adjusted to reflect the true RF value. The distance of a locus from the centromere is therefore

$$RF = \frac{1/2 \text{ number of recombinant asci}}{\text{total number of asci}}$$

Dihybrid crosses may involve two unlinked or two linked genes. As will become apparent below, the relative frequency of asci types allows the determination of linkage or nonlinkage.

First-division segregation of two unlinked loci results in two types of equally frequent $4:4$ patterns, **parental ditype**, PD, and **nonparental ditype**, NPD. Parental ditype means that there are two types of spores and each spore is parental in allelic content. Nonparental ditype means that each spore is recombinant and there are two types of spores. For example,

Parentals: $A\,B \times a\,b$

PD: $A\,B,\,A\,B,\,A\,B,\,A\,B,\,a\,b,a\,b,\,a\,b,\,a\,b$

            $4\,A\,B:4\,a\,b$

NPD: $A\,b,\,A\,b,\,A\,b,\,A\,b,\,a\,B,\,a\,B,\,a\,B,\,a\,B$

            $4\,A\,b:4\,a\,B$

Any deviation from the two $4:4$ patterns for two unlinked loci results from second-division segregation, signaling crossing-over between a gene and the centromere. One example is $A\,b,\,A\,b,\,A\,B,\,A\,B,$ $a\,b,\,a\,b,\,a\,B,\,a\,B$, or $2:2:2:2$. The asci that contain the allelic combinations $A\,B,\,a\,b,\,A\,b,$ and $a\,B$ are called **tetratypes**, T, indicating that there are four different types of meiotic products. A tetratype in unlinked loci indicates that crossing-over has occurred between a gene and its centromere. Whether or not crossing-over occurs, the number of parental ditypes equals the number of nonparental ditypes, and the NPD/T ratio is between $1/4$ and infinity when the two genes are not linked. The RF between a gene and its centromere is calculated separately for each gene, using the formula

$$RF = \frac{1/2 \text{ number of recombinant asci}}{\text{total number of asci}}$$

If two loci are linked, the number of parental ditypes significantly exceeds the number of nonparental ditypes. The NPD/T ratio is between 0 and $1/4$. No crossing-over leads to a $4:4$ pattern, while a single crossover between a gene and its centromere results in a tetratype. Two crossovers result in a parental ditype, a tetratype, or a nonparental ditype, depending on which strands are involved. The RF between a gene and its centromere is calculated separately for each gene, using the formula

$$RF = \frac{1/2 \text{ number of recombinant asci}}{\text{total number of asci}}$$

The RF between the two linked genes is calculated using the following formula:

$$RF = \frac{100\% \, [1/2T + NPD]}{\text{total number of asci}}$$

Because two crossovers can lead to a parental ditype, this formula results in an underestimate of the RF.

These relationships are summarized below:

Unlinked	Linked
PD = NPD	PD >> NPD
NPD/T = 1/4 to infinity	NPD/T = 0 to 1/4

Mitotic crossing-over leading to recombination and **mitotic nondisjunction** can result in **mitotic segregation** of alleles following mitosis. Mitotic segregation has been extensively studied in fungal cells. A **heterokaryon** generated by hyphal fusion in *Aspergillus* consists of two nuclei in a common cytoplasm. Phenotypic variegation indicates mitotic segregation in the heterokaryons.

Human chromosomes have been mapped using **somatic cell hybridization.** Fusion of two nuclei, one human and the other frequently mouse, results in a gradual and random loss of human chromosomes. The presence or absence of human enzymes is correlated with the presence or absence of human chromosomes in several cell lines.

Be sure that you have thoroughly read the entire chapter before you attempt any of the problems.

SOLUTIONS TO PROBLEMS

1. a.   +, +, al–2, al–2, +, +, al–2, al–2

    al–2, al–2, +, +, al–2, al–2, +, +

    b.   The 8 percent value can be used to calculate the distance between the gene and the centromere. That distance is 1/2 the percentage of second division segregation, or 4 percent.

2. a.   *arg–6 al–2* and + +

    b. *arg–6 +, arg–6 al–2, + +,* and *+ al–2*

    c. *arg–6 +* and *+ al–2*

3. The formula for this problem is $f(i) = e^{-m}m^i/i!$

    where $m = 2$ and $i = 0$, 1, and 2.

    a. $f(0) = e^{-2}2^0/0! = e^{-2} = 0.135$

    b. $f(1) = e^{-2}2^1/1! = e^{-2}(2) = 0.27$

    c. $f(2) = e^{-2}2^2/2! = e^{-2}(2) = 0.27$

4. **a.** A region 1 crossover will yield the following chromosomes:

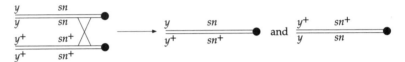

    Mitosis can yield two equally likely results: *y sn/y sn* and *y⁺ sn⁺/y⁺ sn⁺* or both daughter cells *y sn/y⁺ sn⁺*. In the first case, one yellow singed spot will exist in a brown unsinged fly. In the second case, the resulting cells will be wild type.

    b. A region 2 crossover will yield the following chromosomes:

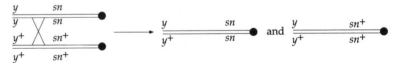

    Mitosis can yield the following combinations:

    y sn/y⁺ sn⁺ and *y⁺ sn/y sn⁺* wild type

      or

    y sn/ y sn⁺ and *y⁺ sn/y⁺ sn⁺* yellow, unsinged spot

5. Rewrite the column headings to note what is missing from the media, and then count the different types of patterns. Growth will occur if the wild-type gene is present or if the medium supplies whatever gene product is missing:

–Leu	–Nic	–Ad	–Arg	Number
+	+	–	–	6
–	–	+	+	4
–	+	–	+	5

(continued on next page)

–Leu	–Nic	–Ad	–Arg	Number
+	–	+	–	4
+	–	–	–	1
+	–	–	+	0
–	+	+	–	0

The first four categories have a $1:1:1:1$ pattern, indicating independent assortment of two chromosomes. Furthermore, the pattern of growth on two of the media types and no growth on two of the media types indicates that two genes are located on each of the two chromosomes, rather than one gene on one chromosome and three genes on the second.

The two missing categories indicate which genes are linked.

Remember that the cross is

arg⁻ ad⁻ nic⁺ leu⁺ × arg⁺ ad⁺ nic⁻ leu⁻.

Growth is not seen in the (–Nic and –Ad) or (–Leu and –Arg) media simultaneously, which means that *nic* is linked to *ad* and *leu* is linked to *arg*. Both *nic* and *ad* assort independently with *leu* and *arg*, suggesting that *nic* is not linked to *leu* and *arg* and that *ad* is not linked to *leu* and *arg*.

   a. The parents were
       ad⁻ nic⁺   leu⁺ arg⁻   ×   ad⁺ nic⁻   leu⁻ arg⁺

   b. Culture 16 resulted from a crossover between *ad* and *nic*. The reciprocal did not show up in the small sample.

   6. This problem is analogous to meiosis in organisms that form linear tetrads. Let red = *R* and blue = *r*. Then meiosis is occurring in an organism that is *Rr* (but there are 4 "alleles" because the "chromosomes" are at the "two-chromatids-per-chromosome" stage), and the "alleles" are at loci far from the centromere. The patterns, their frequencies, and the division of segregation are given below. Notice that the probabilities change as each ball/allele is selected. This occurs when there is sampling without replacement.

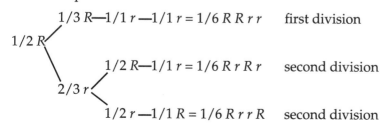

$$1/3\ R{-}1/1\ r{-}1/1\ r = 1/6\ R\,R\,r\,r \quad \text{first division}$$

$$1/2\ R$$

$$1/2\ R{-}1/1\ r = 1/6\ R\,r\,R\,r \quad \text{second division}$$

$$2/3\ r$$

$$1/2\ r{-}1/1\ R = 1/6\ R\,r\,r\,R \quad \text{second division}$$

$1/2\, r$
$\qquad$ $1/3\, r$—$1/1\, R$—$1/1\, R = 1/6\, r\, r\, R\, R$ first division

$\qquad\qquad$ $1/2\, R$—$1/1\, r = 1/6\, r\, R\, R\, r$ second division

$\qquad$ $2/3\, R$
$\qquad\qquad$ $1/2\, r$—$1/1\, R = 1/6\, r\, R\, r\, R$ second division

These results indicate one-third first division segregation and two-thirds second division segregation.

7. a. The formula is $RF = 1/2(1 - e^{-m})$, where recombination $= 0.2$. Therefore, $e^{-m} = 1 - 0.4 = 0.6$, and $m = 0.51$ (from e^{-m} tables). Because an m value of $1.0 = 50$ map units (m.u.), 0.51×50 m.u. $= 25.5$ m.u.

b. The problem is the interpretation of 45 m.u. That could represent two loci approximately 45 m.u. apart, or it could represent two unlinked loci. A χ^2 test is needed for decision making. Hypothesis: no linkage, resulting in a $1:1:1:1$ ratio.

$$\chi^2 = \frac{(58-50)^2 + (52-50)^2 + (47-50)^2 + (43-50)^2}{50}$$

$$= \frac{(64+4+9+49)}{50} = 2.52$$

With 3 degrees of freedom, the probability is greater than 10% that the genes are not linked. Therefore, the hypothesis of no linkage can be accepted.

8. To work these problems, it is first necessary to draw the chromosomes and explore the consequences of crossing-over in different regions. The genes can be assumed to be coupled or in repulsion.

With no crossovers, the pattern is $p\, q$, $p\, q$, $+ +$, $+ +$, a parental ditype. Both genes show an M_I pattern.

Pattern A

With one CO between q and the centromere, the pattern is $p\, q$, $p +$, $+ q$, $+ +$. This is a T, with gene p showing M_I and gene q showing M_{II} segregation.

Pattern B

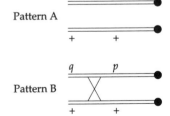

With one CO between p and the centromere and one CO between p and q, the pattern is $p\, q$, $+ q$, $p +$, $+ +$. This is a T, with M_{II} for p and M_I for q. (Note: a 4-strand double would also give the same result.)

Pattern C

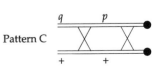

With one CO between p and the centromere, the pattern is $p\,q$, ++, This is a PD, with both genes showing M_{II} segregation.

Pattern D

The pattern is p +, + +, $p\,q$, + q. This is a T, with both genes showing M_{II} segregation.

Pattern E

a. $M_I\,M_I$, PD is pattern A, no crossovers. The probability is

p(no CO from centromere to p)p(no CO from centromere to q)

$= (0.88)(0.80) = 0.704.$

b. $M_I\,M_I$, NPD requires two crossovers between q and the centromere, which cannot occur according to the rules of the problem. The probability is 0.

c. $M_I\,M_{II}$, T is pattern B. The probability is

p(no CO from p to centromere)p(CO between q and centromere)

$= (0.88)(0.2) = 0.176.$

d. $M_{II}\,M_I$, T is pattern C. Because there are two ways to achieve this result, in the following calculation there is an adjustment by a factor of $1/2$. The probability is

$(1/2)$p(CO between p and centromere)p(CO between q and centromere)

$= (0.5)(0.12)(0.2) = 0.012.$

e. $M_{II}\,M_{II}$, PD is pattern D. The probability is

p(CO between p and centromere)p(no CO from q to centromere)

$= (0.12)(0.8) = 0.096.$

f. $M_{II}\,M_{II}$, NPD requires one crossover between p and the centromere and two crossovers between q and the centromere, which cannot occur according to the rules of the problem. The probability is 0.

g. $M_{II}\,M_{II}$, T is pattern E. Because there are two ways to achieve this result, in the following calculation there is an adjustment by a factor of $1/2$. The probability is

$(1/2)$p(CO between p and centromere)p(CO between q and centromere)

$= (0.5)(0.12)(0.2) = 0.012.$

9.

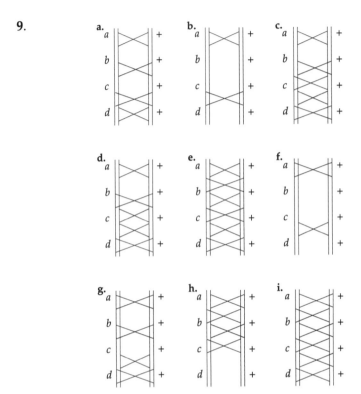

10. Before beginning this problem, classify all asci as PD, NPD, or T and determine whether there is M_I or M_{II} segregation for each gene:

			Asci Type			
1	2	3	4	5	6	7
Type						
PD	NPD	T	T	PD	NPD	T
gene *a* (M)						
I	I	I	II	II	II	II
gene *b* (M)						
I	I	II	I	II	II	II

If PD >> NPD and NPD/T < 1/4, there is linkage. If PD = NPD and NPD/T > 1/4, there is no linkage. The distance between a gene and its centromere = 100%(1/2)(M_{II})/total. The distance between two genes = 100%(1/2T + NPD)/total.

Cross 1: PD = NPD; the genes are not linked.

a–centromere: 100%(1/2)(0)/100 = 0 m.u. Gene *a* is very close to the centromere.

b–centromere: 100%(1/2)(32)/100 = 16 m.u.

●——*a*————— ●————*b*—————
0   16

Cross 2: PD >> NPD; the genes are linked.

$a–b$: $100\%[(1/2)(15) + 1]/100 = 8.5$ m.u.

a–centromere: $100\%(1/2)(0)/100 = 0$ m.u. Gene a is very close to the centromere.

b–centromere: $100\%(1/2)(15)/100 = 7.5$ m.u.

The data contradict because of asci that show an M_I pattern for b even though crossing-over must have occurred between b and the centromere. Therefore, the estimate of 8.5 m.u. between the two genes is the better estimate.

$$\underset{0 \qquad\qquad 8.5}{\bullet \overset{a \qquad\qquad\qquad b}{\rule{6cm}{0.4pt}}}$$

Cross 3: PD >> NPD; the genes are linked.

$a–b$: $100\%[(1/2)(40) + (3)]/100 = 23$ m.u.

a–centromere: $100\%(1/2)(2)/100 = 1$ m.u.

b–centromere: $100\%(1/2)(40 + 2)/100 = 21$ m.u.

Again, the data are contradictory for the same reasons as in Cross 2.

$$\underset{1 \qquad\quad 23}{\bullet \overset{a \qquad\qquad b}{\rule{4cm}{0.4pt}}} \quad \text{or} \quad \underset{1 \qquad\quad 21}{\overset{a \qquad\qquad b}{\rule{4cm}{0.4pt}}}$$

The first diagram is the better interpretation of the data.

Cross 4: PD >> NPD; the genes are linked.

$a–b$: $100\%[(1/2)(20) + 1]/100 = 11$ m.u.

a–centromere: $100\%(1/2)(10)/100 = 5$ m.u.

b–centromere: $100\%(1/2)(18 + 8 + 1)/100 = 13.5$ m.u. Again, the b-centromere distance is underestimated.

$$\underset{5 \qquad\quad 11}{\bullet \overset{a \qquad\qquad b}{\rule{5cm}{0.4pt}}}$$

Cross 5: PD = NPD; the genes are not linked.

a–centromere: $100\%(1/2)(22 + 8 + 10 + 20)/99 = 30.3$ m.u.

b–centromere: $100\%(1/2)(24 + 8 + 10 + 20)/99 = 31.3$ m.u.

For values this large, in tetrad analysis, the genes are considered unlinked to their centromeres.

Cross 6: PD >> NPD; the genes are linked.

$a–b$: $100\%[(1/2)(1 + 3 + 4) + 0]/100 = 4$ m.u.

a–centromere: $100\%(1/2)(3 + 61 + 4)/100 = 34$ m.u.

b–centromere: $100\%(1/2)(1 + 61 + 4)/100 = 33$ m.u.

The b–centromere distance is underestimated. Genes a and b are more than 50 m.u. from the centromere and are 4 m.u. apart.

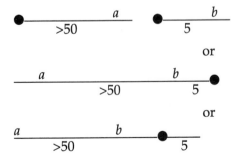

Cross 7: PD >> NPD; the genes are linked.

a–b: $100\%[(1/2)(3 + 2) + 0]/100 = 2.5$ m.u.

a–centromere: $100\%(1/2)(2)/100 = 1$ m.u.

b–centromere: $100\%(1/2)(3)/100 = 1.5$ m.u.

Cross 8: PD = NPD; the genes are not linked.

a–centromere: $100\%(1/2)(22 + 12 + 11+ 22)/100 = 33.5$ m.u.

b–centromere: $100\%(1/2)(20 + 12 + 11 + 22)/100 = 32.5$ m.u.

Same as cross 5.

Cross 9: PD >> NPD; the genes are linked.

a–b: $100\%[1/2(10 + 18 + 2) + 1]/100 = 16$ m.u.

a–centromere: $100\%(1/2)(18 + 1 + 2)/100 = 10.5$ m.u.

b–centromere: $100\%(1/2)(10 + 1 + 2)/100 = 6.5$ m.u.

Cross 10: PD = NPD; the genes are not linked.

a–centromere: $100\%(1/2)(60 + 1 + 2 + 5)/100 = 34$ m.u.

b–centromere: $100\%(1/2)(2 + 1 + 2 + 5)/100 = 5$ m.u.

Cross 11: PD = NPD; the genes are not linked.

a – centromere: 100%(1/2)(0)/100 = 0 m.u.

b – centromere: 100%(1/2)(0)/100 = 0 m.u.

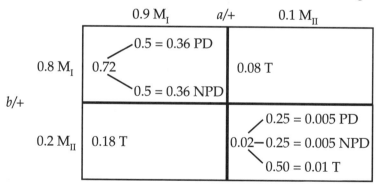

11. The cross is *a* +/+ *b*, with the two genes unlinked. Each gene has a given probability of a crossover between it and the centromere. Remember that map units = 100%[(1/2)(number crossover asci)]/total asci. Therefore, if there are 5 m.u. between a gene and its centromere, there will be 10 percent crossover or second division asci (M_{II}) and 90 percent noncrossover or first division asci (M_I).

A 4 : 4 pattern exists with no crossing-over. Thus, if neither gene shows a crossover, two equally likely patterns are possible: *a b, a b*, ++, ++ (NPD) and *a* +, *a* +, + *b*, + *b* (PD).

If one gene (assume gene *a*) experiences a crossover, the pattern for it is *a*, +, *a*, + or *a*, +, +, *a*. Combined with a 4 : 4 pattern for gene *b*, this would result in four equally likely outcomes: *a b*, + *b*, *a* +, ++ (T); or *a b*, + *b*, ++, *a* + (T); or + *b*, *a b*, ++, *a* + (T); or *a b*, + *b*, ++, *a* + (T).

If both genes experience crossovers, the pattern is 1/4 PD : 1/2 T : 1/4 NPD (you should check to see if you can produce this ratio).

The following table presents the probabilities for both genes:

b/+		*a*/+: 0.9 M_I	*a*/+: 0.1 M_{II}
	0.8 M_I	0.72: 0.5 = 0.36 PD; 0.5 = 0.36 NPD	0.08 T
	0.2 M_{II}	0.18 T	0.02: 0.25 = 0.005 PD; 0.25 = 0.005 NPD; 0.50 = 0.01 T

To understand the above table, look at cell 1. No crossovers occur between either gene and its centromere (p = 0.8 × 0.9). The pattern for a is thus *a a* + + and the pattern for *b* is *b b* + +. The *b*/+ gene can line up in either orientation with the *a*/+ gene: *a b, a b*, ++, ++ or *a* +, *a* +, + *b*, + *b*. Therefore, there is a 1 : 1 chance of *a* +, *a* +, + *b*, + *b* (PD) and *a b, a b*, ++, ++ (NPD). The other cells can be interpreted in a similar manner.

a. 36.5% PD: the total of PD from the table

b. 36.5% NPD: the total of NPD from the table

    c. 27% T: the total of T from the table

    d. 50% recombinants: 1/2 (T) + NPD

    e. 25% ++

12. The frequency of recombinants is equal to NPD + 1/2T. The uncorrected map distance based on RF = (NPD + 1/2T)/total. The corrected map distance = 50(T + 6NPD)/total.

Cross 1:

recombinant frequency   = 4% + 1/2(45%) = 26.5

uncorrected map distance = [4% + 1/2(45%)]/100% = 26.5 m.u.

corrected map distance   = 50[45% + 6(4)]/100% = 34.5 m.u.

Cross 2:

recombinant frequency   = 2% + 1/2(34%) = 19%

uncorrected map distance = [2% + 1/2(34%)]/100% = 19 m.u.

corrected map distance   = 50[34% + 6(2%)]/100% = 29 m.u.

Cross 3:

recombinant frequency   = 5% + 1/2(50%) = 30%

uncorrected map distance = [5% + 1/2(50%)]/100% = 30 m.u.

corrected map distance   = 50[50% + 6(5%)]/100% = 40 m.u.

13. First, classify the asci: 138 T, 12 NPD, and 150 PD, for a total of 300 asci.

    a. The frequency of recombinant asci is 50 percent, which leads to an uncorrected RF of 100%(12 + 69)/300 = 27 m.u. The corrected RF is $m = -\ln(1 - 0.54) = -\ln(0.46) = 0.63$, which is 31.5 m.u.

    b. The general formula is DCOs = 4(NPD). Therefore, DCOs = 4(12) = 48. One-half of them look like tetratypes and one half look like parental ditypes. Therefore

        actual 0 crossovers = PD − 12 = 150 − 12 = 138 or 46%

        actual 1 crossovers = T − 24 = 138 − 24 = 114 or 38%

        actual DCOs = 48 or 16%

    c. To correct for double crossovers, the general formula for the mean number of crossovers is $m = T + 6NPD = [138 + 6(12)]/300 = 0.70$, which is 35 m.u.

14.   a.   The cross is $arg^- \times arg^-$. Because arg^+ progeny result, more than one locus is involved, and each deviation from wild type is recessive. The cross can be rewritten

           $arg\text{-}1^+ \ arg\text{-}2^- \times arg\text{-}1^- \ arg\text{-}2^+$

           A 4 : 0 ascus is a PD ascus, because all spores require arginine. The 3 : 1 ascus must represent a T ascus. The 2 : 2 ascus is an NPD ascus.

    b.   The data support independent assortment of the two genes. PD = NPD = 40, and NPD/T = 40/20 = 2.00.

15.   Because PD = NPD, the *his-?* is not linked to *ad-3*. The T-type ascospores require one crossover between the gene and the centromere. Because only 10 tetrads were analyzed, *his-2* would be expected to produce one-tenth of a T ascus [10(0.01) = 0.1], *his-3* would be expected to produce one T ascus [10(0.1) = 1], and *his-4* would be expected to produce four T asci [10(0.4) = 4]. Only *his-4* is located far enough from its centromere to result in 60 percent T asci. Therefore, *his-?* is *his-4*.

16.   Because the two mutants, when crossed, result in some black spores, two separate genes are involved, and both deviations from wild type are recessive. Let mutant 1 = $w \ t^+$, mutant 2 = $w^+ \ t$, and wild type = $w^+ \ t^+$. The cross involving the two mutants is

    P $w \ t^+$ (white) $\times w^+ \ t$ (tan)

Asci types are

    4 black : 4 white = 4 $w^+ \ t^+$: 4 $w \ t$ (NPD)

    4 tan : 4 white = 4 $w^+ \ t$: 4 $w \ t^+$ (PD)

    4 white : 2 black : 2 tan = 2 $w \ t^+$ (white) : 2 $w \ t$ (white):

                                        2 $w^+ \ t^+$ (black) : 2 $w^+ \ t$ (tan)

    Notice that there are two types of white, indicating that there is an epistatic relationship between w and t. The w allele blocks expression of the t^+ allele.

17.   At meiosis I, normal segregation is between homologous chromosomes. The two attached-X chromosomes segregate together because they structurally are the equivalent of a single chromosome. This produces one daughter cell with two copies of X (disomic) and one daughter cell with no copies of X (nullisomic):

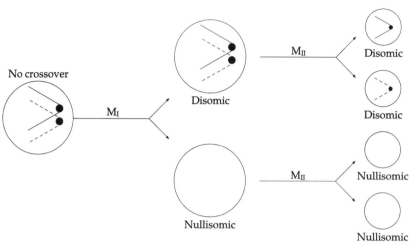

Egg	Sperm	Progeny
XX	X	XXX, nonviable
XX	Y	XXY, viable female
O	X	XO, sterile male
O	Y	OY, nonviable

a. A single crossover between *a* and *b*, involving strands 1 and 2 or involving strands 3 and 4, does not result in recombination. However, a 1-3 (illustrated below), 1-4, 2-3, or 2-4 crossover between *a* and *b* results in recombination.

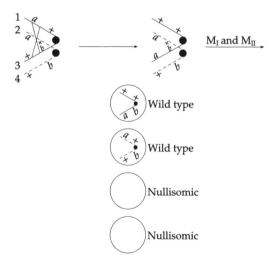

A single crossover between *b* and the centromere, involving strands 1 and 2 or involving strands 3 and 4, does not
result in recombination. A 1-3 (illustrated below) or 2-4
crossover between *b* and the centromere also does not result
in recombination.

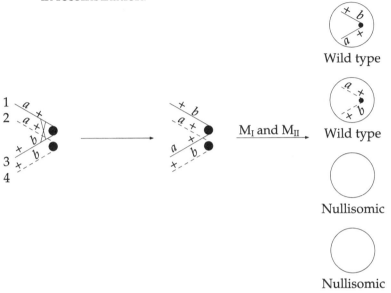

However, a 2-3 (illustrated below) or a 1-4 single crossover
between *b* and the centromere does result in recombination.

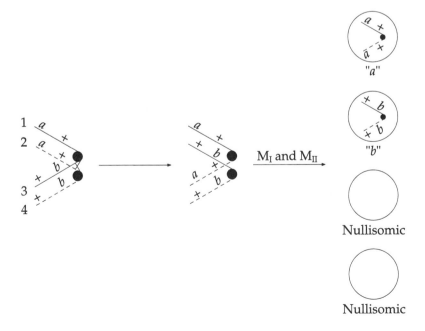

b. With double crossovers, the following are produced.

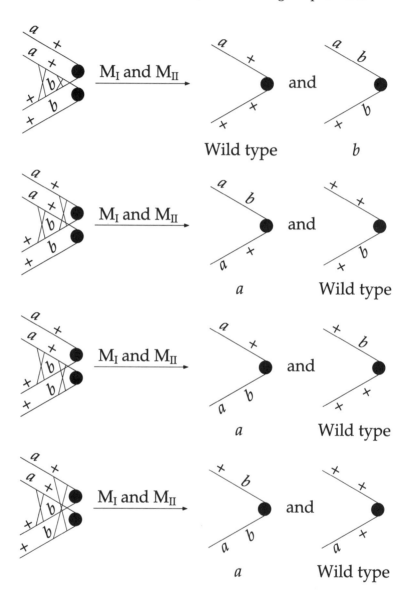

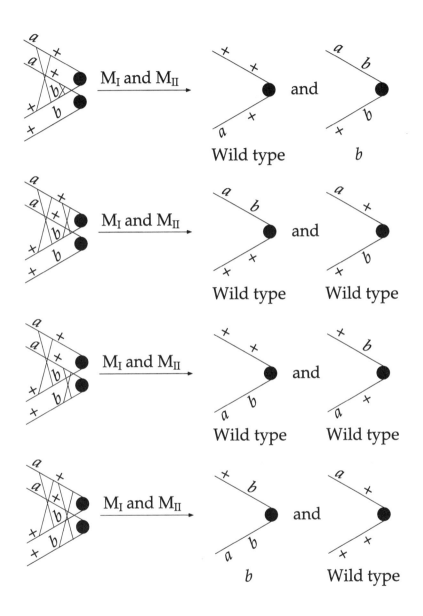

Note that the phenotype in each female (XXY) shows one-half the meiotic products. Thus, each female can be regarded as a half-tetrad.

18.   First classify the asci types. Number 1 is a tetratype (T), number 2 is a parental ditype (PD) and number 3 is a nonparental ditype (NPD).

Recall the following relationships (page 161 of the text). Tetratypes arise from single and double crossovers. Single crossovers yield 100% T asci, and double crossovers yield 50% T asci. Parental ditypes arise from no crossovers (100% PD) and double crossovers (25% PD). Nonparental ditypes arise from 25% of the double crossovers.

Double crossovers would be expected to occur at a frequency of $(0.05)(0.08) = 0.004$. Therefore, the frequency of NPD would be expected to be $1/4 \times 0.004 = 0.001$.

Because PD = NCO + 1/4 DCO, PD = [1 − SCO − DCO] + 1/4 DCO. Substituting the numerical values,

$$PD = 1 - 0.13 - (0.05)(0.08) + 1/4\,(0.05)(0.08)$$

$$= 1 - 0.13 - 0.004 + 0.001 = 0.867.$$

Because T = SCO + 1/2 DCO,

$$T = 0.13 + 1/2\,(0.05)(0.08) = 0.13 + 0.002 = 0.132.$$

Number 1 is a T ascus, which occurs at a frequency of 0.132.

Number 2 is a PD ascus, which occurs at a frequency of 0.867.

Number 3 is an NPD ascus, which occurs at a frequency of 0.001.

19.   First classify the asci types and determine whether they are M_I or M_{II} ascii for each gene:

Type	un	cyh
1. T	II	I
2. T	I	II
3. PD	I	I
4. PD	II	II
5. NPD	II	II
6. T	II	II

Notice that PD (47 + 2) >> NPD (2). The two genes are linked.

a. $un - cyh = 100\%\,[1/2\,T + NPD]/(total\,\#\,asci)$

$$= \frac{100\%\,[1/2\,(15 + 29 + 5) + 2]}{15 + 29 + 47 + 2 + 2 + 5}$$

$$= 100\% \, [1/2 \, (29) + 2]/ \, 100 = 16.5 \text{ m.u.}$$

$$un - \text{centromere} = 100\% \, (1/2)(\# \, M_{II} \text{ asci})/(\text{total } \# \text{ asci})$$

$$= 100\% \, (1/2)(15 + 2 + 2 + 5)/100 = 12 \text{ m.u.}$$

$$cyh - \text{centromere} = 100\% \, (1/2)(\# \, M_{II} \text{ asci})/(\text{total } \# \text{ asci})$$

$$= 100\% \, (1/2)(29 + 2 + 2 + 5)/100$$

$$= 19.0 \text{ m.u.}$$

The map data are self-contradictory because no arrangement of 12 m.u. and 19 m.u. can equal a total distance of 16.5 m.u. Recall that centromeres often give "funny" results when calculating map distances. Also note the first two ascii, which are reciprocals, occur in fairly high frequency, suggesting independent assortment of the two loci even though they are linked. The centromere must be between the two genes.

The final map is

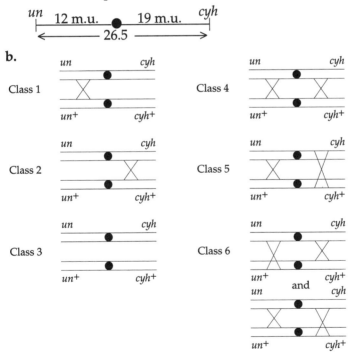

b.

c. Figure 6-14 in the text can be used as a guide to determine the missing tetrads if the number of crossovers is limited to two. Classify the asci types as to the number of crossovers involved using the table from the text:

Type	un	cyh	C O
1. T	II	II	DCO
2. T	I	II	SCO
3. PD	I	I	NCO
4. PD	II	II	DCO
5. NPD	II	II	DCO
6. T	II	II	DCO

The above table indicates that the six basic asci types that result from 0, 1 or 2 crossovers are present, although the reciprocals have not been listed. For example, the reciprocal of type 1 is

un⁺ cyh⁺

un cyh⁺

un⁺ cyh⁺

un cyh

Other missing asci types, such as those given below, result from three or more crossovers.

un⁺ cyh⁺		*un*	*cyh*
un	*cyh*	*un⁺*	*cyh⁺*
un	*cyh*	*un⁺*	*cyh⁺*
un⁺	*cyh⁺*	*un*	*cyh*

The missing asci types probably did not occur because of the low frequency of three or more crossovers and the relatively low number of asci that were studied.

d. Classes 4, 5 and 6 all involve double crossovers. Class 4 involves a 2-strand double crossover, with both crossovers occurring between the centromere and each gene. There is only one way to achieve this result. Class 5 involves a 4-strand double crossover, one between the centromere and *un* and one between *un* and *cyh*. There is only one way of achieving this result. Class 6 involves a 3-strand double crossover, with one between *un* and the centromere and one between the two genes. There are two ways of achieving this result. Therefore, class 6 should occur at twice the frequency of either of the other two classes.

20.   The chromosome map is

leu3   cys2

0   8

The cross is + cys2 × leu3 +. First classify the asci types:

	Type
a.	NPD
b.	PD
c.	T
d.	T
e.	NPD
f.	PD
g.	T

a.   The ascus is a NPD with M_I segregation for both loci. This can happen only when a double crossover occurs. The problem states that double crossovers should not be considered. Therefore, the answer is 0%.

b.   The ascus is a PD with M_I segregation for both loci. This occurs only with no crossovers.

$$
\begin{aligned}
NCO &= 1 - SCO - DCO, \text{ recall that } DCO = 0 \\
&= 1 - SCO \\
&= 1 - T \\
&= 1 - 2\,RF \\
&= 1 - 2\,(0.08) \\
&= 0.84
\end{aligned}
$$

c.   The ascus is a T from a SCO between the centromere and the cys2 allele. SCO occur with a frequency of 0.16, as calculated in part b. However, a single crossover could give four different spore arrangements, of which this is one example. The probability of this specific type of ascus is therefore 1/4 the probability of a SCO, or 0.04.

d–g.   All four ascus types show M_{II} segregation for leu3, which cannot occur. The probability of each type is 0%.

21. The cross is

P $g\,C\,s/g\,C\,s \times G\,c\,S/G\,c\,S$

F_1 $g\,C\,s/G\,c\,S$ wild type

In order to achieve the mutants that were observed, mitotic crossing-over had to occur.

The first set of mutants were $gg\ C\!-\ ss$ and $G\!-\ cc\ S\!-$. A single crossover can yield these results:

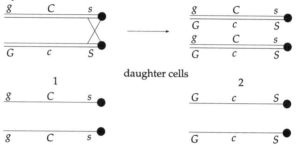

daughter cells

The second set of mutants were $gg\ C\!-\ S\!-$ and $G\!-\ cc\ S\!-$ A single crossover can yield these results:

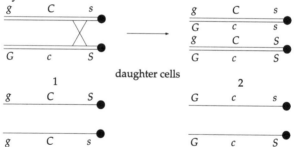

daughter cells

The third mutants were $gg\ C\!-\ S\!-$. A single crossover can yield these results:

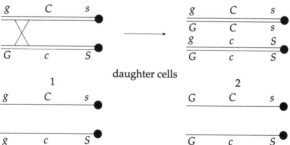

daughter cells

22. Recall that white diploid sectors will have two copies of the chromosome and two copies of each gene. The original chromosomes were

ad col phe pu sm w/ad⁺ col⁺ phe⁺ pu⁺ sm⁺ w⁺ (gene order is alphabetic).

a. The sectors must be ww. To be ww, mitotic crossing-over must have occurred. The following diagram illustrates this for alleles w/w^+ only:

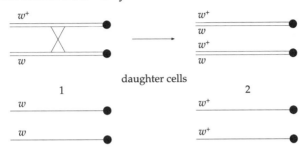

daughter cells

b. Note that any gene distal to the crossover will remain with the w allele if no other crossovers occur, while any gene proximal to the crossover will be separated from the w allele if no other crossovers occur. This means that the closer a proximal gene is to the w allele, the less likely it will be separated from w and the more likely it will be homozygous recessive.

Using this logic, pu (with ww in 100% of the sectors) is distal to w. The col allele is never observed with w, suggesting that it is proximal to it. In other words, col lies very close to the centromere. However, as will be discussed below, on which side of the centromere col is located cannot be determined. The other genes are between w and the centromere: ad (with ww in 95% of the sectors), sm (with ww in 65% of the sectors), and phe (with ww in 41% of the sectors). The final gene order is

centromere —— col —— phe —— sm —— ad —— w —— pu.

c. The relative map distances can be calculated directly from the cosegregation of phenotypes. If two genes are found together X% of the time, then crossing-over occurs between them (100 – X)% of the time.

$w - pu$: 100% – 100% = 0 relative map units. This finding indicates that the relative order determined above may not be exactly correct, because w and pu are so tightly linked. It is possible that the gene order is

centromere —— col —— phe —— sm —— ad —— pu —— w.

Without further information, no choice can be made between the two possibilities.

$w - ad$: 100% – 95% = 5 relative map units

$w - sm$: 100% – 65% = 35 relative map units

$w - phe$: 100% – 41% = 59 relative map units

The w – centromere distance cannot be calculated precisely.

d. The phenotype associated with homozygous *col* was never observed. This means that *col* was very far from *w*. If *col* were between *w* and the centromere, then some of the sectors should have had a *col* phenotype unless *col* is so close to the centromere that no crossing-over occurs between them. If *col* were on the other side of the centromere from *w*, but close to the centromere so that no mitotic crossing-over occurred, then it would never be observed with *w*. Therefore, *col* is very close to the centromere but could be on either arm.

23. Let *gg* = green, *Gg* = yellowish and *GG* = yellow. Mitotic crossing-over can account for the observations:

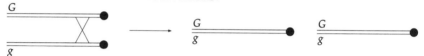

The resulting daughter cells would be *GG* (yellow) and *gg* (green).

24. Ignoring the white allele for a moment, the 1 : 1 : 1 : 1 ratio indicates independent assortment of two units, or chromosomes. The *a* and *c* alleles are found in equal proportions with *b* and *b⁺*, indicating that b/b^+ assorts independently of a^+/a and c^+/c. If w/w^+ were linked on either chromosome, then the white allele would be found more frequently with one gene combination than another. Because it is not, w/w^+ is not linked to either chromosome.

$$\underline{w/w^+} \qquad \underline{a/a^+ \quad c/c^+} \qquad \underline{b/b^+}$$

25. Remember that the segregants are yellow and diploid (80 percent *yy r⁺–*, 20 percent *yy rr*). To get *yy* segregants, crossing-over must occur between *y* and the centromere. There are three possible arrangements:

1. yellow — centromere — ribo

2. centromere — yellow — ribo

3. centromere — ribo — yellow

If 1 is correct, after crossing-over the chromosomes would be

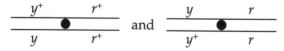

Without a crossover between r and the centromere, no rr segregants would be observed. Because the two genes are far away from each other, a 1 : 1 ratio of ribo-requiring and non – ribo-requiring (wild type for ribo) would be expected.

If 2 is correct, after crossing-over the chromosomes would be

Unless the two genes are more than 50 m.u. apart, most of the yy segregants would be ribo-requiring.

If 3 is correct, crossing-over between r and the centromere would give ribo-requiring segregants, and crossing-over between y and the centromere would give wild type for ribo. Therefore, both types of segregants would be observed with only one crossover. Furthermore, the 80 : 20 ratio suggests that crossing-over occurs more frequently between y and the centromere.

26.   a.   All fpa/fpa diploid segregants experienced a crossover between fpa and the centromere. The data indicate that pro and $paba$ are linked to fpa. The different frequencies are a measure of the distances involved. Because there are no progeny requiring only proline, pro is closer to the centromere than is $paba$.

      b.

●————pro————paba————fpa————
      +   +   +

$pro–paba$: $100\%(71)/154 = 71.4$ relative m.u.

$paba–fpa$: $100\%(35)/154 = 22.7$ relative m.u.

$pro–centromere$: $100\%(9)/154 = 5.8$ relative m.u.

      c. $pro\ paba\ fpa$

27.   α: the only chromosome missing in A and B and present in C is 7.

      β: the only chromosome present in all colonies is 1.

      γ: the only chromosome missing in A and present in B and C is 5.

      δ: the only chromosome present only in B is 6.

      ε: not on chromosomes 1 through 7.

28.   Steroid sulfatase: XP; phosphoglucomutase-3: 6q, esterase D: 13q; phosphofructokinase: 21; amylase: 1p; galactokinase: 17q.

COMMENTS ON THIS MATERIAL

The material covered in Chapter 6 of *An Introduction to Genetic Analysis*, 5th ed., will challenge the very best of students. Students experience more difficulty with this chapter than with any other chapter in the textbook. One reason for this may be insufficient mathematical skills, a problem that cannot be solved here. Another reason this material is so difficult for so many is that it requires the integration of all that you have learned up to this point. It requires a thorough understanding of the foregoing material and systematic application of the problem-solving techniques discussed earlier. As you are struggling with some of these problems, it may help to know that you may have to spend well over an hour in solving a specific problem in this chapter. Persistence, coupled with seeking help when you are truly struck, does pay off in the end.

SELF-TEST

1. One strain (*ad*) of *Neurospora* requires adenine for growth. Another strain (*ylo*) produces yellow conidia. The two strains were crossed, and the following asci observed.

Number of asci	Ascus type
110	4 *ad ylo⁺* : 4 *ad⁺ ylo*
18	2 *ad ylo⁺* : 2 *ad ylo* : 2 *ad⁺ ylo⁺* : 2 *ad⁺ ylo*

　　a. Are the two genes linked?

　　b. Calculate the distance of each gene from its centromere and, if the genes are linked, the distance between the two genes.

2. Two strains of *Neurospora* requiring adenine were crossed and the following asci were observed.

Number of asci	Ascus type
110	4 *ad-1⁺ ad-2⁺* : 4 *ad-1 ad-2*
100	4 *ad-1 ad-2⁺* : 4 *ad-1⁺ ad-2*
80	2 *ad-1 ad-2⁺* : 2 *ad-1⁺ ad-2⁺* : 2 *ad-1 ad-2* : 2 *ad-1⁺ ad-2*

　　a. Are the two genes linked?

　　b. Calculate the distance of each gene from its centromere and, if the genes are linked, the distance between the two genes.

3.   Consider two strains in *Neurospora*, a b^+ and a^+ b. If the genes are linked and a is closer to the centromere than b, diagram the following and identify the ascus type.

   a.   no crossover

   b.   crossover between a and the centromere

   c.   crossover between b and the centromere

   d.   crossover between each gene and the centromere involving two strands

   e.   crossover between each gene and the centromere involving four strands

   f.   two crossovers between gene a and the centromere involving four strands

   g.   two crossovers between gene b and the centromere involving four strands

4.   In *Drosophila* there are two linked recessive genes: y, which causes yellow body color, and br, which causes short bristles. y/y^+ is closer to the centromere than is br^+/br. If a double heterozygote in coupling phase experiences mitotic crossing-over, what are the possible outcomes?

5.   Mitomycin C is a drug that increases the frequency of mitotic crossing-over in cultured human cells. How might it be useful in studying rare recessive alleles?

6.   Human cells were fused with cells of the mouse. Several different lines with varying numbers of human chromosomes were isolated and tested for the enzyme X. The results are tabulated below (+ indicates chromosome or enzyme is present). On which chromosome is gene X?

Cell line	1	2	3	4	5	6	7	8	9	10	Enzyme X
A	+	+	−	−	−	+	+	+	+	+	+
B	+	−	+	+	+	+	+	−	−	+	+
C	−	+	+	+	+	+	−	+	+	+	−
D	−	−	+	−	+	+	−	+	−	−	−
E	−	+	+	−	−	−	+	−	+	−	+

Human chromosomes

7.   Assume that you are studying the effects of what appear to be two different genes but, in reality, the two phenotypic characteristics are caused by a pleiotropic gene. What will be the χ^2 result?

SOLUTIONS TO SELF–TEST

1. **a.** PD = 110, NPD = 0. PD >> NPD. NPD/T = 0/18. Therefore, the two genes are linked.

    b. Gene *ad* shows only first-division segregation. It is very close to the centromere.

    ylo -to-centromere distance: 100%(1/2)(18)/128 = 14.1 m.u.

    ad -to-*ylo* distance: 100%(1/2)(18)/128 = 14.1 m.u.

    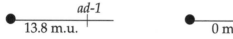

2. **a.** NPD = 100, PD = 110, T = 80. PD almost equals NPD. NPD/T = 100/80 = 1.25. Therefore, the genes are not linked.

    b. *ad-1* to centromere: (100%)(1/2)(80)/290 = 13.8 m.u.

    ad-2 to centromere: (100%)(1/2)(0)/290 = 0 m.u.

    ● ——————————— *ad-1*   ● ———————————— *ad-2*
        13.8 m.u.   0 m.u.

3. **a.** 4 *a b⁺* : 4 *a⁺ b*, PD

    b. 2 *a b⁺* : 2 *a⁺ b* : 2 *a b⁺* : 2 *a⁺ b*, PD

    c. 2 *a b⁺* : 2 *a b* : 2 *a⁺ b⁺* : 2 *a⁺ b*, T

    d. 2 *a b⁺* : 2 *a⁺ b⁺* : 2 *a b* : 2 *a⁺ b*, T

    e. 2 *a⁺ b* : 2 *a b* : 2 *a⁺ b⁺* : 2 *a b⁺*, T

    f. 2 *a⁺ b* : 2 *a⁺ b* : 2 *a b⁺* : 2 *a b⁺*, PD

    g. 4 *a b* : 4 *a⁺ b⁺*, NPD

4. If crossing–over occurs between *y* and the centromere, after recombination both chromosomes would be *y br/y⁺ br⁺*. Depending on the alignment at metaphase, the daughter cells could both be *y br/y⁺ br⁺* (fully wild type), or one cell could be *y br/y br* (single spot that is yellow, with short bristles) and the other could be *y⁺ br⁺/y⁺ br⁺* (fully wild type).

    If crossing–over occurs between the two genes, after recombination one chromosome would be *y br/y br⁺* and the other would be *y⁺ br/y⁺ br⁺*. Alignment at metaphase could yield the following: *y br/y⁺ br* (short bristles) and *y br⁺/y⁺ br⁺* (fully wild type) or *y br/y⁺ br⁺* (fully wild type) and *y br⁺/y⁺ br* (fully wild type).

5. By exposing heterozygous cells in culture to mitomycin C, mitotic recombination would result in mitotic segregation 50 percent of the

time. If the cells could be cloned, lines homozygous for each allele could be isolated and defined.

6. chromosome 7

7. If you assumed independent assortment, the χ^2 will be highly significant. If you assumed some value of linkage, the χ^2 will be highly significant if the assumed value was within the range of most mapping problems. If the linkage was assumed to be very tight, a highly significant χ^2 would require a very large sample size.

SOME TOUGH ADVICE ON HOW TO STUDY GENETICS

It is my sincere hope you have the habit and the methods of critical analysis that have been presented in both your textbook and this *Companion*. At this point in the text, the material becomes much more descriptive. You now have two main tasks: (1) to memorize the presented material and (2) to integrate the new material with all that has come before. The first task, memorization, should be relatively easy. It requires a skill that you have been perfecting since long before you entered kindergarten.

The second task, integration, is quite difficult for many students. For example, in Chapter 11 you will cover the structure of DNA, in Chapter 16 you will put that DNA into chromosomes, and in Chapter 19 you will study recombination at the molecular level. All of these major topics must be integrated with each other and with what you have learned about recombination at the level of transmission genetics.

If at this point your grasp of transmission genetics is weak, go back to Chapter 2 and learn it. You may be able to memorize the following material without a firm foundation in transmission genetics, and you may be able to do very well on tests covering the new material; but, ultimately, that new material will carry little meaning for you unless it can be applied to transmission genetics.

7
Gene Mutation

IMPORTANT TERMS AND CONCEPTS

A gene and its function are not detectable without **variants** to reveal the existence of that gene. Variants arise by two mechanisms: (1) **gene mutation**, which is also known as a **point mutation**, and (2) **chromosome mutation.**

The standard form of a gene is the **wild type.** Any deviation from the standard form is a **forward mutation.** Any change from the forward mutation back toward the standard form is a **reverse mutation**, a **reversion**, or a **back mutation.**

A **somatic mutation** occurs in nonreproductive cells and leads to a **clone** of cells that differs genetically from the rest of the organism. This results in the organism being classed as a **mosaic,** because it has two or more differing cell lines. Somatic mutations can be inherited if the organism undergoes vegetative reproduction.

A **germinal mutation** occurs in reproductive tissue. Germinal mutations can be inherited.

Morphological mutations cause a change in form. **Lethal** mutations result in death. **Conditional** mutations are expressed under the **restrictive** condition and are not expressed under the **permissive** condition. **Biochemical** mutations result in a change in metabolism. Organisms that are nutritionally self-sufficient given a standard set of growth conditions are **prototrophic.** Mutants that require additional supplementation are **auxotrophic. Resistance mutations** confer the ability to grow in the presence of a specific inhibitor such as a poison.

Mutations can be classified by the mode of action of the mutant:

    a. **Hypomorphs** have a reduced phenotype as compared to wild type. The reduction can be in such traits as color or enzyme activity. Increasing the copy number of hypomorph mutants results in an approach to wild-type phenotype.

b. **Hypermorphs** have an increased phenotype as compared to the wild type. The increase can be in such traits as enzyme activity or production of a product.

c. **Amorphs** completely lack a function that the wild type has. The lack can be in such traits as enzyme activity or color.

d. **Antimorphs** result in a phenotype in the opposite direction from that of the wild type. Increasing the copy number of antimorph mutants results in a phenotype that is farther and farther away from the wild type.

e. **Neomorphs** result in a new trait as compared to the wild type.

The **mutational rate** is the number of mutational events per unit time. The **mutational frequency** is the number of mutant individuals per total number of organisms.

Selective systems aid in the detection of rare mutations.

Evolution occurs through mutations, although most mutations are deleterious.

Mutations can be induced by a number of differing techniques, biochemical and physical. Natural and induced mutations are random in direction, in the gene being affected, and in the cell in which they occur.

Be sure that you have thoroughly read the entire chapter before you attempt any of the problems.

SOLUTIONS TO PROBLEMS

1. The petal will now be *Ww*, or blue, either in whole or in part, depending upon the timing of the reversion.

2. Grow cells in the absence of leucine and in the presence of an antibiotic that will kill only proliferating cells. Wash out the antibiotic, and then plate the cells on medium containing leucine.

3. Plate the cells on medium lacking proline. Nearly all colonies will come from revertants. The remainder will be second-site suppressors.

4. Streak the yeast on minimal medium plus arginine. When colonies appear, replica plate them onto minimal medium. The absence of growth in minimal medium will identify the arginine-requiring mutants.

5. Assume that you are working with twenty specific nutrients that were added to the minimal medium. Group the nutrients, with five to a group. [The choice of how many nutrients are included in each group is completely arbitrary.] Test each auxotroph against each group. When an auxotroph grows in one of the groups, test the auxotroph separately against each member of the group. A flow sheet would look something like the following:

Test 1	Growth	Test 2	Growth
group A (1 to 5)	–	11	–
group B (6 to 10)	–	12	–
group C (11 to 15)	+	13	+
group D (16 to 20)	–	14	–
		15	–

These results tell you that nutrient 13 was required for growth.

If a mutant cannot be identified to have a requirement for a specific nutrient, then it may be a double or multiple mutant. Alternatively, it could require an unidentified component of the complete medium.

6. You need to apply the Poisson distribution (Chapter 6) to answer this problem. Mutants were *not* observed (zero class) on 37 plates out of 100. The formula is e^{-un} = number in zero class/total number. Or $e^{-u} \times 10^6$ = 37/100, and $u = -\ln(0.37) \times 10^{-6} = 1/10^{-6}$ cell divisions.

7. There are many ways to carry out this experiment. Using *Drosophila*, you could raise flies with (experimental) and without (control) caffeine added to the diet. You could do the same with mice, rats, cats or dogs, or with mammalian cells in culture. Alternatively, you could inject a solution with or without caffeine into an organism.

8. Stain pollen grains, which are haploid, from a homozygous *Wx* parent with iodine. Look for red pollen grains, indicating mutations to *wx*, under a microscope.

9. The most straightforward explanation is that a mutation from wild type to black occurred in the germ line of the male wild-type mouse. Thus, he was a gonadal mosaic of wild-type and black germ cells.

10. An X-linked disorder cannot be passed from father to son. Because the gene for hemophilia must have come from the mother, the nuclear power plant cannot be held responsible.

It is possible that the achondroplastic gene mutation was caused by exposure to radiation.

11. The mutation rate needs to be corrected for achondroplastic parents and put on a "per gamete" basis, which requires subtracting the two cases for which a parent was achondroplastic and the parents involved in producing those children:

$$(10 - 2)/2 \times (94{,}075 - 2) = 4.25 \times 10^{-5} \text{ gametes}$$

You do not have to worry about revertants in this problem because the problem asks for the net mutation frequency to achondroplasia.

12. The commission was looking for induced recessive X-linked lethal mutations, which would show up as a shift in the sex ratio. A shift in the sex ratio is the first indication that a population has sustained lethal genetic damage. Other recessive mutations might have occurred, of course, but they would not be homozygous and therefore would go undetected. All dominant mutations would be immediately visible, unless they were lethal. If they were lethal, there would be lowered fertility and/or an increase in detected abortions, but the sex ratio would not shift as dramatically.

13. **a.** reddish all over

    b. reddish all over

    c. many small, red spots

    d. a few large, red spots

    e. like part c, but with fewer reddish patches

    f. like part d, but with fewer reddish patches

    g. some large spots and many small spots

14. Because A/deletion has a greater deviation from wild type than $A/+$, the A and $+$ alleles are working against each other. Therefore, the new mutant is an example of an antimorph.

15. If the starting point for comparison is wild type, then the new mutant is a hypomorph because it results in less pigmentation than the wild type.

16.   The new recessive mutation can be expected to be on one of the twelve chromosomes. In order to determine which chromosome, plant lines should be selected that are heterozygous for several distinctive alternatives along the length of each chromosome. For each chromosome, the markers must be no farther apart than 30 map units.

Once the suitable tester lines have been selected, each should be crossed with the line containing the new recessive mutation. Assume that the new mutation is a and that it is located close to the allelic alternatives tall (T) and dwarf (t). Also assume that the a mutation is in a plant line that does not contain the dwarf allele. The cross is

P $a\,T/a\,T \times A\,T/A\,t$

F_1 $a\,T/A\,T$ nonmutant and tall

$a\,T/A\,t$ nonmutant and tall

The next step would be to cross the F_1 with dwarf plants in order to detect which plants are heterozygous for plant height. Once this has been done, the progeny of the appropriate crosses can be evaluated for recombination between the two genes.

For markers on other chromosomes and for markers on chromosome 1 which are further than 30 map units, the appropriate crosses to show heterozygosity in the marker gene will yield ratios indicating independent assortment. Only plant height, under the initial assumptions for this answer, will show a lack of independent assortment in the progeny of the plants heterozygous for both the new mutation and the marker.

17.   The cross is $arg^r \times arg^+$, where arg^r is the revertant. However, it might also be $arg^-\,su \times arg^+\,su^+$, where su^+ has no effect on the arg gene.

   a.   If the revertant is a precise reversal of the original change that produced the mutant allele, 100% of the progeny would be arginine independent.

   b.   If a suppressor mutation on a different chromosome is involved, then the cross is $arg^-\,su \times arg^+\,su^+$. Independent assortment would lead to the following:

   1 $arg^-\,su$ arginine independent

   1 $arg^+\,su^+$ arginine independent

   1 $arg^-\,su^+$ arginine dependent

   1 $arg^+\,su$ arginine independent

   c.   If a suppressor mutation 10 map units from the arg locus occurred, then the cross is $arg^-\,su \times arg^+\,su^+$ but it is now necessary to write the diploid intermediate as $arg^-\,su/arg^+\,su^+$.

The two parental types would occur 90% of the time, and the two recombinant types would occur 10% of the time. The progeny would be

45% *arg⁻ su*   arginine independent

45% *arg⁺ su⁺*   arginine independent

5% *arg⁻ su⁺*   arginine dependent

5% *arg⁺ su*   arginine independent

18.   a.   The results show that the new mutants have the following epistatic relationships: $w^- > p^- > y^- > b^- > o^-$.

b.   There are a total of ten heterokaryon pairs possible. All would have the phenotype of the wild type because of complementation.

c.   The cross is $o^- p^- \times o^+ p^+$. Remember that haploid fungi immediately enter meiosis after gamete fusion, producing haploid progeny. Because the two genes are 16 map units apart, the recombinants will total 16% of the progeny and the parentals will be 84%. The genotypes and phenotypes of the progeny are given below.

42% *o⁻ p⁻*   pink

42% *o⁺ p⁺*   red

8% *o⁻ p⁺*   orange

8% *o⁺ p⁻*   pink

SELF-TEST

1.   Recall the replica plating test. Assume that Lederberg and Lederberg observed that one in a thousand colonies was resistant to penicillin when tested by replica plating. When they next tested the colonies that gave rise to the penicillin-resistant colonies, what percentage of the cells in each colony would be expected to be penicillin-resistant if

a.   resistance is caused by penicillin?

b.   resistance is selected by penicillin?

2.   During the 1940s and into the early 1950s in the United States,

many shoe stores used a continuous X-ray machine to check shoe fit. Frequently, young children would watch their foot bones wiggle in the machine while their mothers tried on shoes. What effect would be expected from this?

3. How can you distinguish a new mutation from a mutation that had not been expressed in prior generations due to epistasis?

4. A child is born with cleft lip and palate, a disorder known to be caused by some environmental agents and also to have several genetic causes (both dominant and recessive forms exist). The parents state that there is no history of the disorder on either side of the family. Is it likely that the child represents a new mutation?

5. A child is born with neurofibromatosis. This is a dominant genetic disorder with the highest rate of mutation known in humans. The high mutation rate of neurofibromatosis is perhaps explained by the fact that it is also a disorder that has reduced penetrance, has variable expressivity, and is very frequently not diagnosed when present. Before coming to the conclusion that a new mutation has occurred with this particular child, what must you do?

6. Are abnormal phenotypes caused by an environmental agent inherited?

7. When Muller constructed the *ClB* strain of *Drosophila*, what was the role of the crossover suppressor *C* in his experimental design? What was the role of *l*? What was the role of *B*?

8. Propose an explanation for the following observations:

    1. dominant X-linked abnormalities in humans are much more rare than recessive X-linked abnormalities;

    2. the ratio of dominant to recessive abnormalities in humans is much lower for genes on the X chromosome than for genes on the autosomes.

SOLUTIONS TO SELF-TEST

1. a. If resistance is caused by exposure to penicillin, then approximately the same frequency of resistance would be observed, 1/1000 cells.

    b. If resistance is already present in the colonies and is simply selected by penicillin, then the range of resistant cells can be from very few (only a subpopulation of the colony is resistant) to 100 percent of the cells (the entire colony is resistant).

2.   The rapidly growing cells giving rise to toenails would be the cells most likely to experience mutation. This could be expressed as very small nails, deformed nails, absence of nails, and even possibly malignancy.

3.   This is very difficult practically in humans, less so in other organisms. In the fruit fly, for instance, if the mutant allele had been blocked from expression, then testcross progeny of sibs of the parents whose progeny first expressed it might also express it. If a new mutation occurred, sibs of the parents whose progeny first expressed it would not be expected to carry the allele.

4.   While it is possible that the child represents a new mutation, it is more likely that environmental exposure or genetic inheritance is the cause. Mutation should be used as the explanation of last resort because the rate of mutation is much lower than the frequency of any specific birth defect.

5.   The parents and all sibs of the child should have a complete physical examination to rule out neurofibromatosis. Many children with this disorder have relatives who, although not diagnosed, have some symptoms of neurofibromatosis.

6.   Those environmental agents that cause mutations would give rise to inherited changes, although the direction of mutation would be random. Those environmental agents that interfere with development without causing mutations (teratogenic agents) would not give rise to inherited changes.

7.   The crossover suppressor prevents the separation of the original lethal mutation from the bar-eye marker by crossing-over. Without the crossover suppressor, there is no way to be sure that a newly induced mutation has not been eliminated from detection and study through crossing-over.
The purpose of the lethal recessive mutation in the ClB chromosome is to eliminate approximately half of the males, all of whom could not possibly be carrying the newly induced mutation.
The bar-eye allele allows for the identification of females carrying the lethal recessive mutation.

8.   A dominant abnormality is going to be expressed, barring epistasis. However, the normal allele in an autosomal heterozygote may be able to ameliorate the expression of the dominant allele. It is for this reason that dominant abnormalities such as achondroplasia are thought to be recessive lethals.

For X-linked genes, however, the male is hemizygous. In addition, after X-inactivation occurs, females are functionally hemizygous for most of the genes on the X chromosome. While the female has the possibility of "genetic buffering" and chance alone can prevent the full expression of the dominant allele, the male has no possibility that a normal allele could ameliorate the expression of the dominant abnormality. Therefore, the disruption caused by an X-linked dominant abnormality would be more directly subjected to selection than the disruption caused by an autosomal dominant abnormality. The rarity of X-linked dominant abnormalities is thus a function of gene expression.

8

Chromosome Mutation I: Changes in Chromosome Structure

IMPORTANT TERMS AND CONCEPTS

Chromosome mutations are changes in the genome involving chromosome parts, whole chromosomes, or whole chromosome sets. They are also known as **chromosome aberrations.** They can be detected either by genetic tests or by viewing the chromosomes under the microscope.

Cytogenetics is the combined study of cells (cytology) and genetics.

Chromosomes can be distinguished by size, centromere position, nucleolar organizers, satellites, and staining patterns.

Specific autosomal chromosomes within a genome are numbered. The larger the chromosome, the smaller the number. If two chromosomes are of the same size, the one with the more centrally positioned centromere has the lower number.

The **primary constriction** is the centromere. The **secondary constriction** is the **nucleolar organizing region**, or NO.

Metacentric chromosomes have the centromere in the middle of the chromosome. **Acrocentric** chromosomes have the centromere off center. **Telocentric** chromosomes have the centromere at the end of the chromosome. **Acentric** chromosomes do not have a centromere. **Dicentric** chromosomes have two centromeres.

A **telomere** is the end of a chromosome. A **satellite** is a small piece of chromosome distal to the nucleolar organizing region.

Heterochromatin is a densely staining region thought to be genetically inert. **Constitutive** heterochromatin does not vary from cell to cell within a species. **Facultative** heterochromatin varies with cell type within a species. **Euchromatin** stains very lightly and is thought to be genetically active.

Banding patterns along the length of chromosomes can occur naturally in some species, such as *Drosophila*, or be induced by various treatments in other species, such as humans.

Endomitosis is a process of chromosome replication not followed by cell division. It leads to an increase in the total number of chromosomes in a cell. In humans, a normal feature of liver and other cells is one round of endomitosis, leading to 92 chromosomes. In *Drosophila* salivary gland cells, endomitosis results in **polytene chromosomes.**

Chromosome rearrangements consist of deletions, duplications, inversions, and translocations.

A **deletion** is the loss of a chromosome segment. A **terminal** deletion results from one chromosome break. An **interstitial** deletion results from two chromosome breaks; the region between the two breaks is lost when chromosome repair occurs. Deletions frequently result in **pseudodominance**, the expression of a recessive gene when present in a single copy. A deletion results in an unpaired loop during synapsis. Homozygous deletions usually are lethal.

A **duplication** is the presence of more than one copy of a chromosomal segment on one chromosome. Adjacent duplicated segments occur in **tandem sequence** with respect to each other (abcdabcd) or they may occur in **reverse order** with respect to each other (abcddcba). Duplications, like deletions, can disturb the genetic balance of the genome, resulting in abnormal development or function. They also supply additional genetic material capable of evolving new functions. Duplications result in an unpaired loop during synapsis.

Inversions result from two chromosome breaks, with a subsequent "flipping" of the middle segment with respect to the two ends, followed by chromosome repair. **Paracentric** inversions do not involve the centromere. Crossing-over in the inverted region of a paracentric inversion leads to an acentric fragment and a dicentric chromosome, which then enters the **breakage-fusion-bridge cycle**, resulting in duplications and deletions. **Pericentric** inversions involve the centromere. Crossing-over in the inverted region of a pericentric inversion leads to duplications and deletions. Inversion heterozygosity results in a reduction of viable recombinant gametes. Inversion heterozygotes have a paired loop during synapsis.

A **translocation** is the movement of a segment of a chromosome to a new location. A **reciprocal translocation** occurs when there is one break in each of two chromosomes followed by an exchange of the acentric fragments. New linkage relations are created by translocations. When nonhomologous chromosomes are involved, pairing at synapsis in the heterozygote results in a cross configuration involving four chromosomes. Synapsis in the homozygote does not result in the cross structure. Translocation heterozygosity leads to greatly reduced fertility because segregation usually results in both duplications and deletions for entire chromosomes.

Position-effect is the alteration in a gene's functioning caused by a change in the gene's location.

Be sure that you have thoroughly read the entire chapter before you attempt any of the problems.

SOLUTIONS TO PROBLEMS

1. a. Deletions lead to a shorter chromosome with missing bands, if banded, an unpaired loop during homologous pairing, and the expression of hemizygous recessive alleles.

    b. Duplications lead to a longer chromosome with repeated bands, if banded, and an unpaired loop during homologous pairing; there may be disturbed development.

    c. Inversions can be detected by banding, and they show the typical twisted homologous pairing for heterozygotes. No crossover products are seen for genes within the inversion in the heterozygote.

    d. Reciprocal translocations can be detected by banding. They show the typical cross structure during homologous pairing, lead to new linkage groups, and show altered linkage relationships. The heterozygote has a high rate of unbalanced gamete production.

2. a. In heterozygotes, the products of crossing-over will be nonviable 25 percent of the time. Thus, the RF will be about three-fourth of the normal value, or 27 percent.

    b. The homozygote will have no trouble with crossing-over, so the RF will be about 36 percent.

3. P $A-\ B-\ C-\ D-\ E-\ F-\ \times\ aa\ bb\ cc\ dd\ ee\ ff$

F_1 1/2 *Aa Bb Cc Dd Ee Ff*

  1/2 *Aa Bb Cc dd ee Ff*

Remember that these genes are linked. Because all progeny flies are *A– B– C– F–*, the wild type must have been homozygous for these genes. Half the progeny received *D E*, which had to have come from the wild-type parent, and half received *d e*, which presumably came from the wild-type parent. No recombinants were seen.

The best explanation is that the wild-type fly was heterozygous *D E/d e* and that a heterozygous inversion spanned these two genes, which blocked all recombination products from being seen.

An alternative explanation is that the wild-type fly was heterozygous for a deletion spanning genes *D* and *E*. With this explanation, the second class of F_1 progeny would be hemizygous for *d* and *e*, or *Aa Bb Cc d e Ff*.

4. **a.** paracentric inversion

    b. deletion

    c. pericentric inversion

    d. duplication

5. From each of the statements concerning the rare cells, you should be able to draw the following conclusions:

Statement	Conclusion
require leucine	*leu⁺* lost
do not mate	one mating type lost
will not grow at 37°C	*un⁺* lost
cross only with *a* type	*a* lost
only nucleus 1 recovered	deletion occurred in nucleus 2

Because *ad-3A⁺* and *nic⁺* function are required by the heterokaryon, these genes must have been retained. Therefore, the most reasonable explanation is that a deletion occurred in the left arm of chromosome 2 and that *leu⁺*, mating type *a*, and *un⁺* were lost.

6. The single waltzing female that arose from a cross between waltzers and normals is expressing a recessive gene when it is present in one copy. That means that the normal allele must have been deleted.

When she was mated to a waltzing male, all the progeny were waltzers. This further supports the conclusion that there was a deletion of the normal allele. Had it been present, one-half of the progeny would be normal.

When she was mated to a normal homozygous male, all the progeny were normal. This indicates that her waltzing was due to a recessive allele and does not represent a dominant variant for waltzing. If a deletion occurred, half of these offspring are heterozygous normal and half are hemizygous normal.

When some of these offspring are mated, the progeny are normal. The offspring are w^+w (normal) or w^+w^* (normal, with deletion). Without a deletion in the normal female, one-fourth of their progeny would be waltzers. With a deletion, progeny homozygous for a deletion would be expected to die. Progeny that are ww^* would be expected to be waltzers. These waltzers were not observed. Because this is the only discrepancy, it must be assumed that not enough crosses were performed.

The cytological data also support the conclusion that a deletion occurred because the abnormal waltzing female and her abnormal progeny had one member of a chromosome pair that was abnormally short.

7. The colonies that would not revert most likely had a deletion within the ad-3B gene. If the gene had not been deleted, at least some reversion would have been seen. Because the gene was deleted, however, there was nothing there for the mutagens to work on. These colonies could grow only with adenine supplementation.

8. Compare deletions 1 and 2: allele b is more to the left than alleles a and c. The order is b (a c), where the parentheses indicate that the order is unknown.

Compare deletions 2 and 3: allele e is more to the right than (a c). The order is b (a c) e.

Compare deletions 3 and 4: allele a is more to the left than c and e, and d is more to the right than e. The order is b a c e d.

Compare deletions 4 and 5: allele f is more to the right than d. The order is b a c e d f.

Allele	Band
b	1
a	2
c	3
e	4
d	5
f	6

9. **a. and b.** When a deletion is crossed with a recessive point mutation in the same gene, the recessive point mutation is expressed. When the deletion and the point mutation are in different genes, wild type is observed. This is exactly like the results seen in a cross between two allelic variants (non-wild-type progeny) and a cross between organisms that have defects in two different genes (wild-type progeny).

Mutant	Defect
1	deletion of at least part of genes *h* and *i*
2	deletion of at least part of genes *k* and *l*
3	deletion of at least part of gene *m*
4	deletion of at least part of genes *k*, *l*, and *m*
5	deletion not within the *h* through *m* genes, or a recessive point mutation

10. **a.** Eighteen map units (m.u.) were either deleted or inverted. A large inversion would result in semisterility, whereas a large deletion would most likely be lethal. Thus, an inversion is more likely.

b.

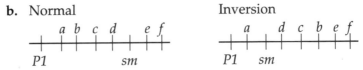

Normal   Inversion

| | a b c d | e f | | | | a | d c b e f | |
| P1 | | sm | | | P1 | sm | | |

c. The semisterility is the result of crossing-over in the inverted region. All products of crossing-over would have both duplications and deletions.

11. The testcross is *P B Q/p B q × p b q/p b q*.

a. To obtain normal eye shape, the bar allele must be deleted. Actually, bar eye is the result of a tandem duplication of a normal allele rather than a variant allele that results in bar eye. Thus, to delete the extra copy of the gene, synapsis must occur out of register between the two chromosomes:

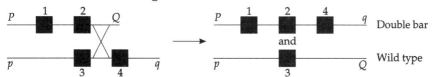

b. In the diagram above, the flanking markers are *P q* and *p Q* after crossing-over. If gene 1 had paired with gene 4, then the wild-type phenotype would have been associated with *P q*, and the double bar would have been with *p Q*.

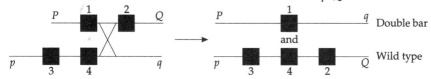

12. a. Classical dominance states that one copy of the dominant allele is sufficient for the dominant phenotype. In this case, the female progeny have one copy of the dominant allele, yet they do not have the dominant phenotype. To explain these results, it must be assumed that both the dominant and the variant alleles have a product and that the phenotype is the result of the ratio of one product to the other.

b. The female parents are v^+v^-/v^+v^-. The ratio of the two alleles is $1:1$, which results in the wild-type phenotype. The male parents are v^-/Y. No dominant alleles are present, and the males are vermilion.

c. The male progeny are v^+v^-/Y, and the ratio of the two alleles is $1:1$, yielding a wild-type phenotype identical to that of their female parents. The female progeny are v^+v^-/v^-. The ratio of dominant alleles to vermilion is $1:2$. Thus, they have the vermilion phenotype.

d. Recall that the choices are hypomorph, hypermorph, amorph, antimorph, and neomorph in Muller's classification and that wild type is deep red. Vermilion is a bright red. Therefore, the vermilion mutation represents a hypomorph of the wild type. Alternatively, because the gene products appear to balance against each other, the vermilion mutation may be an antimorph.

13. The most likely explanation is that one or both break points were located within essential genes, leading to a lethal recessive mutation.

14. **a.** Single crossovers lead to tetratypes. Also, only one-half of the tetratype asci are crossover products, so the 10 m.u. must be multiplied by 2 to yield the right frequencies.

un3⁺ ad3⁺	*un3⁺ ad3⁺*	*un3⁺ ad3⁺*
un3⁺ ad3⁺	*un3⁺ ad3⁺*	*un3⁺ ad3⁺*
un3⁺ ad3⁺	*un3⁺ ad3*	*un3⁺ ad3*
un3⁺ ad3⁺	*un3⁺ ad3*	*un3⁺ ad3*
un3 ad3	*un3 ad3⁺*	*un3 ad3*
un3 ad3	*un3 ad3⁺*	*un3 ad3*
un3 ad3	*un3 ad3*	*un3 ad3⁺*
un3 ad3	*un3 ad3*	*un3 ad3⁺*
80%	10%	10%

b. The aborted spores result from an inversion in the wild type. Crossing-over led to nonviable spores because they were unbalanced. This could be tested by selecting *un3 ad3* double mutants from the wild type and then crossing them with the *un3⁺ ad3⁺* inverted strain. The *un3* to *ad3* distance should be altered.

15. **a.**

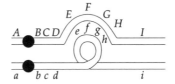

b.

```
1   A  B  C  d  h  G  F  E  D  C  B  A      dicentric

2   I  H  g  f  e  i      acentric

3   a   b c D E F G H I
                                viable
4   a   b c d h g f e i
```

c.

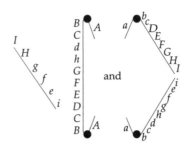

    d. The chromosomes numbered 3 and 4 will give rise to viable progeny. The genotypes of those progeny will be *Aa Bb Cc DD EE FF GG HH II* and *Aa Bb Cc Dd Ee Ff Gg Hh Ii*.

16.   **a.** To construct the maps, look at three genes at a time. For example, the Okanagan sequence for *a*, *b* and *c* is

    a to *b*: 12 m.u.

    a to *c* : 14 m.u.

    b to *c*:   2 m.u.

The only possible sequence is *a b c*

Okanagan sequence:
$$\underset{d}{\quad} \overset{20}{\rule{0pt}{0pt}} \underset{e}{\quad} \overset{3}{\rule{0pt}{0pt}} \underset{a}{\quad} \overset{12}{\rule{0pt}{0pt}} \underset{b}{\quad} \overset{2}{\rule{0pt}{0pt}} \underset{c}{\quad} \overset{15}{\rule{0pt}{0pt}} \underset{f}{\quad}$$

Spain sequence:
$$\underset{f}{\quad} \overset{15}{\rule{0pt}{0pt}} \underset{c}{\quad} \overset{4}{\rule{0pt}{0pt}} \underset{e}{\quad} \overset{3}{\rule{0pt}{0pt}} \underset{a}{\quad} \overset{12}{\rule{0pt}{0pt}} \underset{b}{\quad} \overset{18}{\rule{0pt}{0pt}} \underset{d}{\quad}$$

    b. Diagram the heterozygote during homologous pairing. Crossing-over can occur between *c* and *f* .

	a	*b*	*c*	*d*	*e*	*f*
a	0	0	0	0	0	15
b		0	0	0	0	15
c			0	0	0	15
d				0	0	15
e					0	15
f						15

17.   **a.** The aberrant plant is semisterile, which suggests an inversion. Since the *d–f* and *y–p* frequencies of recombination in the aberrant plant are normal, the inversion must involve *b* through *x*.

    b. To obtain recombinant progeny when an inversion is involved, either a double crossover occurred within the inverted region or single crossovers occurred between *f* and the point of inversion, which occurred someplace between *f* and *b*.

18.   The cross is

    P   *cc bzbz wxwx shsh dd* × *CC BzBz WxWx ShSh DD*

    F_1 *Cc Bzbz Wxwx Shsh Dd*

    Backcross *Cc Bzbz Wxwx Shsh Dd* × *cc bzbz wxwx shsh dd*

a. The total number of progeny is 1000. Classify the progeny as to where a crossover occurred for each type. Then, total the number of crossovers between each pair of genes. Calculate the observed map units (m.u.).

Region	# CO	M.U. Observed	M.U. Expected
$C - Bz$	103	10.3	12
$Bz - Wx$	13	1.3	8
$Wx - Sh$	13	1.3	10
$Sh - D$	186	18.6	20

Notice that a reduction of map units, or crossing-over, is seen in two intervals. Results like this are suggestive of an inversion. The inversion most likely involves the Bz, Wx, and Sh genes in the wild-type plant as compared to the standard stock.

Further notice that all those instances in which crossing-over occurred in the proposed inverted region involved a double crossover. This is the expected pattern.

b. A number of possible classes are missing: four single crossover classes resulting from crossing over in the inverted region, eight double crossover classes involving the inverted region and the noninverted region, and triple crossovers and higher. The ten classes detected were the only classes that were viable. They involved a single crossover outside the inverted region or a double crossover within the inverted region.

c. Class 1 parental; increased due to nonviability of some crossovers

Class 2 parental; increased due to nonviability of some crossovers

Class 3 crossing over between C and Bz; approximately expected frequency

Class 4 crossing over between C and Bz; approximately expected frequency

Class 5 crossing over between Sh and D; approximately expected frequency

Class 6 crossing over between Sh and D; approximately expected frequency

Class 7 double crossover between C and Bz and between Sh and D; approximately expected frequency

Class 8 double crossover between C and Bz and between Sh and D; approximately expected frequency

Class 9 double crossover between Bz and Wx and between Wx and Sh; approximately expected frequency

Class 10 double crossover between Bz and Wx and between Wx and Sh; approximately expected frequency

d. Cytological verification could be obtained by looking at chromosomes during meiotic pairing. Genetic verification could be achieved by crossing two homozygotes for the inversion wild-type.

19. a. and b. The F_1 females are $y\ cv\ v\ f\ B^+\ car/y^+\ cv^+\ v^+f^+\ B^+\ car^+$. These are crossed with $y\ cv\ v\ f\ B\ car/Y$ males.

Class 1: parental

Class 2: parental

Class 3: DCO y–cv and B–car

Class 4: reciprocal of class 3

Class 5: DCO cv–v and v–f

Class 6: reciprocal of class 5

Class 7: DCO cv–v and f–car

Class 8: reciprocal of class 7

Class 9: DCO v–cv and v–f

Class 10: reciprocal of class 9

Class 11: This class is identical to the male parent's X chromosome and could not have come from the female parent. Thus, the male sperm must have donated it to the offspring. In *Drosophila*, sex is determined by the ratio of X chromosomes to the number of sets of autosomes. The ratio in males is 1X : 2A, where A stands for the autosomes contributed by one parent (the ratio in females is 2X : 2A). Thus, this class of males must have arisen from the union of an X-bearing sperm with an egg that was the product of nondisjunction for X and contained only autosomes.

c. Class 11 should have only one sex chromosome, which could be checked cytologically.

20. The inversion results in no viable crossover products from heterozygous females. When *Cu pr/Cu pr* females are crossed with irradiated wild-type males, all female progeny will be heterozygous for the inversion and for any recessive lethal mutation induced by irradiation. They will have curled wings and wild-type eyes (*Cu pr/Cu⁺ pr⁺*?). Each female will carry a different mutation (?), if any were induced. Cross the females individually with a homozygous *Cu pr* male to generate groups of flies with the same mutation. Then, cross the normal-eyed progeny among themselves (*Cu pr/Cu⁺ pr⁺*?). This results in

1/4 *Cu⁺ pr⁺ ?/Cu⁺ pr⁺ ?*   normal wings and eyes

1/2 *Cu pr/Cu⁺ pr⁺*   curled wings and normal eyes

1/4 *Cu pr/Cu pr*   curled wings and purple eyes

If a lethal mutation had been induced, the class with normal wings and eyes would be missing.

21.

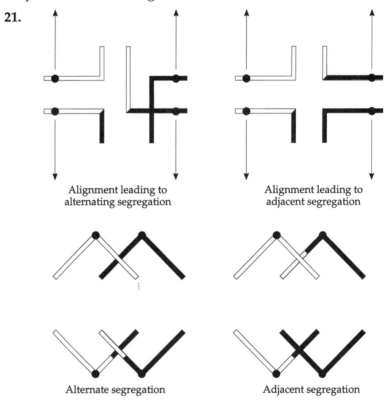

Alignment leading to alternating segregation

Alignment leading to adjacent segregation

Alternate segregation

Adjacent segregation

a.   b.

22. If the *a* and *b* genes are on separate chromosomes, independent assortment should occur, giving equal frequencies of *a b*, *a⁺ b⁺*, *a b⁺*, and *a⁺ b*. This was not observed; instead, the two genes are behaving as if they were linked, with 10 m.u. between them. This behavior is indicative of a reciprocal translocation in one of the parents, most likely the wild type from nature.

At meiosis prior to progeny formation, the chromosomes would look like the following (centromere not included because its position has no effect on the results):

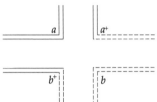

Only alternate segregation avoids duplications and deletions for many genes. Therefore, the majority of the progeny would be parental *a b* and *a⁺b⁺*. The *a b⁺* and *a⁺ b* progeny would result from crossing-over between either gene and the breakpoint locus.

23. Notice that the males have the male parent phenotype and the females have the female parent phenotype. This suggests a translocation of the *Cy* chromosome to the Y chromosome:

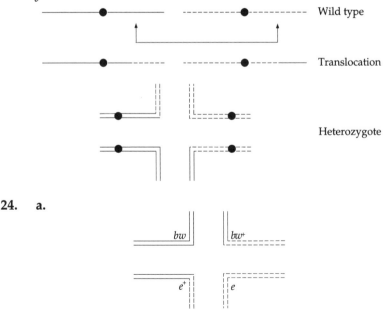

24. **a.**

b. The surviving offspring would result from alternate segregation and would be either *bw e* (brown eye, ebony body) or *bw⁺e⁺* (wild type), in a 1 : 1 ratio.

25. The size of the insertional translocation will determine whether the translocated region or the rest of the region will dominate homologous pairing. Below, it is assumed that the insertion is quite small in relation to the rest of both chromosomes.

The following asci types will be seen:

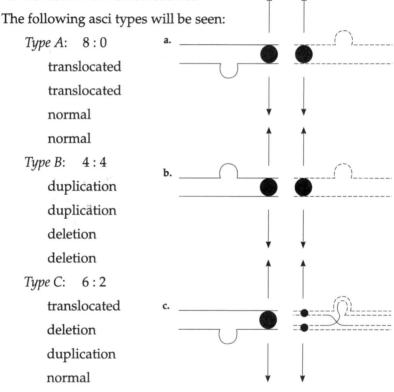

Type A: 8 : 0   a.
      translocated
      translocated
      normal
      normal

Type B: 4 : 4   b.
      duplication
      duplication
      deletion
      deletion

Type C: 6 : 2   c.
      translocated
      deletion
      duplication
      normal

26.

Cross 1: Independent assortment of 2 genes occurred.

Cross 2: Two genes are linked at 1 m.u. distance. Therefore, a reciprocal translocation took place and both genes were very close to the breakpoint. The black spores resulted from alternate segregation, the white from adjacent segregation.

Cross 3: Half the spores were normal, and non-translocated, and half contained both translocated chromosomes.

27. The F₁ is heterozygous for both the translocation and *Pp*. Therefore, it is semisterile. A crossover that occurs within the region from the breakpoint to the centromere will be viable, whereas a crossover that occurs beyond the breakpoint will not be viable. Among the viable crossovers, two-thirds will maintain the link between the P allele and semisterility and one-third will disrupt that linkage. Therefore, the frequency of crossing-over that needs to be considered is 30 m.u. − 20 m.u. = 10 m.u. When the F_1 is backcrossed to the pp parent which does not contain the translocation, the following progeny are obtained, where * denotes the translocation chromosome.

Parentals

    45% $P*/p$ purple, semisterile

    45% p/p green, fully fertile

Recombinants

    5% P/p purple, fully sterile

    5% $p*/p$ green, semisterile

a. green, semisterile = 5%

b. green, fully fertile = 45%

c. purple, semisterile = 45%

d. purple, fully fertile = 5%

e. To solve this problem, recognize that the gametes from the F_1 will occur in the same frequency as the progeny in the backcross. Green, fully fertile plants can arise from the union of two nontranslocated gametes, p, or from the union of two gametes bearing the translocation, p *. Therefore, the probability of obtaining green, fully fertile plants from an F_1 selfing is

$p(pp) + p(pp$ **$) = (0.45)(0.45) + (0.05)(0.05) = 0.2050$

    A third possibility does exist, although it is rather unlikely. If there is fusion of two unbalanced gametes in which the unbalanced genetic components are complementary, then a balanced embryo would result.

28.   The original plant was homozygous for a reciprocal translocation that brought genes P/p and S/s very close together. Because of the close linkage, a ratio suggesting a monohybrid cross, instead of a dihybrid cross, was observed, both with selfing and with a testcross. All gametes are fertile because of homozygosity.

    original plant: $P\,S/p\,s$

    tester: $p\,s/p\,s$

    F_1 progeny: heterozygous for the translocation:

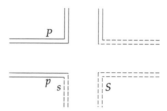

The easiest way to test this is to look at the chromosomes of heterozygotes during meiosis I.

29. The breakpoint can be treated as a gene with two "alleles," one for normal fertility and one for semisterility. The problem thus becomes a two-point cross.

parentals	764	semisterile *Pr*
	727	normal *pr*
recombinants	145	semisterile *pr*
	186	normal *Pr*
	1822	

$100\%(145 + 186)/1822 = 18.17$ m.u.

30.

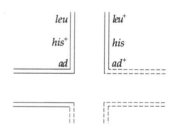

Because the short arm carries no essential genes, adjacent-1 segregation will yield progeny that are viable. Select for leu^+, his^+ and ad^+ by omitting those components from a minimal medium.

31. The percent degeneration seen in the progeny of the exceptional mouse is 51% larger than that seen in the progeny of the normal. One explanation could be a chromosomal inversion. This could be verified by cytological observation of meiotic cells in the mouse. A more likely possibility would be a translocation that could also be checked cytologically.

32. **a.** Breaks in different regions of 17R result in deletion of all genes from the breakpoint.

b. Because there is only 17R from humans, all the human genes expressed must be on 17R.

Notice that only gene *c* is expressed by itself. This means that gene *c* is closest to the mouse material. Next notice that if *c* and one other gene are expressed, that other gene is always *b*. This means *b* is closer to the mouse material than *a* is. The gene order is mouse *−c −b −a*.

The probability of a break between two genes is a function of the distance between them. Of the 200 lines tested, 48 expressed no human activity. Thus, the *c* gene is no more than $(100\%)(24)/200 = 24$ relative m.u. from the mouse material. A break between *c* and *b* (cells express *c* only) occurred in 12 lines, placing these genes $(100\%)(6)/200 = 6$ relative m.u. apart. A break between *b* and *a* (cells express *c* and *b*) occurred in 80 lines, placing these genes $(100\%)(80)/200 = 40$ relative m.u. apart. Finally, 60 clones expressed all three genes, placing gene *a* $(100\%)(60)/200 = 30$ relative m.u. from the end of the chromosome:

mouse ├── 24 m.u. ──*c*── 6 m.u. ──*b*── 40 m.u. ──*a*── 30 m.u. ──┤ end

c. The dye could be used to correlate band presence with gene presence.

33. a. Heterozygous reciprocal translocations lead to duplications and deletions. Therefore, in asci in which crossing-over occurs within the translocated region, each crossing-over event would lead to two white ascospores that abort and two viable dark ascospores. In asci in which no crossing-over occurs within the translocated region, the ascospores would be normal color.

b. Heterozygous pericentric inversions lead to duplications and deletions. Therefore, in asci in which crossing-over occurs within the pericentric inversion, each crossing-over event would lead to two white ascospores that abort and two viable dark ascospores. In asci in which no crossing-over occurs within the pericentric inversion, the ascospores would be normal color.

c. Heterozygous paracentric inversions result in an acentric fragment that has lost some genetic material (deletion) and a dicentric chromosome that has gained some genetic material (duplication) if crossing-over occurs within the paracentric inversion. Therefore, in asci in which crossing-over occurs within the paracentric inversion, each crossing-over event would lead to two white ascospores that abort and two viable dark ascospores. In asci in which no crossing-over occurs within the paracentric inversion, the ascospores would be normal color.

34. Species B is probably the "parent" species. A paracentric inversion in this species would give rise to species D. Species E could then occur by a translocation of $z\ x\ y$ to $k\ l\ m$. Next, species A could result from a translocation of $a\ b\ c$ to $d\ e\ f$. Finally, species C could result from a pericentric inversion of $b\ c\ d\ e$.

35. The assumptions are that half of the gametes from a single heterozygous translocation are nonviable and that the two parents have the same chromosomes involved in translocations.

The progeny of crosses between parents with translocations is referring to the F_1 progeny, in which the parental generation was heterozygous. Designate the parents as follows:

A: (T1 T2 N1 N2)

B: (T1 T2 N1 N2)

The gametes will be

A:	1/4 (T1 T2)	B:	1/4 (T1 T2)
	1/4 (N1 N2)		1/4 (N1 N2)
	*1/4 (T1 N2)		*1/4 (T1 N2)
	*1/4 (T2 N1)		*1/4 (T2 N1)

where * equals an unbalanced gamete.

Fertilization between balanced gametes will occur 4(1/4)(1/4), or 4/16 of the time. An additional 2/16 of the fertilizations will lead to a balanced fetus even though both gametes were unbalanced, for example, (T2 N1) × (T1 N2). Therefore, 6/16 of the progeny are viable and 10/16 are nonviable.

SELF-TEST

1. A new mutant that causes a rough coat appears in mice. Chromosome analysis reveals that one number 3 chromosome is slightly shorter than its homolog and that two interstitial chromosome bands are missing. What is the best interpretation of the new mutant?

2. When the mutant in Problem 1 above is crossed with a wild-type mouse, all the progeny are wild type. A cross of F_1 progeny with the mutant parent results in approximately 50 percent stillborn offspring. Explain these results.

3. A dicentric chromosome has the following gene sequence:

$$a\,b\,c \quad \bullet \quad d\,e\,f\,g\,h \quad \bullet \quad i\,j\,k$$

If, at anaphase, a break occurred between genes f and g, what would be the chromosome composition of each daughter cell after the S phase?

4. In the following inversion heterozygote, diagram the consequences of crossing-over between genes D and E.

A	B	C	D	E	F	G	H
a	b	g	f	e	d	c	h

5. Discuss the role that inversions might have played in evolution.

6. In species X, it is known that gene A is 10 m.u. from gene B. When a heterozygote in repulsion was testcrossed, the following was observed:

490 $Aa\,bb,$ normal fertility

500 $aa\,Bb,$ semisterility

4 $aa\,bb,$ normal fertility

6 $Aa\,Bb,$ semisterility

What can be concluded about genes A and B?

7. A man had two different wives and, altogether, produced six early miscarriages and two stillborn children with multiple abnormalities. What is the best conclusion regarding the man?

8. The chromosomes of the man in Problem 7 were examined. It was found that he had the following for chromosomes 8 and 9. Diagram synapsis.

Chromosome 8: $A \bullet B\,C\,D\,E\,F\,G\,3\,2\,1$ and $a \bullet e\,d\,c\,b\,f\,g\,h\,i$

Chromosome 9: $1\,2\,3\,4 \bullet 5\,6$ and $i\,h\,4 \bullet 5\,6$

SOLUTIONS TO SELF-TEST

1. A deletion.

2. The stillborn offspring were homozygous for the deletion. The deletion is a recessive lethal.

3. Prior to synthesis the daughter cells would be $abc \cdot def$ and $gh \cdot ijk$, where the dot indicates the centromere. The f and g ends would behave as if they were "sticky" during S, resulting in the following dicentric chromosomes:

$$\underline{a\,b\,c \bullet d\,e\,f\,f\,e\,d \bullet a\,b\,c} \quad \text{duplication of } abcdef, \text{ deletion of } ghijk$$

$$\underline{k\,j\,i \bullet h\,g\,g\,h \bullet i\,j\,k} \quad \text{duplication of } ghijk, \text{ deletion of } abcdef$$

4. The two strands not involved in crossing-over would give rise to parental chromosomes. The recombinant strands would be

$$\underline{A\,B\,C\,D\,e\,g\,f \bullet a\,b} \quad \text{duplication of } ab, \text{ deletion of } h$$

$$\underline{H\,G\,F \bullet E\,d\,c\,h} \quad \text{duplication of } h, \text{ deletion of } ab$$

5. Inversion heterozygotes cannot yield viable recombinant products for the region that is inverted. They give rise only to parental gametes. Homozygotes for the normal or the inverted sequence have no difficulty in producing recombinant gametes. Therefore, an inversion acts as a barrier to subpopulations within a species. Over time, two subpopulations may diverge sufficiently to generate two separate species.

6. More than likely, one of the genes has been translocated to a nonhomologous chromosome. The $a\,B$ chromosome was the one involved.

7. The man had either a large inversion or a translocation.

8. The man had both a translocation and an inversion:

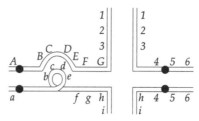

9
Chromosome Mutation II: Changes in Number

IMPORTANT TERMS AND CONCEPTS

The **monoploid number** is the number of chromosomes in the basic set of chromosomes. It usually equals the number of chromosomes in a gamete. **Euploid** organisms have integer multiples of the monoploid number. A **diploid** organism has twice the monoploid number of chromosomes. A **haploid** organism has one monoploid number of chromosomes. A **polyploid** organism has more than twice the monoploid number of chromosomes. Examples of polyploids are **triploid, tetraploid, pentaploid,** and **hexaploid.**

An **aneuploid** has more or fewer chromosomes than an integer multiple of the monoploid number. Addition of one or more chromosomes produces a **hyperdiploid.** Loss of one or more chromosomes produces a **hypodiploid.** A **monosomic** lacks one chromosome. A **nullisomic** lacks both homologous chromosomes. A **trisomic** has an extra chromosome in a diploid. A **disomic** has an extra chromosome in a haploid.

Colchicine and its less toxic derivative colcemid disrupt the mitotic spindle and block mitosis. They produce polyploids.

Polyploids that have an even-integer multiple of the monoploid number are fertile because each chromosome can pair during meiosis. Those that have an odd-integer multiple of the monoploid number are infertile because one chromosome from each of the multiple homologous chromosomes cannot pair during meiosis.

An **autopolyploid** is composed of multiple sets of chromosomes from one species. The diploid derivative is fertile. An **allopolyploid** is composed of multiple sets of chromosomes from different species. An

amphidiploid is an allopolyploid from two species. The diploid intermediate is not fertile.

Plants tolerate both polyploidy and aneuploidy much more easily
than do higher animals.

**Be sure that you have thoroughly read the entire chapter before
you attempt any of the problems.**

SOLUTIONS TO PROBLEMS

1. Klinefelter syndrome   XXY male

   Down syndrome   trisomy 21

   Turner syndrome   XO female

2. (1) Do somatic cell fusion between *AA* and *A'A'* plants.

   (2) Cross *AA* with *A'A'*, and then double the chromosomes with
   colchicine treatment.

3. **a.** 3, 3, 3, 3, 33, 33, 0, 0

   b. 7, 7, 7, 7, 8, 8, 6, 6

4. **a.** If a 6*x* were crossed with a 4*x*, the result would be 5*x*.

   b. Cross *AA* with *aaaa* to obtain *Aaa*.

   c. The easiest way is to expose the *Aa** plant cells to colchicine
   for one cell division. This will result in a doubling of chromosomes to yield *AAa*a**.

   d. Cross 6*x* (*aaaaaa*) with 2*x* (*Aa*) to obtain *Aaaa*.

   e. Obtain haploid cells from a plant and obtain resistant
   colonies by exposing them to the herbicide. Then expose the
   resistant colonies to colchicine to obtain diploids.

5. **b.**

6. To solve this problem, first recognize that *B* can pair with *B* one-
third of the time (leaving *b* to pair with *b*) and that *B* can pair with *b* two-
thirds of the time. If *B* pairs with *B*, the result is *Bb*, *Bb*, *Bb*, *Bb*, occurring
one-third of the time. If *B* pairs with *b*, the resulting tetrad can be of two
equally frequent types, depending on how the pairs align with respect to
each other. One type is *BB*, *BB*, *bb*, *bb*; the second is *Bb*, *Bb*, *Bb*, *Bb*.

7. The gametes produced by a tetraploid *AAaa*, when there is no pairing of chromosomes from the same parent, are *Aa* only. Thus, 100 percent of the progeny would be *AAaa*, and the phenotypic ratio is 16 : 0. Tetraploid *BBbb*, with pairing from the same parent only, would result in *BB* and *bb* gametes. The progeny would be 25 percent *BBBB*, 50 percent *BBbb*, and 25 percent *bbbb*. The phenotypic ratio would be 3 : 1.

8. Consider the following table, in which "L" and "S" stand for 13 large and 13 small chromosomes, respectively:

Hybrid	Chromosomes
G. *hirsutum* × G. *thurberi*	S, S, L
G. *hirsutum* × G. *herbaceum*	S, L, L
G. *thurberi* × G. *herbaceum*	S, L

Each parent in the cross must contribute one-half of its chromosomes to the hybrid offspring. It is known that G. *hirsutum* has twice as many chromosomes as the other two species. Furthermore, its chromosomes are composed of chromosomes donated by the other two species. Therefore, the genome of G. *hirsutum* must consist of one large and one small set of chromosomes. Once this is realized, the rest of the problem essentially solves itself. In the first hybrid, the genome of G. *thurberi* must consist of one set of small chromosomes. In the second hybrid, the genome of G. *herbaceum* must consist of one set of large chromosomes. The third hybrid confirms the conclusions reached from the first two hybrids.

The original parents must have had the following chromosome constitution:

G. *hirsutum*	26 large, 26 small
G. *thurberi*	26 small
G. *herbaceum*	26 large

G. *hirsutum* is a polyploid derivative of a cross between the two Old World species. This could easily be checked by looking at the chromosomes.

9. a. To do this problem you must first recognize that each allele can pair with any other allele within a gene. For a moment, pretend that you can distinguish all four alleles and, for simplicity's sake, number them 1 (*F*), 2 (*F*), 3 (*f*), and 4 (*f*). The combinations now become 1-2, 1-3, 1-4, 2-3, 2-4 and 3-4. In other words, for each gene there are six combinations. Changing the numbers into letters, the gametes for *F*/*f* would be: 1/6 *FF*, 4/6 *Ff* and 1/6 *ff*.

When two genes are considered, the gametes are

$$
1/6\ FF
\begin{cases}
1/6\ GG = 1/36\ FF\ GG \\
4/6\ Gg = 4/36\ FF\ Gg \\
1/6\ gg = 1/36\ FF\ gg
\end{cases}
$$

$$
4/6\ Ff
\begin{cases}
1/6\ GG = 4/36\ Ff\ GG \\
4/6\ Gg = 16/36\ Ff\ Gg \\
1/6\ gg = 4/36\ Ff\ gg
\end{cases}
$$

$$
1/6\ ff
\begin{cases}
1/6\ GG = 1/36\ ff\ GG \\
4/6\ Gg = 4/36\ ff\ Gg \\
1/6\ gg = 1/36\ ff\ gg
\end{cases}
$$

b. The cross is *FFff GGgg* × *FFff GGgg*. For *FFFf GGgg*, consider each gene separately. The combination *FFFf* can be achieved in two ways:

$$
\begin{aligned}
p(FFFf) &= [p(FF) \times p(Ff)] + [p(Ff) \times p(FF)] \\
&= (1/6 \times 4/6) + (4/6 \times 1/6) \\
&= 4/36 + 4/36 = 8/36 = 2/9
\end{aligned}
$$

The combination *GGgg* can be achieved in three ways:

$$
\begin{aligned}
p(GGgg) &= [p(GG) \times p(gg)] + [p(gg) \times p(GG)] + [p(Gg) \times p(Gg)] \\
&= (1/6 \times 1/6) + (1/6 \times 1/6) + (4/6 \times 4/6) \\
&= 1/36 + 1/36 + 16/36 = 1/2
\end{aligned}
$$

Therefore

$$
p(FFFf\ GGgg) = 2/9 \times 1/2 = 1/9
$$

and

$$
\begin{aligned}
p(ffff\ gggg) &= p(ffff) \times p(gggg) \\
&= 1/6 \times 1/6 \times 1/6 \times 1/6 = 1/1296
\end{aligned}
$$

10. e. Only achondroplasia is a gene disorder rather than a disorder characterized by an abnormal chromosome number.

11.   One of the parents of the woman with Turner syndrome (XO) must have been a carrier for colorblindness, an X-linked recessive disorder. Because her father has normal vision, she could not have obtained her sole X from him. Therefore, nondisjunction occurred in her father. The sperm lacking an X chromosome fertilized the egg carrying the col-

orblindness allele. The nondisjunction event could have occurred during either meiotic division.

If the colorblind patient had Klinefelter syndrome (XXY), then both Xs must carry the allele for colorblindness. Therefore, nondisjunction had to occur in the mother. Remember that during meiosis I, given no crossover between the gene and the centromere, allelic alternatives separate from each other. During meiosis II, identical alleles on sister chromatids separate. Therefore, the nondisjunctive event had to occur during meiosis II because both alleles are identical.

12. a. If most individuals were female, this suggests that the normal allele has been lost (by nondisjunction or deletion) or is nonfunctional (X-inactivation) in the colorblind eye.

   b. If most of the individuals were male, this suggests that the male might have two or more cell lines (he is a mosaic, X^{normal} $Y/X^{cb}Y$) or that he has two X chromosomes (he has Klinefelter syndrome) and that the same processes as in females could be occurring.

13. If the fluorescent spot indicates a Y chromosome, then two spots are indicative of nondisjunction. Presumably, exposure to dibromochloropropane increases the rate of nondisjunction. This could be tested in several ways. The most straightforward would be to expose male animals to the chemical, look for an increase in double-spotted sperm over those not exposed, and also examine testicular cells to observe the rate of nondisjunction with and without exposure. Alternatively, specific crosses could be set up that would reveal nondisjunction upon exposure to the chemical. If X-linkage in fruit flies is used for the assay, white-eyed females exposed to the chemical should have a higher rate of nondisjunction than do unexposed females. When crosses to red-eyed males are done, nondisjunction of the X chromosome would result in white-eyed females and red-eyed males.

14. One possibility is that the mean age of mothers at birth dropped significantly. Because the older mother is at higher risk for nondisjunction, this would result in the observation. Hospital records could be used to check the age of mothers at birth between 1952 and 1972, as compared with a 20-year period prior to 1952. Another possibility is an increase of amniocentesis amongst older mothers followed by induced abortion of trisomy-21 fetuses. Because pregnant women 35 and older routinely undergo amniocentesis, the rate for this population may have fallen while the rate for the younger population remained unchanged. This also could be checked through hospital records.

15. a. loss of one X in the developing fetus after the two-celled stage

   b. nondisjunction leading to Klinefelter syndrome (XXY), followed by a nondisjunctive event in one cell for the Y chromosome after the two-celled stage, leading to XX and XXYY

   c. nondisjunction for X at the one-celled stage

   d. either fused XX and XY zygotes or fertilization of an egg and polar body by one sperm bearing an X and another bearing a Y, followed by fusion

   e. nondisjunction of X at the two-celled stage or later

16. Remember that nondisjunction at meiosis I leads to the retention of both chromosomes in one cell, while at meiosis II it leads to the retention of both sister chromatids in one cell.

   1. trisomy 21; nondisjunction at meiosis II in the female

   2. trisomy 21; nondisjunction at meiosis I in the female

   3. normal; normal meiosis in both parents

   4. trisomy 21; nondisjunction at meiosis II in the male

   5. normal; nondisjunction in the female (meiosis I) and the male (either meiotic division)

   6. Klinefelter syndrome; nondisjunction for the sex chromosomes in the male meiosis I

   7. monosomy 21–trisomy 21 in a male zygote; occurrence of mitotic nondisjunction for the 21^c chromosome fairly early in development

   8. sexual mosaic; fused XX and XY zygotes or, as in Problem 15d, fused fertilized egg and fertilized polar body

17. *Type a:* The extra chromosome must be from the mother. Because the chromosomes are identical, nondisjunction had to have occurred at M_{II}.

   Type b: The extra chromosome must be from the mother. Because the chromosomes are not identical, nondisjunction had to have occurred at M_I.

   Type c: The mother correctly contributed one chromosome, but the father did not contribute any chromosome 4. Therefore, nondisjunction occurred in the male during either meiotic division.

   Type d: One cell line lacks a maternal contribution while the other has a double maternal contribution. Because the two lines are complementary, the best explanation is that nondisjunction occurred in the developing embryo during mitosis.

Type e: Each cell line is normal, indicating that nondisjunction did not occur. The best explanation is that the second polar body was fertilized and was subsequently fused with the developing embryo. Alternatively, a pair of twins fused.

18. **a.** The cross is *PPp* × *pp*.

The gametes from the trisomic parent will occur in the following proportions:

1/6 *p*

2/6 *P*

1/6 *PP*

2/6 *Pp*

Only gametes that are *p* can give rise to potato leaves, because potato is recessive. Therefore, the ratio of normal to potato will be 5 : 1.

b. The cross is *Pp* × *pp*. The ratio of normal to potato will be 1 : 1.

19. The generalized cross is *AAA* × *aa*, from which *AAa* progeny were selected. These progeny were crossed with *aa* individuals, yielding the results in the table in the textbook. Assume for a moment that each allele can be distinguished from the other, and let 1 = *A*, 2 = *A* and 3 = *a*. The gametic combinations possible are

1-2 (*AA*) and   3 (*a*)

1-3 (*Aa*) and   2 (*A*)

2-3 (*Aa*) and   1 (*A*).

Because diploid progeny were examined in the cross with *aa*, the haploid gametic ratio would be 2*A* : 1*a*, and the diploid ratio would also be 2 wild type : 1 mutant. The table indicates that y is on chromosome 1, cot is on chromosome 7, and h is on chromosome 10.

20. Radiation could have caused point mutations or induced recombination, but nondisjunction is the more likely explanation.

21. P   *a b⁺ c d⁺ e* × *a⁺ b c⁺ d e⁺*

Selection for *a⁺ b⁺ c⁺ d⁺ e⁺*

Because this rare colony gave rise to both parental types among asexual (haploid) spores, the best explanation is that the rare colony initially contained both marked chromosomes due to nondisjunction. That is, it was disomic. Subsequent mitotic nondisjunction yielded the two parental types, possibly because the disomic was unstable.

22. Before attempting these problems, draw the chromosomes. The cross is

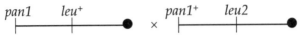

$$pan1 \quad leu^+ \qquad \times \qquad pan1^+ \quad leu2$$

a. The aborted spores arise from nondisjunction. Nondisjunction at meiosis I would produce 4 $n+1$ ($pan1^+$ $leu2/pan1$ $leu2^+$, viable) : 4 $n{-}1$ (nonviable).

b. If, at meiosis II, the chromosome carrying $pan1$ experienced nondisjunction, the progeny would be 2 $pan1$ leu^+ ($n+1$) : 2 $n{-}1$: 4 $pan1^+$ $leu2$ (n).

c. Consider the following crossovers (2-3, followed by 2-4):

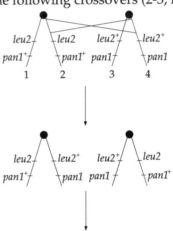

2 $leu2$ $pan1^+$ (n) : 2 $leu2^+$ $pan1$ (n) : 2 $leu2^+$ $pan1/leu2$ $pan1^+$ ($n+1$) : 2 aborted ($n-1$)

The four chromatids would be ($leu2$ $pan1^+$, $leu2^+$ $pan1$) and ($leu2^+$ $pan1$, $leu2$ $pan1^+$). If the second chromosome experienced nondisjunction, it would give rise to 2 fully prototrophic : 2 aborted spores. The first chromosome would give rise to 2 leu-requiring : 2 pan-requiring spores.

23. The two chromosomes are

$$b_1 \quad b^+ \qquad\qquad b^+ \quad b_2$$

If one of the centromeres becomes functionally duplex before meiosis I, the homologous chromosomes will separate randomly. This will result in one daughter cell having one chromosome with one chromatid, and the second daughter cell having one chromosome with one chromatid and a second chromosome with two chromatids. Meiosis II will lead to a nullisomic (white) and a monosomic (buff) from the first daughter cell and a disomic (black) and a monosomic (buff) from the second daughter cell.

If both centromeres divide prematurely, each daughter cell will get two chromosomes, each with one chromatid. All the ascospores will be black.

If nondisjunction occurred at meiosis I, the result would be one-half black (disomic) and one-half white (nullisomic) spores. Nondisjunction at meiosis II for one of the cells would result in two buff spores (normal meiosis II) and one white (nullisomic) and one buff (two copies of the same gene).

Normal meiosis will yield all buff spores because no crossing-over occurs between the two genes.

24. Aneuploidy is the result of nondisjunction. Therefore, any system that will detect nondisjunction will work. One of the easiest is that discussed in Problem 15. Cross white-eyed females with red-eyed males and look for the reverse of X-linkage in the progeny. Compare populations unexposed to any environmental pollutants with those exposed to different suspect agents.

25. **a.** *B. campestris* was crossed with *B. napus*, and the hybrid had 29 chromosomes consisting of 10 bivalents and 9 univalents. *B. napus* had to have contributed a total of 19 chromosomes to the hybrid. Therefore, *B. campestris* had to have contributed 10 chromosomes. The 2n number in *B. campestris* is 20.

When *B. nigra* was crossed with *B. napus*, *B. nigra* had to have contributed 8 chromosomes to the hybrid. The 2n number in *B. nigra* is 16.

B. oleracea had to have contributed 9 chromosomes to the hybrid formed with *B. juncea*. The 2n number in *B. oleracea* is 18.

b. First list the haploid and diploid number for each species:

Species	Haploid	Diploid
B. nigra	8	16
B. oleracea	9	18
B. campestris	10	20
B. carinata	17	34
B. juncea	18	36
B. napus	19	38

Now, recall that a bivalent in a hybrid indicates that the

chromosomes are essentially identical. Therefore, the more bivalents formed in a hybrid, the closer the two parent species.

Three crosses result in no bivalents, suggesting that the parents of each set of hybrids are not closely related:

Cross	Haploid Number
B. juncea × B. oleracea	18 × 9
B. carinata × B. campestris	17 × 10
B. napus × B. nigra	19 × 8

Three additional crosses resulted in bivalents, suggesting a closer relationship among the parents:

Cross	Haploid Number	Bivalents	Univalents
B. juncea × B. nigra	18 × 8	8	10
B. napus × B. campestris	19 × 10	10	9
B. carinata × B. oleracea	17 × 9	9	8

Note that in each cross the number of bivalents is equal to the haploid number of one species. This suggests that the species with the larger haploid number is a hybrid composed of the second species and some other species. In each case, the haploid number of the unknown species is the number of univalents. Therefore, the following relationships can be deduced:

B. juncea is an amphidiploid formed in the cross of B. nigra and B. campestris.

B. napus is an amphidiploid formed in the cross of B. campestris and B. oleracea.

B. carinata is an amphidiploid formed in the cross of B. nigra and B. oleracea.

These conclusions are in accord with the three crosses that did not yield bivalents:

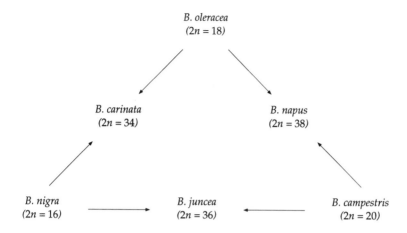

26.   a.   Before considering function, simply list the gametes and their frequency in both parents. In this cross, the parents have the same chromosome constitution, so they have the same outcomes:

Female and Male

2/6	*P*
2/6	*Pp*
1/6	*PP*
1/6	*p*

Next, consider whether the gametes are functional in each sex:

Female	Functional	Final Frequency
2/6 *P*	100%	4/9
2/6 *Pp*	50%	2/9
1/6 *PP*	50%	1/9
1/6 *p*	100%	2/9

Male	Functional	Final Frequency
2/6 *P*	100%	2/3
2/6 *Pp*	0%	0
1/6 *PP*	0%	0
1/6 *p*	100%	1/3

Now, a table can be constructed for the frequency of functional gametes from each sex:

		Female		
	4/9 P	2/9 Pp	1/9 PP	2/9 p
Male 2/3 P	8/27 PP	4/27 PPp	2/27 PPP	4/27 Pp
1/3 p	4/27 Pp	2/27 Ppp	1/27 PPp	2/27 pp

The ratio of purple to white is 25 : 2.
    The same method was used to solve the remaining parts of this problem. The results are given below.

b.   17 purple : 10 white

c.   4 purple : 5 white

SELF-TEST

1.   Prior to meiosis I, a germ cell in a human male experienced the translocation of one entire chromosome 21 to a chromosome 15. What are the chromosome complements of each resulting sperm? If each sperm fertilizes a normal egg, what is the outcome?

2.   In *Drosophila*, there is a recessive gene, *ey*, on the fourth chromosome that leads to an eyeless phenotype. A male trisomic for chromosome 4 with the genotype ey^+ ey^+ ey is crossed with an eyeless female. What will be the genotypes and phenotypes of their progeny?

3.   How many chromatids are found in prophase of a pentaploid cell when $x = 4$?

4.   The diploid number of the mouse is $2n = 44$. How many different trisomics could be formed?

5.   A woman who is monosomic for X has Turner syndrome. A man who is disomic for X has Klinefelter syndrome. A normal couple produce a child with hemophilia, an X-linked recessive disorder. What are the possible genotypes of that child? In which parent did nondisjunction occur?

6.   The Abyssinian oat is a tetraploid with 28 chromosomes. Common oat is a hexaploid from the same series. How many chromosomes are in the common oat?

7.   A chimpanzee was born at the Yerkes Primate Center in Atlanta that had all the characteristics of Down syndrome. By analogy with humans, what chromosome abnormality does this chimp have?

SOLUTIONS TO SELF-TEST

1. Meiosis I could result in the 15-21 translocation chromosome in one cell and autonomous chromosomes 15 and 21 in the other cell. At meiosis II, each cell would give rise to two cells that are identical to it. When they fertilize normal eggs, there would be two completely normal embryos and two embryos that would develop normally but would be translocation heterozygotes.

Meiosis I could result in disomy 21, with a 15-21 translocation, and nullisomy 21. Both sperm types would result in nonviable embryos.

Meiosis I could result in disomy 15, with a 15-21 translocation, and nullisomy 15. Both sperm types would result in nonviable embryos.

2. The cross is *ey ey* × *ey⁺ey⁺ey*. Gametes from the male will be

      1/6 *ey⁺ ey⁺*   1/3 *ey⁺*

      1/6 *ey*   1/3 *ey⁺ + ey*

The progeny will be

      1/6 *ey⁺ ey⁺ ey* wild type   1/3 *ey⁺ ey*   wild type

      1/6 *ey ey*   eyeless   1/3 *ey⁺ ey ey* wild type

3. (2 chromatids/chromosome)(5 sets of chromosomes/cell)(4 chromosomes/set) = 40 chromatids/cell.

4. 22; all except for the sex chromosomes would very likely be nonviable.

5. First, the mother must be heterozygous for hemophilia. The child could have four genotypes: (1) $X^h X^h$ female, nondisjunction in both parents. (2) $X^h O$ female nondisjunction in father. (3) $X^h X^h Y$ male, nondisjunction in mother. (4) $X^h Y$ male, normal. The child could also be a normal XY male, with no nondisjunction involved.

6. If $4x = 28$, $x = 7$ and $6x = 42$.

7. The chimp had trisomy of its smallest autosome.

10

Recombination in Bacteria and Their Viruses

IMPORTANT TERMS AND CONCEPTS

The **prokaryotes** are composed of **blue-green algae** (**cyanobacteria**) and **bacteria. Bacteriophages**, or **phages**, are viruses that reproduce in bacteria.

Conjugation is the one-way transfer of DNA from one bacterium to another. The ability to transfer DNA by conjugation is dependent upon the presence of the **F**, or **fertility**, **factor**.

The F factor is an **episome**, a genetic particle that can exist either free in the cytoplasm or integrated into the host chromosome.

Cells carrying the F factor are **F⁺** (free in cytoplasm), **Hfr** (integrated into bacterial chromosome), or **F′** (F factor in cytoplasm, with chromosomal genes inserted into it). Cells lacking the F factor are **F⁻**.

Cells with the F factor produce **pili**, which are proteinaceous structures that attach to the F⁻ cell. Cells with the F factor also produce a **conjugation tube**, through which genes are transferred.

F⁺ cells transfer genes located on the F factor. Hfr cells transfer chromosomal genes and, rarely, the F factor. F′ cells transfer both chromosomal and F factor genes in a process called **sexduction.**

After the transfer of genes, recombination can occur between the transferred genes (**exogenote**) and the F⁻ **endogenote**. There is a **gradient of transfer** of chromosomal genes.

Transformation is the process by which cells take up naked DNA from their environment. The DNA subsequently recombines into the bacterial recipient.

Phage infection of a bacterial cell can result in cell destruction, **lysis**, or a change in the characteristics of the bacterial cell, **lysogeny**. Lysis results in a **plaque**, or clear area, in the bacterial lawn.

A **virulent** phage cannot integrate into the bacterial chromosome and therefore always causes lysis. A **temperate** phage can integrate into the bacterial chromosome and therefore causes lysogeny. When integrated, the virus is called a **prophage**.

Phage characteristics include plaque morphology, host range, and burst size.

Transduction is the movement of genes from one bacterial cell to another with the phage as the vector. **Generalized** transduction results from lysis, frequently without a preceding lysogeny; each bacterial gene has an equal chance of being transduced. **Specialized** transduction results from lysogeny; genes close to the site of prophage insertion are transduced.

Be sure that you have thoroughly read the entire chapter before you attempt any of the problems.

SOLUTIONS TO PROBLEMS

1. While the interrupted-mating experiments will yield the gene order, it will only be relative to fairly distant markers. Thus, the precise location cannot be pinpointed with this technique. Generalized transduction will yield information with regard to very close markers, which makes it a poor choice for the initial experiments because of the massive amount of screening that would have to be done. Together, the two techniques allow, first, for a localization of the mutant (interrupted-mating) and, second, for precise determination of the location of the mutant (generalized transduction) within the general region.

2. This problem is analogous to forming long gene maps with a series of three-point testcrosses. Write the four sequences so that they overlap:

```
M  Z  X  W  C
         W  C  N  A  L
               A  L  B  R  U
                     B  R  U  M  Z
```

The regions with the bars above or below are identical in sequence. Therefore, the order of markers on the circular map is:
M–Z–X–W–C–N–A–L–B–R–U–M–Z – – – etc.

3. An F⁻ strain will respond differently to an F⁺ (L) or an Hfr (M) strain. Thus strains 2, 3, and 7 are F⁻. Strains 1 and 8 are F⁺, and strains 4, 5, and 6 are Hfr.

4. a. Agar type   Selected genes

1	c^+
2	a^+
3	b^+

    b. The order of genes is revealed in the sequence of colony appearance. Because colonies first appear on agar type 1, which selects for c^+, c must be first. Colonies next appear on agar type 3, which selects for b^+, indicating that b follows c. Allele a^+ appears last. The gene order is c b a. The three genes are roughly equally spaced.

    c. In this problem you are looking for cotransfer, which results in no growth because the Hfr strain is d^-. Therefore, the farther a gene is from d, the more growth that will occur. From the data, d is closest to b. It is also closer to a than it is to c. The gene order is c b d a.

    d. With no A in the agar, the medium is equivalent to agar type 2, and the first colonies should appear at about 17.5 minutes.

5. First, carry out a series of crosses in which you select in a long mating each of the auxotrophic markers. Thus, select for Arg⁺T1ʳ. In each case score for penicillin resistance. Although not too informative, these crosses will give the marker which is closest to Penʳ by showing which marker has the highest linkage. Then do a second cross concentrating on the two markers on either side of the penʳ locus. Suppose that the markers are ala and glu. You can first verify the order by taking the cross in which you selected for Ala⁺, the first entering marker, and scoring the percentage of both Penʳ and Glu⁺. Because of the gradient of transfer, the percentage of Penʳ should be higher than the percentage of Glu⁺ among the selected Ala⁺ recombinants.

Then, take the mating in which Glu⁺ was the selected marker. Since this marker enters last, one can use the cross data to determine the map units by determining the percentage of colonies that are Ala⁺Penʳ, and by the number of Ala⁻Penʳ colonies, as shown in Figure 10-13.

6. a. Determine the gene order by comparing arg^+ bio^+ leu^- with arg^+ bio^- leu^+. If the order were arg leu bio, four crossovers would be required to get arg^+ bio^+ leu^-, while only two would be required to get arg^+ bio^- leu^+. If the order is arg bio leu, four crossovers would be required to get arg^+ bio^- leu^+, and only two would be required to get arg^+ bio^+ leu^-. The gene order is arg bio leu.

b. The arg–bio distance is estimated by the arg^+ bio^- leu^- colony type. RF = 100%(48)/376 = 12.76 m.u.

The bio–leu distance is estimated by the arg^+ bio^+ leu^- colony type. RF = 100%(8)/376 = 2.12 m.u.

7. To solve this problem, draw the Hfr and recipient chromosomes in both crosses and note the number of crossovers needed to get Z_1^+ Z_1^+ for the two possible gene orders.

Order 1:

Hfr $\quad\quad$ Z_1^- Z_2^+ ade^+ str^s

recipient $\quad$ Z_1^+ Z_2^- ade^- str^r

Order 2:

Hfr $\quad\quad$ Z_2^- Z_1^+ ade^+ str^s

recipient $\quad$ Z_2^+ Z_1^- ade^- str^r

From the number of crossovers required to get Z^+ ade^- str^r, the order must be ade Z_2 Z_1.

8. In crosses A and B, the only types that will grow are pro^+ (lac-x^+ lac-y^+) ade^+. Both crosses require a crossover between the pro and the lac genes, and between the lac genes and the ade gene. In cross A, if x is to the left of y, one crossover is required; and if y is to the left of x, two crossovers are required. The opposite is true for cross B. Single crossovers are more frequent than double crossovers.

X	Y	Cross A	Cross B	Conclusion
1	2	173	27	1 is to the left of 2
1	3	156	34	1 is to the left of 3
1	4	46	218	4 is to the left of 1
1	5	30	197	5 is to the left of 1
1	6	168	32	1 is to the left of 6
1	7	37	215	7 is to the left of 1

(continued on next page)

1	8	226	40	1 is to the left of 8
2	3	24	187	3 is to the left of 2
2	8	153	17	2 is to the left of 8
3	6	20	175	6 is to the left of 3
4	5	205	17	4 is to the left of 5
5	7	199	34	5 is to the left of 7

The sequence is *pro*-4-5-7-1-6-3-2-8-*ade*.

9. The most straightforward way would be to put an Hfr at both ends of the same sequence and measure the time of transfer between two specific genes. For example,

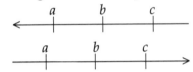

10. a. To survive on the selective medium all cultures must be ery^r. Keep in mind that 300 of these cells were tested under four separate conditions.

    If 263 colonies can grow when only ery is added, they must be arg^+ aro^+ ery^r. The remaining 37 cultures are mutant for one or both genes.

    The 264 cultures that can grow on ery + arg are ery^r aro^+. They may or may not be arg^+. Those that cannot grow are aro^-. Therefore, $300 - 264 = 36$ are ery^r aro^-. They may or may not be arg^+.

    The 290 cultures that grow on ery + aro must be arg^+, and the 10 that cannot grow must be arg^-. They may or may not be aro^+.

    Now this information can be assembled in a table. First write what has been determined experimentally:

	arg^+	arg^-		
aro^+	263	?	+	264
aro^-	?	?		36
	290	+ 10		300

Now the unknown values can be filled in.

263	ery^r	arg^+	aro^+
27	ery^r	arg^+	aro^-
1	ery^r	arg^-	aro^+
9	ery^r	arg^-	aro^-
300			

b. Recombination in the *aro-arg* region is represented by two genotypes: *aro⁺ arg⁻* and *aro⁻ arg⁺*. The frequency of recombination is

100%(1 + 27)/300 = 9.3 m.u.

Recombination in the *ery-arg* region is represented by two genotypes: *aro⁺ arg⁻* and *aro⁻ arg⁻*. The frequency of recombination is

100%(1 + 9)/300 = 3.3 m.u.

Recombination in the *ery-aro* region is represented by three genotypes: *arg⁺ aro⁻*, *arg⁻ aro⁻* and *arg⁻ aro⁺* The frequency of recombination is

100%(27 + 9 + 1)/300 = 12 m.u.

c. The ratio is 28 : 10, or 2.8 : 1.0.

11. The best explanation is that the integrated *pro⁺* was sexducted onto an F′ factor that was transferred into recipients early in the mating process. These cells now carry the F factor and are able to transmit F⁺ in the second cross as part of the F′ factor, which still carries *pro⁺*.

12. The high rate of integration and the preference for the same site originally occupied by the sex factor suggest that the F′ contains some homology with the original site. The source of homology could be a fragment of the sex factor or it could be a chromosomal fragment.

13. Here, we first need to carry out a cross with the Hfr and F⁻, in which we select for Ala⁺Strʳ. If the Hfr donates the *ala* region late, then we should do a short, interrupted mating. If it donates this region early, then we should use a Rec⁻ strain that cannot incorporate a fragment of the donor chromosome by recombination. The colonies from the cross should then be used in a second mating to another Ala⁻ strain to see whether we can donate easily the *ala* gene, which would indicate that we have recieved and F′ *ala*. To do this we need another marker. If we had an F⁻ that was also Ala⁻ and T1ʳ, then we could do the second cross selecting for Ala⁺T1ʳ.

14. **a. and b.**

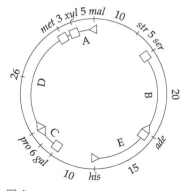

☐ first to enter
▷ last to enter

    c. A: select for *xyl⁺*

        B: select for *ser⁺*

        C: select for *gal⁺*

        D: select for *met⁺*

        E: select for *ade⁺*

15. **a.** If the two genes are far enough apart to be located on separate DNA fragments, then the frequency of double transformants should be the product of the frequency of the two single transformants, or (4.3%) × (0.40%) = 0.017%. The observed double transformant frequency is 0.17 percent, a factor of 10 greater than expected. Therefore, the two genes are located close together and are cotransformed at a rate of 0.17 percent.

      b. Here, when the two genes must be contained on separate pieces of DNA, the rate of cotransformation is much lower, confirming the conclusion in part a.

16. **a.** Notice that each gene was transferred into about one-tenth of the cells (single drugs tested). Also notice that pairwise testing gives low values whenever B is involved but fairly high rates when any drug but B is involved. This suggests that the gene for B resistance is not close to the other three genes and that the low rates come from double crossovers.

      b. To determine the relative order of genes for resistance to A, C, and D, notice that the frequency of resistance to AC is approximately the frequency of resistance to ACD. Also notice that AD resistance is roughly 50 percent higher. This suggests that the gene for D resistance is between the other two genes.

    17. The expected number of double recombinants is (0.01)(0.002)(100,000) = 2. Interference = 1 − [(observed DCO)/(expected DCO)] = 1 − 5/2 = − 1.5. By definition, the interference is negative.

18. **a.** m–r: The two parentals are + + + and *m r tu*. The crossovers between *m* and *r* are

          m + tu   162

          m + +   520

          + r tu   474

          + r +   <u>172</u>

                      1328

Therefore the distance is 100%(1328)/10,342 = 12.8 m.u.

r–tu: use the same approach as above to show that the distance is 100%(2152)/10,342 = 20.8 m.u.

m–tu: by the approach above, the distance is 100%(2812)/10,342 = 27.2 m.u.

b. Because m and tu are farthest apart, the sequence is m r tu. At this point, the distance between m and tu can be corrected for double crossovers (classes + r + and m + tu). The final m–tu distance is the sum of the two smaller distances, or 12.8 + 20.8 = 33.6.

c. Recall that I = 1 – c.c. = 1 – (observed DCO/expected DCO). The observed DCO is 162 + 172 = 334. The expected DCO would be (0.128)(0.208)(10,342) = 275. c.c. = 1.2. I = 1 – 1.2 = –.2. A negative value for I indicates that the occurrence of one crossover makes a second crossover more likely to occur than it would have been without that first crossover. That is, more double crossovers occur than are expected.

19. a. I: minimal plus proline and histidine

II: minimal plus purines and histidine

III: minimal plus purines and proline

b. The order can be deduced from cotransfer rates. It is *pur-his-pro*.

c. The closer the two genes, the higher the rate of cotransfer. *His* and *pro* are closest.

d. *Pro⁺* transduction requires a crossover on both sides of the *pro* gene. Because *his* is closer to *pro* than *pur*, you get the following:

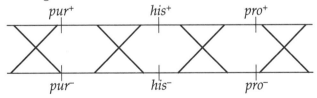

A *pur⁺ his⁻ pro⁺* genotype requires four crossovers. If you select for *pro⁺ pur⁺*, then the probability of *his⁺* is very much larger than the probability of *his⁻*.

20.   In several percent of the cases, Gal⁺ transductants arise from recombination between the λdgal transducing phage and the chromosome, without the transducing phage remaining intergrated in the chromosome.

21. **a.** Specialized transduction is at work here. It is characterized by the transduction of one to a few markers.

   b. The prophage is located in the *cys–leu* region, which is the only region that gave rise to colonies when tested against the six nutrient markers.

22.

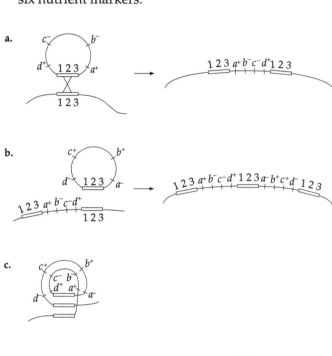

23. **a.** If *trp1* and *trp2* are alleles, then a cross between strains A and B will never result in *trp+*, unless recombination occurs within the *trp* gene. If they are not allelic, there will be *trp+* colonies. Check these colonies for the possibility of recombination.

   b. Infect strain C with the Z phage and use the progeny to infect strain B cells (which are immune because they are lysogenic for Z). The strain B cells should be plated onto minimal medium and minimal medium plus cysteine.

If the order is *cys trp2 trp1*, two crossovers will result in *cys⁺ trp2⁺ trp1⁺*, and the number of colonies on the two media should be approximately the same.

If the order is *cys trp1 trp2*, four crossovers are required for *cys⁺ trp1⁺ trp2⁺*. Therefore, the number of colonies on medium containing cysteine would be greater than the number of colonies on minimal medium.

24.   Recognize that if a compound is not added and growth occurs, the E. *coli* has received the genes for it by transduction. Thus, the BCE culture must have received *a⁺* and *d⁺*. The BCD culture received *a⁺* and *e⁺*. The ABD culture received *c⁺* and *e⁺*. The order is thus *d a e c*. Notice that *b* is never cotransduced and is therefore distant from this group of genes.

25.   a.   100%(3 + 10)/50   =   26%

b.   100%(10 + 13)/50   =   46%

c.   *pdx* is closer as determined by cotransduction rates.

d.   If the order is *pur pdx nad*, four crossovers are required to get *pur⁺ pdx⁺ nad⁺*. If the order is *nad pur pdx*, two crossovers are required to get wild type:

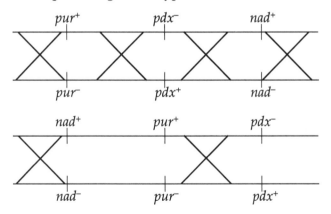

Because completely wild type occurred less frequently than the other gene combinations, the order is *pur pdx nad*.

26.   a.   The colonies are all *cys⁺* and either + or − for the other two genes.

b.   (1) *cys⁺ leu⁺ thr⁺/⁻*

(2) *cys⁺ leu⁺/⁻ thr⁺*

(3) *cys⁺ leu⁺ thr⁺*

c. Because none grew on minimal medium, no colony was *leu⁺ thr⁺*. Therefore, medium (1) had *cys⁺ leu⁺ thr⁻*, and medium (2) had *cys⁺ leu⁻ thr⁺*. The remaining cultures were *cys⁺ leu⁻ thr⁻*, and this genotype occurred in 100% − 56% − 5% = 39% of the colonies.

d.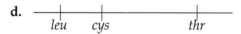

27. To isolate the special transducing particles of phage Ø 80 that carried *lac⁺*, the researchers would have had to induce the phage with UV and then use these lysates to transduce a Lac⁻ strain to Lac⁺. Lac⁺ colonies would then be used to make a new lysate, which should be highly enriched for the *lac⁺* transducing phage.

SELF-TEST

1. Could transformation also occur in eukaryotic cells? What techniques would you use?

2. Could transduction also occur in eukaryotic cells? What techniques would you use?

3. Four Hfr strains donate the markers shown in the order given below. All the Hfr strains are derived from the same F⁺ strain. What is the order of these markers in the original F⁺?

    Strain 1: Q W D M T

    Strain 2: A X P T M

    Strain 3: B N C A X

    Strain 4: B Q W D M

4. A mutant strain is plated onto a complete medium. Replica plates that have minimal medium supplemented by various amino acids are prepared from the original plate.

    a. From the results below, determine the genotype of the mutant.

    b. Determine the genotype of each of the colonies found.

        Replica 1: minimal medium + Arg and Lys → 1 colony

        Replica 2: minimal medium + Arg and Ser → 0 colonies

        Replica 3: minimal medium + Lys and Ser → 1 colony

5.   A cross is made between an Hfr $a^+ b^+ c^+$ and an *E. coli* strain that is $a^- b^- c^-$. It is known that c enters the recipient last, so cells are selected only for c^+. The exconjugants are tested for a^+ and b^+. The results follow:

$a^+ b^+ c^+$	300	$a^+ b^- c^+$	3
$a^- b^+ c^+$	0	$a^- b^- c^+$	80

    a. What is the gene order?

    b. What are the map distances in recombination units?

SOLUTIONS TO SELF-TEST

1.   Transformation is defined as the uptake of naked DNA from the environment followed by a recombination event that leads to change in cellular characteristics. The transformation of eukaryotic cells is routinely utilized in somatic cell genetics. When intact chromosomes are utilized, the process is known as chromosome-mediated-gene-transfer (CMGT). When naked DNA is utilized, the process is known as DNA-mediated-gene-transfer (DMGT).

2.   Transduction is the transfer of genetic material from one cell to another mediated by a virus vector. A form of generalized transduction is used in somatic cell genetics. A virus particle is fractionated into its component genetic material and protein from the viral capsid. Naked DNA from the cells selected as donor is mixed with the viral protein. The hybrid viral particle containing DNA from the donor cells reconstitutes itself by a process known as self-assembly. These hybrid viruses can now be used to transduce cells.

3.   Q W D M T P X A C N B Q

4.   **a.** *lys⁻ ser⁻ arg⁻*, a triple mutant

    b. replica 1:   *lys⁻ ser⁺ arg⁻*

        replica 3:   *lys⁻ ser⁻ arg⁺*

5.   **a.** *c a b*

    b. *c–a*: 100%(80)/383 = 20.9 m.u.

        a–b: 100%(3)/383 = 0.78 m.u.

11

The Structure of DNA

IMPORTANT TERMS AND CONCEPTS

The **transforming principle** is DNA.

DNA is made of four **nucleotides.** A nucleotide contains a phosphate group, a deoxyribose sugar, and one of four **bases.** A **nucleoside** contains a deoxyribose sugar and one of four bases. The bases are **adenine, guanine, cytosine,** and **thymine.** Adenine and guanine are **purines**; thymine and cytosine are **pyrimidines.** The number of thymine bases plus cytosine bases equals the number of adenine bases plus guanine bases.

DNA is a right-handed **double helix.** The nucleotides are connected by **phosphodiester bonds**, and the chains of the helix are held together by **hydrogen bonds.** The two chains are **antiparallel.** The orientation of deoxyribose within a chain provides the polarity of the chain.

Replication of the DNA is **semiconservative.** Each chain acts as a **template** during replication. Replication proceeds from the origin **bidirectionally.** A **primer**, composed of RNA, begins the replication process. The primer is made by an **RNA polymerase**, often called **primase. DNA polymerase** catalyzes the reactions that lead to **polymerization** of nucleotides. **DNA ligase** ligates two DNA molecules together. **DNA helicases** disrupt hydrogen bonds between the two strands, leading to kinks and twists in the DNA. **DNA topoisomerase** converts DNA from one topological form to another, removing kinks and twists. **DNA gyrase** can induce twisting and coiling of DNA, leading to **supercoiling.**

Each chromatid is composed of a single DNA helix.

Be sure that you have thoroughly read the entire chapter before you attempt any of the problems.

SOLUTIONS TO PROBLEMS

1. Because A = T, G = C, and A + T + G + C = 1, 1 – 2T = G + C. Therefore

$$1 - 2T = 2C. \ C = 1/2(1 - 2T) = 1/2 \ (1 - 0.30) = 35 \text{ percent.}$$

2. Because the percent G equals the percent C, the percent of each in the molecule is 1/2(48%) = 24%. Because A + T + G + C = 1.0,

$$A + T = 1 - G - C = 1 - 24\% - 24\% = 52\%. \ A = T.$$

Therefore, the frequency of both A and T is 1/2(52%) = 26%.

3.

f. Models b and e are ruled out by the experiment. The results were compatible with semiconservative replication, but the exact structure could not be predicted from the results. Experiments can *prove* only a negative and never a positive. In this experiment, it was proven that DNA replication does *not* occur conservatively at either the DNA or chromosomal level.

4. The results suggest that the DNA is replicated in short segments that are subsequently joined by enzymatic action (DNA ligase). Because DNA replication is bidirectional, because there are multiple points along the DNA where replication is initiated, and because DNA polymerases work only in a 5'→3' direction, one strand of the DNA is always in the wrong orientation for the enzyme. This requires synthesis in fragments.

5. Replication requires that the enzymes and initiation factors of replication have access to the DNA. One possible answer is that the heterochromatic regions, being more condensed than euchromatin, require a longer period to decondense to the point where replication can be initiated. A second possibility is that the heterochromatic regions, which are generally located at centromeres and telomeres in many organisms, "anchor" the chromosome to the nuclear membrane. Embedded in part in the nuclear membrane, these regions could require extra time to disentangle so that replication may proceed. A third possibility involves the mechanism of heterochromatization. Genes that are inactive in a given cell type are generally heterochromatic. This mechanism may also specifically delay replication. Many other possibilities can be proposed.

6. **a.** A very plausible model is of a triple helix, which would look like a braid, with each strand interacting by hydrogen bonding to the other two.

b. Replication would have to be terti-conservative. The three strands would separate, and each strand would dictate the synthesis of the other two strands.

c. The reductional division would have to result in three daughter cells, and the equational would have to result in two daughter cells, in either order. Thus, meiosis would yield six gametes.

7. Chargaff's rules are that A = T and G = C. Because this is not observed, the most likely interpretation is that the DNA is single stranded. The phage would first have to synthesize a complementary strand before it could begin to make multiple copies of itself.

8. Remember that there are two hydrogen bonds between A and T, while there are three hydrogen bonds between G and C. Denaturation involves the breaking of these bonds, which requires energy. The more bonds that need to be broken, the more energy that must be supplied. Thus the temperature at which a given DNA molecule denatures is a function of its base composition. The higher the temperature of denaturation, the higher the percentage of GC pairs.

9. Deletions and duplications at the DNA level would look exactly like the same events during homologous pairing of chromosomes at the duplex DNA level:

Inversions would have two possibilities, depending on the relative length of the inverted and noninverted regions:

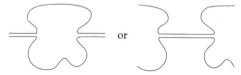

10. **a.** The first shoulder appears before strand interaction takes place, suggesting that the complementary regions are in the same molecule. This is called a palindrome:

ATGCATGGCCA————————TGGCCATGCAT

TACGTACCGGT———————ACCGGTACGTA

When the strands separate, each strand can base-pair with itself:

ATGCATGGCCA

TACGTACCGGT

b. The second shoulder represents sequences that are present in many copies in the genome (repeated sequences). Because they are at a higher concentration than are sequences present in only one copy per haploid genome (unique sequences), they have a higher probability of encountering each other during a given time period.

11. First realize that the repeated and unique sequences could be completely interspersed, partially interspersed, or completely segregated from each other in the chromosomal DNA. The distribution of these two types of sequences will affect the reannealing curves observed.

Extract the DNA from the cells. Do separate renaturation curves for unsheared DNA and DNA sheared to fragments of just a few kilobases. If there is generalized interspersion, then the part of the curve corresponding to the annealing of unique sequences will be farther to the left for the unsheared sample compared to the sheared sample. This is because the interspersed repeated sequences in the unsheared sample will facilitate pairing.

You might also examine the rapidly annealing DNA from the unsheared sample by electron microscopy. Interspersion would result in partial duplexes, with unmatched single-stranded regions (unique-sequence DNA) interspersed.

12. This observation suggests that the mouse cancer cells have copies of the virus genome integrated into them. Thus, it may be that the viral genes somehow alter cell function, triggering malignancy. Alternatively, the viral genome may carry one or more genes that directly result in malignancy. In either case, viral infection may also be the mechanism by which human malignancy is triggered in some instances.

13. The data suggest that each chromosome is composed of one long, continuous molecule of DNA.

14. Let the broken line indicate DNA that has incorporated bromodeoxyuridine and the unbroken line indicate normal DNA.

After one round   After two rounds   After three rounds

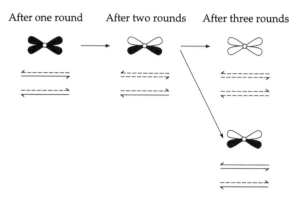

SELF-TEST

1. Which of the following two sequences would you be more likely to find in an organism that grows in a hot spring? Why?

    a. 3' ATATCTGATTTAT 5'

    b. 3' GGGCGTGGGCGGA 5'

2. a. By most genetic measures, chimpanzees and gorillas are closer to each other than humans are to either. Several years ago (1990), DNA hybridization was used as a measure of genetic relatedness, and the results indicated that humans and chimpanzees are the closest pair. The results were confirmed independently. This conclusion has been hotly contested by a number of researchers. What are their possible arguments?

    b. Recently (1992), a new analysis of the old fossil evidence supported the molecular conclusion that chimpanzees are closer to humans genetically than they are to gorillas. Does this new analysis change your answer to the above question?

3. If a DNA sequence is 3' ATTGC 5', what is its complementary sequence?

4. Assume that a single break occurred in a DNA chain. Which enzyme is capable of connecting the two pieces?

5. Buoyant density is a measure of molecular density during centrifugation. The more dense a molecule, the faster it will pellet in a given solution. The buoyant density (ρ) of DNA molecules in 6 M CsCl increases with the molar content of G + C nucleotides according to the following formula:

$$\rho = 1.660 + 0.00098 \, (G + C)$$

Find the molar percentage of G + C in DNA from *Streptococcus pneumoniae*, in which $\rho = 1.700$. What is the A + T molar content?

6.   Which enzyme initiates transcription in bacteria?

7.   Which enzyme fills gaps during DNA replication in bacteria?

8.   Which enzyme is the primary DNA replication enzyme in bacteria?

9.   What class of enzymes is responsible for changing DNA topology?

10.   Which enzyme unwinds DNA during replication?

11.   Graph DNA content within chromosomes as a cell goes through mitosis and then through meiosis.

SOLUTIONS TO SELF-TEST

1.   b.   The sequence with a high GC content, because of the three hydrogen bonds per GC base pair, is more resistant to melting than is the sequence with a high AT content, since there are only two hydrogen bonds per AT base pair.

2.   a.   The objections have ranged from the highly technical to the highly slanderous. One scientific objection is that DNA hybridization is a much more complex process than has been recognized. Another scientific objection revolves around the statistical analysis that was conducted. A third is that because the results contradict the results obtained by several other approaches, DNA hybridization simply is not a good measure of genetic relatedness.

      b.   While the scientific objections that were raised have yet to be answered, the furor over the molecular analysis and/or the specific findings may have biased the reanalysis of the fossil evidence. Alternatively, the molecular analysis may have tipped the scales for some who were bothered by the old analysis of the fossil data and yet could not point to specific pieces of fossil evidence that indicated definitively that chimpanzees were closer to humans than to gorillas.

          The student needs to remember that scientific interpretation is conducted by humans. All humans have a set of biases; in some those biases are much stronger than in others. In the past, bias has led to the dismissal of elegant experiments (the work of Avery, MacLeod and McCarty on DNA as the transforming principle, as an example), and the complete acceptance of unproven facts (the initial acceptance of semi-conservative replication although no proof existed when it was proposed, as an example). There is every reason to think that these two "nonscientific" processes are still occurring within science today.

3.   3' GCAAT 5'

4.   DNA ligase

5.   The equation is $1.700 = 1.660 + 0.00098(G + C)$. $G + C = 40.8$ percent. Because $(A + T) + (G + C) = 1.0$, the $A + T$ molar percentage is 59.2.

6.   primase

7.   DNA polymerase I

8.   DNA polymerase III

9.   topoisomerases

10.   helicase

11.

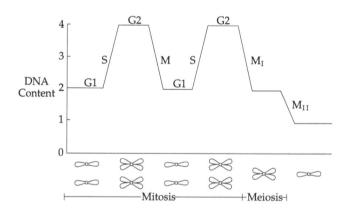

12

The Nature of the Gene

IMPORTANT TERMS AND CONCEPTS

Genes control biochemical reactions by controlling the production of enzymes. **Enzymes** are proteins, which consist of one or more chains of **amino acids** linked together by **peptide bonds.** A **polypeptide** is a chain of amino acids. One or more polypeptides exist in each enzyme. A protein-encoding gene specifies the sequence of amino acids in a polypeptide.

A change in base sequence can lead to a change in amino acid sequence, which can result in an alteration of function of the enzyme.

Both **recombination** and **mutation** can occur within a gene. The smallest unit of both recombination and mutation is a single nucleotide pair.

A **cistron** is the equivalent of a gene. It is a genetic region within which normally no complementation occurs between mutations.

Be sure that you have thoroughly read the entire chapter before you attempt any of the problems.

SOLUTIONS TO PROBLEMS

1. The defective enzyme that results in albinism may not be able to detoxify a chemical component of Saint-John's wort that the wild-type enzyme can detoxify. In fact, the plant contains a chemical that is made toxic by light (a phototoxin).

2. Lactose is composed of one molecule of galactose and one mole-

cule of lactose. A secondary cure would result if all galactose and lactose is removed from the diet. The disorder would be expected not to be dominant, because one good copy of the gene should allow for at least some, if not all, breakdown of galactose. In fact, the disorder is recessive.

3. Amniocentesis can be used to detect chromosomal abnormalities and any single-gene abnormalities for which there is a test. Thus, Down syndrome, Turner syndrome, and other chromosomal abnormalities can be detected. Furthermore, biochemical disorders such as galactosemia, Tay-Sachs disease, sickle cell anemia, and phenylketonuria can be detected. Amniocentesis would thus be useful whenever there is a family history of chromosomal or biochemical disorders and whenever there is a history of parental exposure to mutagens (X rays or chemicals). It would also be useful when the maternal age is over 35, because the rate of nondisjunction is elevated in this population.

4.   **a.** The main use is in detecting carrier parents and in diagnosing a disorder in the fetus.

   b. Because the values for normal individuals and carriers overlap for galactosemia, there is ambiguity if a person has 25 to 30 units as a result. That person could be either a carrier or normal.

   c. These genes are phenotypically dominant but are incompletely dominant at the molecular level. A minimal level of enzyme activity apparently is enough to ensure normal function and phenotype.

5. One less likely possibility is a germ-line mutation. More likely is that each parent was blocked at a different point in a metabolic pathway. If one were *AA bb* and the other were *aa BB*, then the child would be *Aa Bb* and would have sufficient levels of both resulting enzymes to produce pigment.

6. Assuming homozygosity for the normal gene, the mating is *AA bb × aa BB*. The children would be normal, *Aa Bb* (see Problem 5).

7.   **a.** Complementation refers to genes within a cell, which is not what is happening here. Most likely, what is known as cross-feeding is occurring, whereby a product made by one strain diffuses to another strain and allows growth of the second strain. This is equivalent to supplementing the medium. Because cross-feeding seems to be taking place, the suggestion is that the strains are blocked at different points in the metabolic pathway.

   b. For cross-feeding to occur, the growing strain must have a block that occurs earlier in the metabolic pathway than does the block in the strain from which it is obtaining the product for growth.

   c.   E-D-B

   d.   Without some tryptophan, no growth at all would occur, and the cells would not have lived long enough to produce a product that could diffuse.

8.

Experiment	Result	Interpretation
v into *v* hosts	scarlet	defects in same gene
cn into *cn* hosts	scarlet	defects in same gene
v into wild-type hosts	wild type	wild type provides *v* product
cn into wild-type hosts	wild type	wild type provides *cn* product
cn into *v* hosts	scarlet	*v* cannot provide *cn* product; *cn* later than *v* in metabolic pathway
v into *cn* hosts	wild type	*cn* provides *v* product; *v* defect earlier than *cn*

A simple test would be to grind up *cn* animals, inject *v* larvae with the material, and look for wild-type development.

9.

$$bw^+$$

no pigment (white) $\xrightarrow{}$ scarlet

no pigment (white) $\xrightarrow{}$ brown

$$st^+$$

Scarlet plus brown results in red.

10.   **a.**   The later a compound is in a pathway, the more mutants for which it can support growth. Therefore,

   E $\longrightarrow$ A $\longrightarrow$ C $\longrightarrow$ B $\longrightarrow$ D $\longrightarrow$ G

   b.   A block is indicated by the fact that no growth takes place if a compound is provided that is already being made. Growth occurs if a compound that cannot be made by the organism is supplied.

   Mutant 1:   grows on D and G; the block is at the conversion of B to D.

> *Mutant 2:* grows on B, D and G; the block is at the conversion of C to B.
>
> *Mutant 3:* grows on G; the block is at the conversion of D to G.
>
> *Mutant 4:* grows on B, C, D and G; the block is at the conversion of A to C.
>
> *Mutant 5:* grows on all but E; the block is at the conversion of E to A.

    c.   1,3 + 2,4: 1,3 would accumulate D and require G; 2,4 would require B, D, or G but could then make G for 1,3 growth. Therefore, growth would occur.

        1,3 + 3,4: 1,3 would require G and accumulate B; 3,4 would require B, D, or G and accumulate C. Neither can help the other to grow

        1,2 + 2,4 + 1,4: 1,2 would require D or G and would accumulate B; 2,4 would require B, D, or G and accumulate C; 1,4 would require D or G and would accumulate B. Therefore growth would occur.

11. **a.** When $m = 0.5$, $e^{-m} = 0.60$. Therefore, 60 percent of the meioses will not have a crossover.

    b. Because RF $= 1/2(1 - e^{-m})$, RF $= 1/2(1 - 0.6) = 0.20$. That is, there are 20 m.u. between the two genes.

    c. The recombinants will be $1/2(val\text{-}1\ val\text{-}2)$ and $1/2(val\text{-}1^+\ val\text{-}2^+)$. Therefore, $1/2$RF $= (val\text{-}1^+\ val\text{-}2^+) = 10$ percent.

    d. Remember that accumulation of substance x means the gene responsible for converting substance x to the next metabolic substance is defective. Also, if substance y permits growth, it is beyond a block in a metabolic pathway.

$$\longrightarrow B \underset{val\text{-}1}{\longrightarrow} A \underset{val\text{-}2}{\longrightarrow} \text{valine}$$

12. **a.** A defective enzyme A (from m_2m_2) would yield red petals.

    b. Purple, because it has a wild-type allele for each gene.

    c. 9 M_1- M_2- purple

        3 m_1m_1 M_2- blue

        3 M_1- m_2m_2 red

        1 m_1m_1 m_2m_2 white

   d. Because they do not produce a functional enzyme.

13.   a. white

      b. blue

      c. purple

      d. P bb DD × BB dd

          F_1 Bb Dd × Bb Dd

          F_2 9 $B-$ $D-$ purple

               3   bb $D-$ white

               3   $B-$ dd blue

               1   bb dd white or 9 : 3 : 4

14.   The *cis* and *trans* burst size should be the same if the mutants are in different cistrons, and if they are in the same cistron, the *trans* burst size should be zero. Therefore, assuming rV is in A, rW also is in A, and rU, rX, rY, and rZ are in B.

15.   The cross is *pan2x pan2y⁺* × *pan2x⁺ pan2y*.

      a. If one centromere precociously divides, that will put three chromatids in one daughter cell and one in the other.

Daughter Cell 1:   Daughter Cell 2:

  $pan2x$ $pan2y^+$ $pan2x^+$ $pan2y$
——————————————●   ——————————————●
                                            $pan2x$ $pan2y^+$
                          ——————————————●   ——————————————●

            After meiosis II and mitosis, the first daughter cell would give rise to two pale (*pan2x + pan2y⁺*) and two white, aborted (nullisomic) ascospores, while the second daughter cell would give rise to two black (*pan2x pan2y⁺* / *pan2x⁺ pan2y*) and two pale (*pan2x⁺ pan2y*) ascospores. The same result (4 pale : 2 colorless : 2 black) would occur if only the other centromere divided early.

      b. If both centromeres divided precociously, each daughter cell would be *pan2x pan2y⁺*/*pan2x⁺ pan2y*. This would lead to 4 colorless (nullisomic) and 4 black (disomic) ascospores.

16.   a. The mutant does not complement any other mutant. The best interpretation is that it is a deletion.

      b. Complementation groups do not complement within a group (−) but do complement between groups (+). Notice that mutants 1, 5, 8, and 9 complement all others but do not complement within the group. The same holds for mutants 2, 3, 4, and 12 as a group and mutants 6, 7, 10, 11, and 13 as a group. These are the three complementation groups.

c. Mutants 1 and 2 are in different cistrons, so the cross can be written $1 + \times + 2$. Assuming independent assortment, the progeny would be

1/4 1 + eye^-

1/4 1 2 eye^-

1/4 + 2 eye^-

1/4 + + eye^+

or 3 eye^- : 1 eye^+

Mutants 2×6 also complement each other. If independent assortment existed, a 3 : 1 ratio would be observed. Because the ratio is 113 : 5, there is no independent assortment and the cistrons are linked. Only one of the two recombinant classes can be distinguished: 5 eye^+. Because the recombinants should be of equal frequency, the total number of recombinants is 10 out of 118, which leads to 100% (10/118) = 8.47 m.u. distance between the cistrons.

Mutant 14 includes the same cistron (no complementation) as mutant 1.

d. There are three complementation groups; therefore there are three loci, plus mutant 14. Because two of the groups are independently assorting, mutant 14 is a very large deletion spanning the three loci (and they are therefore on the same chromosome), or it is a separate fourth locus that in some fashion controls the expression of the other three loci, or it is a double mutant with a point mutation within one complementation group (1, 5, 8, 9) and a deletion spanning the two linked complementation groups.

e. Two groups are linked, with 8.5 m.u. between them: (2, 3, 4, 12 and 6, 7, 10, 11, 13), and the third group is either on a separate chromosome or more than 50 m.u. from the two other groups.

17. The best interpretation is that rW is a deletion spanning rZ and rD. Alternatively, it could be a double point mutation in rZ and rD. If it is a double point mutation, then a cross of rW with a mutant between rZ and rD (rZ–D) should yield wild type at a low frequency (double crossover). If it is a deletion, no wild type will be observed.

P $+ rZ–D + \times rZ + rD$ (rW)

Double recombinants: $+ + +$ and $rZ\ rZ–D\ rD$

18. **a.** A point mutation within a deletion yields no growth (–), while a point mutation external to a deletion yields growth (+). Only mutant c fails to complement deletion 1, so it is within the deletion and the other mutants are not. Mutant d is in the overlapping region of deletions 2 and 3, while mutant e is in the small region of deletion 2 that is not over-lapped by other deletions. The partial order is therefore $c\ e\ d$. Mutant a is within the nonoverlapped deletion 3, and mutant b is within deletions 3 and 4. The final map is

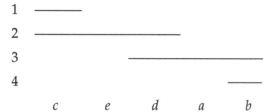

    1
    2
    3
    4

       c   e   d   a   b

    b. The suggestion is that deletion 4 spans both cistrons. This does not affect the conclusions from part a.

19. **a.** Here, + indicates nonoverlapping and - indicates overlap-ping. Therefore, 1 overlaps 3 and 5, 2 overlaps 5 only, 3 over-laps all but 2, 4 overlaps 3 only, and 5 overlaps all but 4. Putting all these pieces together yields the deletion map

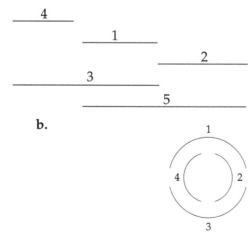

    4
         1
              2
         3
              5

    b.

         1
    4   2
         3

20. **a.** The values equal one-half of the recombinants. Because the problem asks for relative frequency, however, it is not neces-sary to convert to real m.u. Therefore, the distances are

1–2:	14	2–3:	12
1–3:	2	2–4:	6
1–4:	20	3–4:	18

The only map possible is

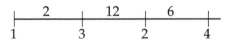

b. no

21. This is like any other mapping problem when the reciprocal cannot be detected: the detected class is multiplied by 2. Rewrite the crosses and results, using parentheses to indicate unknown order, so that it is clear what the results mean:

Cross 1: *his-2*⁺ (*a, b*⁺) *nic-2*⁺ × *his-2* (*a*⁺, *b*) *nic-2*

Cross 2: *his-2*⁺ (*a, c*⁺) *nic-2* × *his-2* (*a*⁺, *c*) *nic-2*⁺

Cross 3: *his-2* (*b, c*⁺) *nic-2* × *his-2*⁺ (*b*⁺, *c*) *nic-2*⁺

Results:

Genotype	Cross 1	Cross 2	Cross 3
his-2 nic-2	DCO between *a* and *b*, and *b* and *nic*	1 CO between *a* and *c*	DCO between *b* and *c*, and *b* and *nic*
his-2⁺ *nic-2*⁺	DCO between *a* and *b*, and *his* and *a*	as above	DCO between *b* and *c*, and *his* and *c*
his-2 nic-2⁺	1 CO between *a* and *b*	DCO between *a* and *c*, and *nic* and *c*	1 CO between *b* and *c*
his-2⁺ *nic-2*	3 CO between *a* and *b*, *his* and *a*, and *b* and *nic*	DCO between *a* and *c*, *his* and *a*	3 CO between *b* and *c*, *his* and *c*, and *b* and *nic*

Putting all this information together, the only gene sequence possible is *his-2 a c b nic-2*. To calculate the genetic distances, it is necessary to multiply the frequency of recombinants by 2 because reciprocals are not seen:

a–b: 100%(2)(15)/41,236 = 0.072 m.u.

a–c: $100\%(2)(6)/38{,}421 = 0.031$ m.u.

b–c: $100\%(2)(5)/43{,}600 = 0.023$ m.u.

The final map is

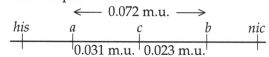

22.   Class I mutants are probably deletions, while the class II mutants are probably point mutations. A homozygous deletion would be expected to be lethal, while point mutations would be expected to be recessive. The heterozygote shows both phenotypes because the point mutation can be expressed when paired with a deletion.

To test this interpretation, cross a class I mutant for eye effects with a class II mutant for wings. The heterozygote should show only dominant eye effects, because the class I mutant should be normal for the class II point mutation. Next, cross the heterozygote to another class II mutant, this time for bristles. The progeny should be 1/2 wild type : 1/2 class I eye mutant.

23.   **a.**   The allele s^n will show dominance over s^f because there will be only 40 units of square factor in the heterozygote.

b.   Here, the functional allele is recessive.

c.   The allele s^f may become dominant over time in two ways: (1) it could mutate slightly, so that it produces more than 50 units, or (2) other modifying genes may mutate to increase the production of s^f.

24.   Pleiotropic effects result from interaction between gene products. As an example, sickle cell anemia results from a point mutation in the globin portion of hemoglobin. The phenotype can include joint damage, brain damage, kidney damage, etc. These effects can be labeled pleiotropic, but because the molecular, cellular, and organismal bases for the damage are understood, the term *syndrome* is usually used. As another example, a gene product (an enzyme) may act in the branch point of a metabolic pathway. The lack of this gene product would then result in two or more deficiencies, and each endpoint effect would be labeled a pleiotropic effect. A third example would be a gene product that is a regulatory protein (Chapters 17 and 23), which can alter many functions simultaneously.

25.   **a.**   One mutant cannot utilize the CAP produced by the wild-type allele of the other gene. Thus, there must be two pools of CAP in the cell, and neither pool is available for use in the alternative metabolic pathway. This could occur through membrane sequestering of each reaction.

b. Because the *pyr-3* enzyme controls two consecutive metabolic steps, the suggestion is that CAP is not released by the enzyme. This accounts for the inability of *pyr-3⁺* to compensate for *arg-3* mutants, but not vice versa. The *pyr-3* enzyme must have at least two active sites.

c. Partial suppression most probably results from a buildup in CAP to the point where some of it is released by the nonfunctional enzymes. When released, it is available for utilization through complementation.

d. Again, the facts suggest that the biochemical pathways are kept separate.

e. In rats, there are no separate pools of CAP.

26. Benzer used the Poisson distribution to make his calculations. While he knew the number of 1 and 2 occurrence sites, he did not know the total number of occurrence sites. Therefore, he had to assume that the Poisson distribution was applicable.

The equation is

$$f(i) = e^{-m}m^i / i!$$
$$e^{-m}m^i / i!$$

The terms:

$$f(0) = e^{-m}m^0 / 0! = e^{-m}$$
$$f(1) = e^{-m}m^1 / 1! = e^{-m}m^1 = 117 \text{ (from Figure 12-33)}$$
$$f(2) = e^{-m}m^2 / 2! = e^{-m}m^2 / 2 = 53 \text{ (from Figure 12-33)}$$

These equations can be used to determine the value of *m*:

$$f(2)/f(1) = (e^{-m}m^2/2)/(e^{-m}m^1) = 53/117$$
$$m/2 = 53/117$$
$$m = 0.9059$$

The number of 0 occurrences is

$$f(0)/f(1) = e^{-m}/e^{-m}m$$
$$f(0) = f(1)/m = 117/0.9059 = 129.15$$

27. a. *Cross 1 × 2:* All purple F_1 indicates that two genes are involved. Call the defect in 1 *aa* and the defect in 2 *bb*. The cross is

$$P \quad aa \ BB \times AA \ bb$$

F$_1$ *Aa Bb*

If the two genes assort independently, a 9 : 7 ratio of purple : white would be seen. A 1 : 1 ratio indicates tight linkage. The cross above now needs to be rewritten

P *a B/a B × A b/A b*

F$_1$ *a B/A b*

F$_2$ 1 *a B/a B* (white : 2 *a B/A b* (purple) : 1 *A b/A b* (white)

Cross 1 × 3: Again, an F$_1$ of all purple indicates two genes. The 9 : 7 F$_2$ indicates independent assortment. Therefore, let the cross 3 defect be symbolized by *d*:

P *a B/a B DD × A B/A B dd*

F$_1$ *a B/A B Dd × a B/A B Dd*

F$_2$ 9 *A– BB D–*   (purple)

3 *aa BB D–*   (white)

3 *A– BB dd*   (white)

1 *aa BB dd*   (white)

Cross 1 × 4: All white F$_1$ and F$_2$ indicates that the two mutations are in the same gene. The cross is

P *a B/a B DD × a B/a B DD*

F$_1$ same as parents

F$_2$ same as parents

b. *Cross 2 × 3:*

P *A b/A b DD × A B/A B dd*

F$_1$ *A b/A B Dd*   (purple)

F$_2$ 9 *A– B– D–*   (purple)

3 *A b/A b D–*   (white)

3 *A– B– dd*   (white)

1 *A b/A b dd*   (white)

Cross 2 × 4: same as cross 1 × 2

28. Mutants *a* and *e* have point mutations within the same cistron. The other point mutations are all in different cistrons. There are at least four cistrons involved with leucine synthesis.

With the exception of two crosses ($a \times e$, $b \times d$), the frequency of prototrophic progeny is approximately 25 percent. This indicates independent assortment of a plus e with b, d, and c; and c with b and d. Cistrons b and d are linked: RF = 100%(4)/500 = 0.8 m.u.

29.   a.   There are three cistrons:

   Cistron 1: mutants 1, 3, and 4

   Cistron 2: mutants 2 and 5

   Cistron 3: mutant 6

 b. Diagram the heterozygotes that yield *star*⁺ gametes, using parentheses to indicate unknown order:

  1–6: A (1⁺, 6) B/a (1, 6⁺) $b \longrightarrow a$ (1⁺, 6⁺) B

  2–4: A (2⁺, 4) B/a (2, 4⁺) $b \longrightarrow a$ (2⁺, 4⁺) B

  To determine cistron order within the 1–6 cross, note that the order A 1 6 B would require three crossovers, while the order A 6 1 B would require one crossover. The order is more likely A/a 6 (1, 3, 4) B/b.
  To determine cistron order from the 2–4 cross, note that the order A 2 4 B would require three crossovers, while the order A 4 2 B would require one crossover. The order is more likely A/a (4, 1, 3) (2, 5) B/b. The final order is A/a 6 (1, 3, 4) (2, 5) B/b.

SELF-TEST

1. The following point mutations were crossed with the following deletions. In the table below, + indicates complementation, – indicates no complementation. Order the genes along the deletion map.

Point Mutations	Deletions				
	A	B	C	D	E
1	–	+	+	+	+
2	+	–	+	–	+
3	+	–	–	+	+
4	+	+	–	+	+
5	–	+	–	+	–

2.   Consider the following metabolic pathway. If L produces the same phenotype as L', what would be the expected phenotypic ratio in an F_1 dihybrid cross?

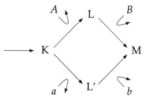

3.   Several mutants are isolated that can grow when they are supplied with substance D. The mutants were tested for growth when provided with precursors of D. In the following table, + indicates growth and – indicates no growth. What is the order of compounds in the metabolic pathway?

Mutants	A	B	C	D
1	–	–	+	+
2	+	–	+	+
3	–	–	–	+

4.   Two deaf parents gave rise to a normal-hearing child. What is the minimum number of cistrons involved?

5.   Two mutants known to be in the same cistron were able to complement each other. How can you explain this?

SOLUTIONS TO SELF-TEST

1.
```
          A
                   C
                            B
      E                D
  1      5     4    3       2
```

2.   14 : 2

3.   B → A → C → D

4.   two

5.   The end product of the wild-type gene contained at least two identical polypeptides. The mutant product of one allele interacted with the mutant product of the second allele in such a way that normal or nearly normal function resulted.

13
DNA Function

IMPORTANT TERMS AND CONCEPTS

RNA is a single-stranded nucleic acid composed of a phosphate group, a ribose sugar, and one of four bases: adenine, guanine, cytosine, and uracil. The ribose sugar provides the polarity to the molecule.

Transcription results in an RNA strand that is complementary to a DNA strand. Only one DNA strand is usually transcribed off a given region of a DNA helix. Along the helix, however, transcription can switch between one strand and the other numerous times, depending on the location of **promoters.** A promoter is the site for the initiation of transcription. For protein-encoding genes, the product of transcription is **mRNA.** Both **tRNA** and **rRNA** are also transcribed, but not translated.

Translation is the ribosome-mediated production of a polypeptide, using the information encoded in mRNA. A **codon** is a sequence of three DNA bases that specifies an amino acid. The **genetic code** is the set of correspondences between nucleotide triplet codons and amino acids. The code is **degenerate.**

Wobble is the sloppy pairing between the anticodon of a tRNA molecule and the codon in the mRNA.

RNA processing consists of the addition and/or removal of one or more bases in an RNA molecule plus, in eukaryotes, the splicing out of **intron** transcript sequences. An intron is a sequence within the amino acid–encoding region of a gene that is transcribed but not translated. An **exon** is the coding region in eukaryotic genes that is transcribed and translated into an amino acid sequence.

Be sure that you have thoroughly read the entire chapter before you attempt any of the problems.

SOLUTIONS TO PROBLEMS

1.   Because RNA can hybridize to both strands, the RNA must be transcribed from both strands. This does not mean, however, that both strands are used as a template within each gene. The expectation is that only one strand is used within a gene but that different genes are transcribed in different directions along the DNA. The most direct test would be to purify a specific RNA coding for a specific protein and then hybridize it to the λ genome. Only one strand should hybridize to the purified RNA.

2.   a.   The data do not indicate whether one or both strands are used for transcription in either case.

      b.   If the RNA is double-stranded, the percentage of purines (A + G) would equal the percentage of pyrimidines (U + C), and the AG/UC ratio would be 1.0. This is clearly not the case for *E. coli*, which has a ratio of 0.80. Therefore, *E. coli* RNA is single-stranded. The ratio for *B. subtilis* is 1.02. Either the RNA is double-stranded, or there is an equal number of purines and pyrimidines in each strand.

3.   A single nucleotide change should result in three adjacent amino acid changes in a protein. One and two adjacent amino acid changes would be expected to be much rarer than the three changes. This is directly the opposite of what is observed in proteins.

4.   It suggests very little evolutionary change between *E. coli* and humans with regard to the translational apparatus. The code is universal, the ribosomes are interchangeable, the tRNAs are interchangeable, and the enzymes involved are interchangeable.

5.   There are three codons for isoleucine: 5′AUU 3′, 5′AUC 3′, and 5′AUA 3′. An unacceptable anticodon is 3′ UAU 5′ because it would also recognize the codon for *Met*, 5′AUG 3′. Possible anticodons (using Figure 13-18) are 3′ UAA 5′ (complementary), 3′ UAG 5′ (complementary), and 3′ AUI 5′ (wobble).

6.   a.   As shown in Figure 13-18, there are eight cases in which knowing the first two nucleotides does not tell you the specific amino acid.

      b.   If you knew the amino acid, you would not know the first two nucleotides in the cases of Arg, Ser, and Leu (Figure 13-18).

7.   The codon for amber is UAG. Listed below are the amino acids that would have been needed to be inserted to continue the wild-type chain and their codons:

glutamine	CAA, CAG*
lysine	AAA, AAG*
glutamic acid	GAA, GAG*
tyrosine	UAU*, UAC*
tryptophan	UGG*
serine	AGU, AGC, UCU, UCC, UCA, UCG*

In each case, the codon that has an asterisk by it would require a single base change to become UAG.

8. a. The codons for phenylalanine are UUU and UUC. Only the UUU codon can exist with randomly positioned A and U. Therefore, the chance of UUU is $(1/2)(1/2)(1/2) = 1/8$.

    b. The codons for isoleucine are AUU, AUC, and AUA. AUC cannot exist. The probability of AUU is $(1/2)(1/2)(1/2) = 1/8$, and the probability of AUA is $(1/2)(1/2)(1/2) = 1/8$. The total probability is thus 1/4.

    c. The codons for leucine are UUA, UUG, CUU, CUC, CUA, and CUG, of which only UUA can exist. It has a probability of $(1/2)(1/2)(1/2) = 1/8$.

    d. The codons for tyrosine are UAU and UAC, of which only UAU can exist. It has a probability of $(1/2)(1/2)(1/2) = 1/8$.

9. a. 1U : 5C: The probability of a U is 1/6, and the probability of a C is 5/6.

Codons	Amino Acid	Probability	Sum
UUU	Phe	$(1/6)(1/6)(1/6) = 0.005$	Phe = 0.027
UUC	Phe	$(1/6)(1/6)(5/6) = 0.023$	
CCC	Pro	$(5/6)(5/6)(5/6) = 0.578$	Pro = 0.693
CCU	Pro	$(5/6)(5/6)(1/6) = 0.116$	
UCC	Ser	$(1/6)(5/6)(5/6) = 0.116$	Ser = 0.139
UCU	Ser	$(1/6)(5/6)(1/6) = 0.023$	
CUC	Leu	$(5/6)(1/6)(5/6) = 0.116$	Leu = 0.139
CUU	Leu	$(5/6)(1/6)(1/6) = 0.023$	

1 Phe : 25 Pro : 5 Ser : 5 Leu

b. Using the same method as above, the final answer is 4 stop : 80 Phe : 40 Leu : 24 Ile : 24 Ser : 20 Tyr : 6 Pro : 6 Thr : 5 Asn : 5 His : 1 Lys : 1 Gln.

c. All amino acids are found in the proportions seen in Figure 13-18.

10. a. $(GAU)_n$ codes for Asp (GAU), Met (AUG), and stop (UGA). $(GUA)_n$ codes for Val (GUA), Ser (AGU), and stop (UAG). One reading frame contains a stop codon.

b. Each of the three reading frames contains a stop codon.

c. The way to approach this problem is to focus initially on one amino acid at a time. For instance, line 4 of Table 13-10 indicates that the codon for Arg can be AGA or GAG. Line 7 indicates it can be AAG, AGA, or GAA. Therefore, Arg is at least AGA. That also means that Glu is GAG (line 4). Lys and Glu can be AAG or GAA (line 7). Because no other combinations except the ones already mentioned result in either Lys or Glu, no further decision can be made with respect to them. However, taking wobble into consideration, Glu may also be GAA, which leaves Lys as AAG.

Next, focus on lines 1 and 5. Ser and Leu can be UCU and CUC. Ser, Leu, and Phe can be UUC, UCU, and CUU. Phe is not UCU, which is seen in both lines. From line 14, CUU is Leu. Therefore, UUC is Phe, and UCU is Ser.

The footnote for Table 13-10 says that line 13 is in the correct order. In line 13, if UCU is Ser (see above), then Ile is AUC, Tyr is UAU, and Leu is CUA.

Continued application of this approach will allow the assignment of an amino acid to each codon.

11.   *Mutant 1:*   A simple substitution of Arg for Ser exists, suggesting a nucleotide change. Two codons for Arg are AGA and AGG, and one codon for Ser is AGU. The final U for Ser could have been replaced by either an A or a G.

Mutant 2:   The Trp codon (UGG) changed to a stop codon (UGA or UAG).

Mutant 3:   Two frameshift mutations occurred:

5′ GCN CCN (–U)GGA GUG AAA AA(+U or C) UGU/C CAU/C 3′.

Mutant 4:   An inversion occurred after Trp and before Cys. The DNA original sequence was

3′ CGN GGN ACC TCA CTT TTT ACA/G GTA/G 5′

Therefore, the complementary RNA sequence was

    5′ GCN CCN UGG AGU GAA AAA UGU/C CAU/C 3′

The DNA inverted sequence became

    3′ CGN GGN ACC AAA AAG TGA ACA/G GTA/G 5′
                    ^   ^

Therefore, the complementary RNA sequence was

    5′ GCN CCN UGG UUU UUC ACU UGU/C CAU/C 3′
                ^   ^

12. old: AAA/G AGU CCA UCA CUU AAU GCN GCN AAA/G
               ‾
     new: AAA/G GUC CAU CAC UUA AUG GCN GCN AAA/G
                                  +

Plus (+) and minus (−) are indicated in the appropriate strands.

13.   e.   With an insertion, the reading frame is disrupted. This will result in a drastically altered protein from the insertion to the end of the protein (which may be much shorter or longer than wild type because of altered stop signals).

14.   If the anticodon on a tRNA molecule also was four bases long, with the fourth base on the 5′ side of the anticodon, it would suppress the insertion. Alterations in the ribosome can also induce frameshifting.

15.   3′ CGT   ACC   ACT   GCA   5′
      5′ GCA   TGG   TGA   CGT   3′
      5′ GCA   UGG   UGA   CGU   3′
      3′ CGU   ACC   ACU   GCA   5′

      NH₃-Ala-Trp stop nothing

16.   f, d, j, e, c, i, b, h, a, g

17.   a.   (40 aa)(3 nucleotides/aa) = 120 nucleotides

      b.   This is actually a three-point cross. At meiosis, the alignment is

                              I   II
            mutant 1: Gln   C   A   A/G
            mutant 2: Ser   A   G   U/C

      The progeny from this cross are the two parental types plus

            Arg   AGA/G   1 CO at II

Arg	CGN	1 CO at I
His	CAC/U	1 CO at II
Asn	AAC/U	DCO
Lys	AAA/G	1 CO at I

Notice that the distance between any two adjacent nucleotides is constant. This means that the frequency of recombination between adjacent nucleotides should be constant. The data on Asn can be ignored because they represent a DCO. Likewise, the data on Arg can be ignored because the Arg frequency results from two separate crossovers. The best data are twice the frequency of His or Lys, which is 4×10^{-7}.

18. Cells in long-established culture lines usually are not fully diploid. For reasons that are currently unknown, adaptation to culture frequently results in both karyotypic and gene dosage changes. This can result in hemizygosity for some genes, which allows for the expression of previously hidden recessive alleles.

19. **a–b.** First look for stop signs. Next look for the initiating codon, AUG (TAC in DNA). Only the upper strand contains a code exactly five amino acids long:

DNA   3′ TAC GAT CTT TAA GGC ACT 5′

RNA   5′ AUG CUA GAA AUU CCG UGA 3′

protein   Met   Leu   Glu   Ile   Pro   stop

The strand, obviously, is read from right to left as written in your text and is written above in reverse order from your text.

c. Remember that polarity must be taken into account. The inversion is

$\longleftarrow$

DNA   5′ TAC ATG CTA GAA ATT CCG TGA AAT GAT CAT GTA 3′

                        start   ∧

RNA   stop 3′ CUU UAA GGC ACU UUA CUA GUA 5′

amino acids   HO-7   6   5   4   3   2   1-NH$_3$

d.

DNA   3′ ATG TAC TAG TAA AGT GCC TTA AAG ATC GTA CAT 5′

mRNA 5′ UAC AUG AUC AUU UCA CGG AAU UUC UAG 3′

              ∧1   2   3   4   5   6   7 ∧

            start   stop

Codon 4 is 5′ UCA 3′, which codes for Ser.

Anticodon 4 is 3′ AGU 5′.

SELF-TEST

1. If the anticodon sequence is 3′ AUG 5′, what is the sequence of the nontranscribed DNA?

2. A mutation in the β-globin gene, a component of hemoglobin, results in a shortened polypeptide even though the immature (before splicing) mRNA transcript was of the correct length. Propose two different causes for the short polypeptide.

3. What would be the effect of an inversion within a gene?

4. What would be the effect of an inversion of an entire gene, including all its control sequences?

5. What is the role of tRNA?

6. What is the role of rRNA?

7. Are tRNA and rRNA transcribed? Translated?

8. Distinguish between missense and nonsense mutations.

9. What is the source of rRNA at the chromosomal level?

10. The DNA of a species contains 33 percent G. What can you say about the percentage of G seen in the RNA?

SOLUTIONS TO SELF-TEST

1. 3′ CAT 5′

2. One cause could be the introduction of a stop codon. A second cause could be a change of the splicing site so that splicing eliminates more bases in the mRNA than it should.

3. At the very least, the amino acid sequence would be changed for the inverted region. Stop codons might also be generated.

4. No effect should be seen.

5. A tRNA molecule acts as an adapter between mRNA and amino acids.

6.   Although rRNA molecules are found in ribosomes, their exact function is unknown.

7.   Both are transcribed; neither is translated.

8.   A missense mutation changes a codon so that it stands for a wrong amino acid. A nonsense mutation changes a codon so that it means "stop" to the translation system.

9.   The nucleolar organizing region (NOR), located at the secondary constriction, contains the rRNA genes. It is the site of ribosome assembly.

10.   The percentage of G in DNA is not a good predictor of the percentage of G in the RNA. Differential transcription of genes occurs. Furthermore, the species may have a highly repetitive, GC-rich or AT-rich fraction, which would not be transcribed.

14

Recombinant DNA

IMPORTANT TERMS AND CONCEPTS

Recombinant DNA molecules are made from nonhomologous DNA.

Vectors are small, well-characterized molecules that contain an origin of replication so that inserted fragments can be replicated. Prokaryotic vectors include plasmids, the λ phage, cosmids, and single-stranded phages. **Expression vectors** allow for the transcription and translation of inserted DNA because they contain the start signals for both processes. **Shuttle vectors** allow for transcription and translation in two or more host cells.

Restriction enzymes are naturally occurring bacterial enzymes that make sequence-specific cuts in DNA. The resulting fragments, which have **sticky (cohesive) ends**, can then be inserted into vectors. Terminal transferase is used to generate sticky ends in their absence through a process known as **tailing.**

Restriction maps can be generated through the use of restriction enzymes. The maps vary with the species.

Cloning is the production of a large number of specific segments of DNA through the insertion of the DNA into a vector that allows for replication.

Cloning strategies include: **shotgunning** and the construction of a **gene bank** or **gene library.**

Southern blotting is the transfer of single-stranded DNA from an electrophoresis gel to a nitrocellulose filter. **Northern blotting** is the transfer of single-stranded RNA from an electrophoresis gel to a nitrocellulose filter. **Western blotting** is the transfer of proteins from an electrophoresis gel to a nitrocellulose filter.

Complementary DNA, or cDNA, is made from mature mRNA by using the bacterial enzyme **reverse transcriptase**.

Chromosome walking allows the analysis of very large segments of DNA.

Two sequence-determination methods exist: **base-destruction sequencing** and **dideoxy sequencing.**

The **polymerase chain reaction (PCR)** allows for the amplification of a specific region of DNA.

Be sure that you have thoroughly read the entire chapter before you attempt any of the problems.

SOLUTIONS TO PROBLEMS

1. GTTAAC occurs, on average, every 4^6 bases. GGCC occurs, on average, every 4^4 bases.

2. Isolate the DNA and separate the two strands. Test each strand for the ability to hybridize with mRNA produced by the phage.

3.

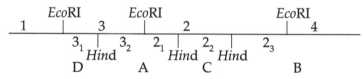

4. a. In situ hybridization using the polytene chromosomes would be the easiest way to identify chromosomal regions. Use whole-cell DNA from embryos lacking the region of interest. Next, using the clones that do not hybridize with the whole-cell DNA, do in situ hybridization onto wild-type polytene chromosomes.

   b. Either Southern blotting or colony hybridization would identify a clone coding for a specific tRNA.

5. Reading from the bottom the sequence is

Hind-Hae-Hae-Hind-Hae-Hae-Hae-Hind-Hind-Hae-Hind-Hae-EcoRI

6. Reading from the bottom up,

left column: GGTACAACTATATATCAATTATAAAC

right column: GGATCTATTCTTATGATTATATAG

7.   The XY male contains every sequence found in the XX female, plus the DNA sequence of the Y chromosome. Therefore, the DNA from a female can be used to purify DNA from the Y chromosome. Isolate, denature, and fix the DNA from a female to a column. Pour denatured DNA from a male through the column several times to remove all sequences complementary to the female. The remaining single-strand DNA will be Y chromosome DNA.

8.   This problem assumes a random distribution of nucleotides.

*Alu*I $(1/4)^4$ = every 256 nucleotide pairs

*Eco*RI $(1/4)^6$ = every 4096 nucleotide pairs

*Acy*I $(1/4)^4(1/2)^2$ = every 1024 nucleotide pairs

9.   a.   The restriction map of pBR322 with the mouse fragment inserted is shown below. The 2.5-kb and 3.5-kb fragments would hybridize to the pBr322 probe.

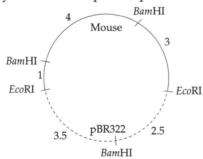

   b.   A protein 400 amino acids long requires a minimum of 1200 nucleotide bases. Only fragment 3 is long enough (3000 bp) to contain two or more copies of the gene.

10.   a.

   | 2.5 | *Hind* | 3.0 | *Sma* | 2.0 |

   b.

2.5	*Hind*	3.0	*Sma*	2.0
	1.5		1.5	
		*Eco*R		

11.   a.   1200 nucleotides

   b.   At 2 hours the viral transcript contains a nontranscribed intron sequence, which does not hybridize to the cDNA. The RNase removed the sequence, leaving behind 500- and 700-base fragments:

500 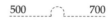 700

By 10 hours, the transcript has been spliced out, and a perfect hybrid forms between the 1200-base viral mRNA and the cDNA:

1200

   c. It takes a minimum of 2 hours to transcribe and splice the mRNA and then translate it into protein.

12. Assuming that the same genes from different species have approximately the same base sequence, use the β-tubulin gene cloned from *Neurospora* to isolate the β-tubulin gene from *Podospora*.

Isolate plasmids from *Neurospora* using ethidium bromide and cesium chloride.

Cleave the *Podospora* DNA with *Eco*RI. Next, use denatured DNA from the cloned *Neurospora* gene to isolate the sequence from single-stranded *Podospora* DNA. Finally, melt the double-stranded DNA, releasing the desired sequence.

Once the desired sequence has been isolated, cleave the *E. coli* plasmid with *Eco*RI. Mix this DNA with the isolated sequence and add ligase.

Some of the plasmids will contain the desired sequence; they will lack resistance to tetracycline. The rest of the plasmids will not have the desired sequence; they will be resistant to tetracycline.

Introduce the plasmids into *E. coli* cells that are Kan^S Tet^S using a calcium chloride precipitation. Select for Kan^R, killing off all *E. coli* that did not incorporate the plasmid.

Identify which resulting clones contain the desired sequence by isolating DNA from each clone, transferring it to a nitrocellulose filter, denaturing it, and probing with P^{32}-labeled DNA from *Neurospora*.

13. **a. and b.**

		8.0		7.4		4.5	2.9	6.2
*Eco*RI								
*Bam*HI	6.0			12.9			10.1	
	6.0	2.0	7.4	3.5	1.0	2.9		6.2

X

SELF-TEST

1. When a fetus is being diagnosed for sickle-cell anemia using recombinant technology and the mother is heterozygous, would contamination of the amniotic fluid by maternal cells lead to a false conclusion?

2.   A linear fragment of DNA is cleaved with the individual restriction enzymes A and B, and then with a combination of the two enzymes. The fragments obtained are

enzyme A   3.0 kb, 5.6 kb

enzyme B   2.5 kb, 6.1 kb

enzymes A and B   0.5 kb, 2.5 kb, 5.6 kb

Draw a restriction map.

SOLUTIONS TO SELF-TEST

1.   Yes; the maternal cells would indicate normal hemoglobin in the fetus.

2.

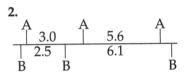

15
Applications of Recombinant DNA

IMPORTANT TERMS AND CONCEPTS

Two methods exist for making specific alterations of genes: **site-directed mutagenesis** and **gene synthesis.**

Once specific genes have been altered, they can be inserted into a cell through various techniques: transformation (exposing the cell to "naked" DNA), the use of vectors, injection, and transduction (transport into the cell by a virus), to name a few.

Transgenic organisms are organisms that develop from a cell into which new DNA has been introduced. Both **gene inactivation** and **regulation** have been studied in this way. **Gene therapy** has been conducted in animals.

Amniocentesis involves the removal and analysis of fetal amniotic fluid and cells. A number of genetic diseases can be diagnosed this way.

RFLP analysis can be used to screen for genetic disease.

Pulsed field gel electrophoresis is used to electrophorese chromosome-sized pieces of DNA.

Chromosome jumping establishes widely spaced markers along a chromosome that can be used for finely detailed mapping.

Be sure that you have thoroughly read the entire chapter before you attempt any of the problems.

SOLUTIONS TO PROBLEMS

1.   Plant 1 shows a typical heterozygous testcross result when crossed with the wild-type kanamycin-sensitive plant. This indicates that a single copy of the gene integrated. The cross is

P $K^r K^s \times K^s K^s$

F_1 1 $K^r K^s$ resistant

1 $K^s K^s$ sensitive

From this result, it can be concluded that resistance is dominant to sensitivity.

Plant 2 results in a 3 : 1 ratio in a testcross. There are two ways this ratio can be achieved in a testcross: if the plant is actually a tetraploid or if there are two separate integrations that assort independently. Assuming tetraploidy, the cross is

P $K^r K^r K^r K^s \times K^s K^s$

F_1 3 $K^r K^s$ resistant

1 $K^s K^s$ sensitive

Assuming two separate integrations, the cross is

P $K^{r1}/K^{s1} \ K^{r2}/K^{s2} \times K^{s1}/K^{s1} \ K^{s2}/K^{s2}$

F1 $K^{r1}/K^{s1} \ K^{r2}/K^{s2}$ 25% resistant

$K^{s1}/K^{s1} \ K^{r2}/K^{s2}$ 25% resistant

$K^{r1}/K^{s1} \ K^{s2}/K^{s2}$ 25% resistant

$K^{s1}/K^{s1} \ K^{s2}/K^{s2}$ 25% sensitive

The gene of interest should assort with kanamycin resistance.

2.   Pulsed field gel electrophoresis involves the movement through a gel of chromosome-sized pieces of DNA. Unless the overall size of a chromosome is changed, it should always migrate to the same relative position.

 a.   7 bands identical to wild type

 b.   7 bands identical to wild type

 c.   The largest and smallest bands would be expected to disappear. Two new intermediate bands would appear, unless they happen to co-migrate with one of the other five wild-type bands.

 d.   One band would be larger than expected and one would be smaller than expected, when compared to the wild-type.

e. 7 bands identical to wild type

f. 6 bands

g. The largest wild-type band would be missing and an even larger new band would be present.

3. The first task is to get the bacterial vector containing the gene of interest into the cell type which you wish to test. This can be accomplished by one of several means such as "shooting" the vector into the cell or producing transformed plants.

Assuming that you also have a resistance gene in the vector, you can select for that gene. Once the tissue is expressing the resistance gene, indicating possible integration of the vector into the plant chromosome, you can assay for the protein of interest or for production of its mRNA.

The quick way would be to do a Northern blot on the roots.

4. This is a cross between strains 1 and 2, with bands as the "genes." Because the sum of the bands from a single probe is much less heavy than the total molecular weight involved in the DNA spanning the two sites, you do not have to worry about the two probes detecting part of the same fragment. Before looking at the ascospores, consider the parents, using both probes separately and simultaneously:

Strain 1			Strain 2		
A	B	A+B	A	B	A+B
				__ 5.5	__
__	4.0	__			
				3.0	__
__	2.0	__			
__	1.5	__			
__	1.0	__			

If there is no recombination, a 4 : 4 ascus results (first division segregation) with the A+B pattern of strain 1 (4) and the A+B pattern of strain 2 (4).

If a crossover occurs between the marker and a centromere, a 2 : 2 : 2 : 2 pattern would be seen that is an alternation of the A+B patterns of strains 1 and 2.

If a single crossover occurs between the two RFLP sites, there will also be a 2 : 2 : 2 : 2 ascus. Each strain pattern will be seen among the parentals. The recombinants will be reciprocal and have the following patterns, where the subscripts refer to the strain source of the pattern:

A_1+B_2	A_2+B_1
—	5.5
4.0	—
3.0	—
—	2.0
1.5	—
—	1.0

5.   The missing *Eco*RI restriction site can be assayed for all members of the family. DNA isolated from blood (white blood cells) of each individual would be digested with *Eco*RI, electrophoresed, transferred by Southern blot, and then probed.

If the restriction site is missing within an individual, that person would then know that he carries the allele for cystic fibrosis. Those who have the restriction site could be relieved of worry about carrying the allele.

The two individuals carry within the same gene two different mutations that lead to cystic fibrosis. Because two copies of a cystic fibrosis gene, whether or not the defect is exactly the same, leads to expression of the disorder, 25% of the children from this mating would have cystic fibrosis.

6.   One approach would be to "knock out" wild-type function and then observe the phenotype. To do this, follow the one-step protocol described for Figure 15-11. Insert a selectable gene into the cloned gene of interest. Linearize the plasmid and use it for transformation of yeast cells. Select for the selectable gene. Another possibility is site-directed mutagenesis (pp. 441-443).

7.   After electrophoresis, Southern blot the gel and probe with radioactive copies of the cloned gene.

8.   Insert cloned glucuronidase with a plant promoter in the correct orientation into either a seed or numerous different tissues. If the former approach is used, grow mature plants in the presence of X-gluc and assay the tissues for pigment. If the latter approach is used, expose the tissues to X-gluc and assay.

9.   a.   Let B = bent tail, b = normal tail, r_1 = 3.8 kb, and r_2 = 1.7 kb. The cross is $Bb\ r_1r_2 \times bb\ r_1r_1$. Among the bent progeny are

40% $Bb\ r_1r_1$

60% $Bb\ r_1r_2$

Eliminating the contribution of the wild-type parent, the progeny are

40% $B\ r_1$

60% $B\ r_2$

If independent assortment exists, a $1:1$ ratio of $r_1 : r_2$ will be seen; r_1 and r_2 are clearly not assorting independently. Therefore, the two genes are linked with 40 m.u. between them.

b. The original cross is $B\ r_2/b\ r_1 \times b\ r_1/b\ r_1$. The wild-type progeny for tail conformation are

60% $b\ r_1/b\ r_1$

40% $b\ r_2/b\ r_1$

10. a. 1: $A1, B2$

   2: $A2, B1$

   3: $A1, B1$

   4: $A2, B2$

b. Spores 3 and 4 are parental types, occurring in 70 percent of the population. Spores 1 and 2 are recombinants, occurring in 30 percent of the population.

c.

$\underline{A \qquad\qquad 30 \qquad\qquad B}$

SELF-TEST

1. RNA from the vesicular stomatitis virus (VSV), which causes characteristic visible effects in cultured cells, was mixed with the protein coat of the rhabdovirus RD114, along with reverse transcriptase. RD114 is also an RNA virus. Virions were formed and used to infect cell lines generated by the fusion of human and mouse cells (recall that these cells will selectively lose human chromosomes). The cell lines were scored for their ability to support VSV infection. In the table below, a + indicates either chromosome present or infection and a − indicates either chromosome absent or no infection.

   a. Which human chromosome contains a gene that codes for a cell receptor for RD114?

b. What is the role of the reverse transcriptase in this experiment?

c. What would be the implication if no human chromosome could be linked with the presence of a cell receptor to the virus?

	Human Chromosome														
Cell Line	1	2	4	6	7	10	12	14	17	18	19	21	22	X	VSV Infection
1	+	+	+	−	−	+	+	−	−	−	+	−	−	−	+
2	−	+	−	+	−	+	−	+	+	−	+	−	+	−	+
3	+	−	+	−	+	−	+	−	+	+	+	+	−	+	+
4	+	−	+	−	+	+	+	+	−	−	−	+	−	−	−
5	+	+	−	−	−	+	−	−	+	+	−	−	+	+	−

2. *Herpes simplex* virus, type I, which causes cold sores, has a gene for thymidine kinase (*TK*). This virus was used to infect mouse cells that were previously grown under conditions that would kill any cell that expressed *TK* (they were TK^-). The mouse genome was known to contain only one copy of the gene prior to beginning this experiment. After infection, the cells were grown under conditions in which *TK* expression was required (they became TK^+). Using some of "the tricks of the trade" the chromosomes from those mouse cells that stably expressed *TK* were isolated and inserted into Chinese hamster cells that were previously grown under conditions that would kill any cell that expressed *TK* (they were TK^-). The Chinese hamster cells were then grown under conditions in which *TK* expression was required for survival (they became TK^+). Several independently derived Chinese hamster cell lines that stably expressed *TK* were isolated. Chromosome preparations were made from each of these cell lines and stained with both Giemsa and Hoechst dye (a fluorescent dye that detects AT-rich segments of DNA). In each cell line, a single Hoechst-positive chromosome was observed and identified as a mouse chromosome with Giemsa banding. However, the mouse chromosome was different in the different cell lines. The Chinese hamster lines that expressed *TK* stably were then grown under conditions in which *TK* expression killed the cells. Again, chromosomes were isolated from each cell line and stained with both Hoechst and Giemsa. In some of the cell lines, the entire mouse chromosome had disappeared. In others, a mouse chromosome was present. However, some of the lines contained an intact chromosome while others contained only a portion of the mouse chromosome. When the different Chinese hamster cell lines were then switched again to conditions that required *TK* expression, only a few lines were capable of survival. No cell line that had lacked a mouse chromosome was capable of growing under conditions that required *TK* expression. No cell line that contained a portion of the mouse chromosome was capable of growing under conditions that required *TK* expression. Only some of the cell lines, but not all, that contained an intact mouse chromosome were capable of growing under conditions that required *TK* expression.

    a. What is implied if TK^+ activity in the mouse cell line can be transferred along with a chromosome to the Chinese hamster cell line?

    b. Did the *Herpes simplex TK* gene insert in a specific site in the mouse genome?

    c. Is there any evidence that the *TK* gene was deleted in the Chinese hamster cell lines?

    d. Is there any evidence of gene regulation in these experiments?

    e. Do Chinese hamster cells contain any extended regions that are AT-rich?

3.   Eukaryotic cells in culture have been demonstrated to phagocytose polystyrene balls, calcium phosphate crystals, and numerous other substances that cells are not normally exposed to. How can this ability to phagocytose large particles be exploited to study gene expression?

4.   When mouse cells in culture are exposed to exogenous DNA in the presence of calcium phosphate precipitate, both the DNA and the crystals of calcium phosphate enter the cells by a process that looks like phagocytosis when viewed by electron microscopy. The DNA is intimately associated with the crystals. Within 24 hours, the phagocytic vesicles appear to be undergoing exocytosis, the secretion of the vesicle contents into the surrounding medium. If selection for an introduced marker is applied, a very small portion of the mouse cells will survive, and testing reveals that the selected marker is being expressed. Some cell lines will stably express the selected marker. The key event in this process seems to be the quality of the coprecipitate formed. Why is it that very few cells express the selected marker?

5.   In the previous problem, it is stated that some cells stably express the selected marker. That means that expression continues in the absence of selection. When recipient chromosomes are examined in these stable expression lines, frequently one or more chromosomes have new bands that were not there prior to the introduction of the exogenous DNA. The new band locations differ from line to line. What do these observations suggest?

SOLUTIONS TO SELF-TEST

1. **a.** The only chromosome that has the same pattern of "+" and "−" as the VSV infection is chromosome 19 in humans. Therefore, chromosome 19 in humans codes for a cell surface protein that can be used by the RD114 virus.

  b. The reverse transcriptase makes a DNA copy of the RNA viral genome so that the genome can insert into the human chromosome.

  c. Either the virus cannot infect humans or the cell receptor was not being expressed in the hybrid cells.

2. **a.** The *TK* gene was inserted into the structure of the mouse chromosome.

  b. Because the mouse genome has only one site for the thymidine kinase gene and the viral *TK* gene was inserted into several different mouse chromosomes, all but one integration must have occurred at a nonhomologous site.

  c. Those hamster cells that were first grown under conditions prohibiting *TK* expression and then were unable to grow under conditions requiring *TK* expression had lost either the entire mouse chromosome or a portion of it. The obvious interpretation was that at least the *TK* gene was deleted.

  d. The hamster cell lines that contained an intact mouse chromosome and were capable of growth, sequentially, under conditions that required *TK* expression, required *TK* nonexpression and required *TK* expression, appear to have been regulating the expression of the viral *TK* gene when it was inserted into the mouse chromosome and then transferred into the hamster cell line.

  e. No. The centromere of each mouse chromosome is AT-rich but no Hoechst-positive centromeres exist among the Chinese hamster chromosomes.

3. The ability to take in large particles can be exploited to get cells to take in exogenous DNA. When isolated DNA is co-precipitated with calcium phosphate onto the surface of cells in culture, a small portion of those cells can later express a selectable gene that was contained in the DNA but not in the recipient cells. This is known as eukaryotic transformation.

4. Most of the DNA that enters the cells through phagocytosis leaves the cells through exocytosis. The DNA that passes into the nucleus must escape the phagocytic vesicle, perhaps by the calcium phosphate crystals dissolving the vesicle membranes.

5.   The suggestion is that stable expression is correlated with the appearance of new chromosome bands. This, in turn, suggests that stable expression is brought about by integration, perhaps through a recombination-like process, of the introduced DNA in the chromosomes. The varying locations of the bands suggest that integration is random.

16

The Structure and Function of Eukaryotic Chromosomes

IMPORTANT TERMS AND CONCEPTS

A **eukaryotic chromosome** is composed of a single, continuous molecule of DNA complexed with proteins. One class of proteins associated with the DNA is the **histones.** There are four major histones: **H2A, H2B, H3,** and **H4.** Two molecules of each of the histones form a structure called a **nucleosome.** The DNA wraps twice around a nucleosome, and there is a nucleosome approximately every 200 base pairs of DNA. Nucleosomes associate to form the **solenoid** structure with the help of another histone, **H1.** The solenoid structure is arranged in loops from the **scaffold.** The scaffold contains **topoisomerase II**, which probably functions to prevent problems caused when DNA must unwind during replication and transcription.

DNA complexed with protein is called **chromatin. Euchromatin,** which is light staining, contains genetically active regions. **Heterochromatin**, which is darkly staining, is thought to be mostly genetically nonfunctional, although some genes may exist in these regions. Some portions of the genome are always heterochromatic (constitutive heterochromatin). Frequently, the DNA contained in the heterochromatic region is **satellite DNA.** Constitutive heterochromatin may play a structural and/or functional role in the chromosome. Some portions of the genome are heterochromatic in some cells and not in others (facultative heterochromatin). Faculative heterochromatin consists of genes that are nonfunctional in the specific cell in which it is seen. One example is the **inactivated X chromosome** constituting the **Barr body** (Chapter 3). Another example is an "eye gene" in a liver cell.

A **position effect** is seen when genes are translocated from euchromatin into or near heterochromatin.

Chromosome bands, whether naturally occurring as in *Drosophila* or induced by staining techniques such as the Giemsa banding procedures, are species distinctive. The Giemsa light bands are relatively GC-rich, tend to replicate early in S, and contain mainly the "housekeeping" genes (those genes that are active in all cells). The Giemsa dark bands are AT-rich, tend to replicate late in S, and contain mostly tissue-specific genes.

Eukaryotic DNA can be classified as **single copy, repetitive,** and **spacer.** Single-copy DNA is composed of protein-encoding genes that are present in only one copy. The repetitive DNA contains both functional and nonfunctional sequences, and the multiple copies can be either in tandem or dispersed throughout the genome. Functional sequences include the rRNA genes, the tRNA genes, families of coding genes (the human globins, as an example) along with their associated pseudogenes, and telomeric DNA. Such genes may or may not encode a protein. The repetitive sequences with no known function include the DNA in the centromere region, variable number tandem repeats (VNTRs), and transposable elements.

The **nucleolus** forms in the **nucleolar organizing region** (NO or NOR), which is located at the **secondary constriction** of chromosomes. It is the site of rRNA synthesis and ribosome assembly.

Be sure that you have thoroughly read the entire chapter before you attempt any of the problems.

SOLUTIONS TO PROBLEMS

1. a. Half the bands in the child should be derived from the mother and half from the father. A child cannot contain a band that is not seen in either parent, unless a germ cell mutation has occurred. F2 is among the group of men who could be a father to the child in question.

    b. If the bands in the child are numbered from the top to the bottom, there are a total of 22 bands. The following bands are from the mother: 1, 4, 5, 10, 12, 13, 14, 15, 16, 17, 18, 19, 20, and 21. The remaining bands are from the presumed father.

c. No.

d. A mutation occurred that altered, eliminated or made a restriction site.

e. The cellular DNA is cut with a restriction enzyme and electrophoresed. This results in a continuous "smear" of DNA along the length of the gel. Discrete bands are seen because the probe is detecting regions that are complementary to it. The multiple bands on the gel indicate a repetitive sequence that is of variable distance from a restriction site from repeat to repeat. The probe most likely is detecting a subsection of the piece of DNA that is seen in the band.

2. In order to answer this problem, assume that the wild-type allele makes a product which is necessary for life and that the recessive lethal lacks that product.

a. The *Su(var)* mutant would suppress the variable expression of the wild-type allele, allowing full wild-type phenotype. If the gene product is diffusible, the organism would be wild type. If the gene product is not diffusible, then the organism would still have a wild-type phenotype because each cell makes the gene product.

b. The *E(var)* mutant would enhance the heterochromatin effect, leading to much less wild-type expression. This would, in turn, allow expression of the recessive lethal allele. If the gene product is diffusible, a few cells may be capable of producing it, which would probably not allow viability. If the product is not diffusible, then most cells would die, leading to organismal death.

c. Without either suppression or enhancement, variegation would result. If the product is diffusible, the organism would be partially wild type, but would still probably die. If it is not diffusible, then most cells would die, resulting in organismal death.

3. a. One locus on each of the homologous chromosomes would be indicated.

b. Both ends of all chromatids would be indicated.

c. The chromosomal satellite region on all chromosomes containing NORs would be indicated.

d. Many small regions on many chromosomes would be indicated.

e. Many larger regions on many chromosomes would be indicated.

f. Centromeres, telomeres and NORs would be indicated.

4. On average, each DNA fragment contains 2 SINE sequences. Assuming that all SINEs have the same orientation, then each fragment of DNA should be able to undergo complementary pairing with one or more fragments.

5. a. The pattern of suspect 1 is compatible with including him among the group of individuals who could have committed the rape.

b. Suspects 2 and 3 could not have committed the rape.

6. To work this problem, number bands in the two parents, then use those numbers to identify bands in their children. If the mother has bands 1–4, marked with an asterisk, and the father has bands 5–8, not marked, the children have the following set of bands:

Child 1	Child 2	Child 3	Child 4
1*	6	1*	1*
6	2*	5	5
7	3*	4*	7
3*	8	8	4*

Note that four bands are present in each person but that a total of eight different bands exist in this family. Each child receives two bands from each parent. There are, therefore, two loci that are being detected with the probe. The loci are not linked. Four alleles are being detected for each locus.

7. a. Isolate DNA from the cells, cut it with a restriction enzyme, and electrophorese the fragments. After Southern blotting, probe with radioactive transposon sequences.

b. You could disrupt the transposon and look for a loss of the abnormal phenotype. Also, you could do a full linkage analysis.

c. The transposon could have inserted in spacer DNA.

d. Although as many as 182 protein-encoding genes may exist on chromosome 3 in yeast, only 34 have been identified by the detection of a mutant phenotype. If those unidentified genes were disrupted by insertion of a transposon, the disruption may not have been identified.

The 30 : 70 split may reflect the basic mutability of the genome, with 30% of the genome composed of spacer DNA and 70% composed of genes. If this is true, then more mutagenesis should lead to more detection of genes.

SELF-TEST

1.   On average there is a nucleosome every 200 base pairs of DNA. What is the relationship between genes and the DNA wrapped around the nucleosome?

2.   The *Xenopus* frog usually has two nucleoli per cell. Some frogs have only one nucleolus, and that mutation is called anucleate. If two *Xenopus* frogs each heterozygous for the anucleate deletion are crossed, what would be the result?

3.   RFLP DNA analysis is now being used in paternity suits. The following data were generated for one such case. Is the alleged father possibly the true father?

Mother	Child	Alleged father
‾‾‾‾	‾‾‾‾	
‾‾‾‾		‾‾‾‾
‾‾‾‾	‾‾‾‾	
‾‾‾‾	‾‾‾‾	
‾‾‾‾	‾‾‾‾	‾‾‾‾
‾‾‾‾	‾‾‾‾	‾‾‾‾

4.   The DNA from three closely related species is heat-denatured. The melting points are A $= 86.1°C$, B $= 86.3°C$, and C $= 85.7°C$. Which two species are more closely related? Why?

5.   Pseudogenes are never transcribed. What kinds of evolutionary changes could result in nontranscription of an originally active gene?

6.   RFLP analysis is also now being used in criminal cases such as rape and murder. What complications exist here that do not exist in paternity suits?

7.   What is satellite DNA and what is the underlying reason why it can be identified?

8.   You are studying the globin gene in chickens by the use of S1 nuclease, which cleaves only single-stranded DNA. Digestion of pancreatic DNA plus nucleosomes indicates that the globin gene is not susceptible to digestion. Digestion of DNA plus nucleosomes from red blood cells, which are nucleated in the chicken, indicates that several sites in the 5' control region of the gene are cleaved by S1 nuclease. What do these findings suggest?

SOLUTIONS TO SELF-TEST

1.   The average protein-encoding gene is approximately 100 amino acids long. That requires 3 × 100 DNA bases, at a minimum. Genes have associated promoter regions and they may have intervening sequences (introns). In addition, immature mRNA transcripts have leaders and trailers, also coded by a gene. Thus, the average gene may be several thousand base pairs long. The DNA associated with a nucleosome is, on average, 200 base pairs. Simple mathematics should convince you that one gene cannot wrap around one nucleosome. There does not seem to be any correlation between a gene and a nucleosome. The nucleosome must be viewed as a simple packaging mechanism.

2.   The cross is Aa × Aa. The AA progeny should have two nucleoli, the Aa progeny should have one nucleolus, and the aa progeny should have no nucleoli. The aa progeny would be expected to die as soon as the maternally derived ribosomes stored in the egg are used up during development.

3.   The child does not have any band that could not have come from either his mother or the alleged father. Furthermore, he has a band that is present in the alleged father but not in his mother. It is possible that the alleged father is the true father.

4.   Species A and B have the least difference between melting points, which means the least difference between G–C : A–T ratio. Because the DNA total content is more closely related between these two, the best interpretation is that they are the more closely related species. However, other supporting data would have to be gathered before this conclusion would be anything but tentative.

5.   Promoter sequences may have been deleted or mutated so that initiation of transcription does not occur. A mutated control factor (protein) may bind to the initiation site permanently and block initiation.

6.   There are two major complications: the limits of detection versus the differences between individuals and the frequency of the "alleles."

RFLP analysis detects only a subset of the sequences in a particular band. On the basis of the subset of sequences that are detected, band size is calculated and used to make comparisons between evidence and the suspect. Electrophoresis cannot detect differences in band size of less than approximately 200 bases. Because a difference in only one base may exist between individuals, the differences between individuals are greater than the differences that can be detected. With regard to the frequency of each allele, the information in Chapter 25 is important here. Different ethnic and geographic populations have been found to differ for every gene that has been studied, and the same differences can be expected to exist for RFLP probes. Without the proper population studies, there is no way to know if a "match" is extremely rare or very common within a population.

7.   Satellite DNA is DNA that migrates either above or below the main band of DNA during centrifugation. It is not in the main band because its average density is either greater than (GC-rich) or lighter than (AT-rich) the average for main-band DNA. Depending upon the species, satellite DNA can be localized to the centromeres, the telomeres, and the nucleolar organizing regions of the chromosome.

8.   Cells that do not produce globin have no single-stranded regions in the globin gene, while cells actively producing globin have single-stranded regions in that gene. It may be that gene activation is accompanied by single-stranded control regions. Gene activity may also require a looser association of DNA with the nucleosomes.

17

Control of Gene Expression

IMPORTANT TERMS AND CONCEPTS

Gene regulation is the regulation of transcription for specific genes. In prokaryotes, it is most often mediated by proteins that react to environmental signals by raising or lowering the rate of transcription.

An **operon** consists of two or more cistrons plus the regulatory signals that affect their transcription. Regulation occurs through the **promoter**, the *I* **locus**, and the **operator**. The **coordinately controlled genes** are transcribed in a **polycistronic** message. **Polar mutations** affect the gene within which they map and also reduce or eliminate the expression of all genes distal to the site of mutation in the polycistronic message.

Negative control is the blocking of transcription by a repressor protein that binds to an **operator**. The relief of **repression** is called **induction**.

The *lac* **operon** is under negative control. In the *lac* operon, **constitutive mutants** result in continuous expression in an unregulated fashion. Some are mutants of the *I* locus, I^-. The *I* locus determines the synthesis of a **repressor molecule**, which blocks activation of a gene or genes. An **operator constitutive mutation**, O^c, also results in unrepressed synthesis.

Positive control is the activation of transcription by a protein factor. **Catabolic repression** of the *lac* operon is an example of positive control. Here, the operon is activated by the presence of a large amount of CAP-cAMP.

Some operons are under both positive and negative control. The arabinose operon is an example.

Genes involved in the same metabolic pathway are frequently tightly clustered on prokaryotic chromosomes.

Feedback inhibition is the inhibition of the first enzyme in a metabolic pathway by the end product of that pathway, as exemplified in tryptophan biosynthesis. This is achieved by a process known as **attenuation**, an alteration of the secondary structure of the newly formed mRNA in the leader region.

Eukaryotic regulation is controlled by the **promoter, enhancers**, and **upstream activating sequences.** Several proteins have been identified that interact with these sites. Some steroid hormones also bind at these sites.

Genetic redundancy and **gene amplification** are cellular mechanisms that ensure an adequate supply of vital gene products.

Be sure that you have thoroughly read the entire chapter before you attempt any of the problems.

SOLUTION TO PROBLEMS

1.   The *I* gene determines the synthesis of a repressor molecule, which blocks expression of the *lac* operon and which is inactivated by the inducer. The presence of the repressor, I^+, will be dominant to the absence of a repressor, I^-. I^s mutants are unresponsive to an inducer. For this reason, the gene product cannot be stopped from interacting with the operator and blocking the *lac* operon. Therefore, I^s is dominant to I^+.

2. O^c mutants do not bind the repressor product of the *I* gene, and therefore, the *lac* operon associated with the O^c operator cannot be turned off. Because an operator controls only the genes on the same DNA strand, it is *cis* (on the same strand) and dominant (cannot be turned off).

3.   **a.** Comparing lines 1 and 2, *a* and *c* in a + or – state do not affect the expression of the Z gene. Therefore, *b* is the Z gene.
       In line 6, the *I* gene is functioning in a *trans* configuration, indicating that *c* is *I*. This leaves *a* as the *O* region, which is confirmed by line 7.

   b. *Line 1:* $a^- = O^c$

   Line 2: $c^- = I^-$

   Line 3: $c^- = I^-$ or I^s

Line 4: $a^- = O^c$, and $c^- = I^-$ or I^s

Line 5: $a^- = O^c$, and $c^- = I^-$

Line 6: $a^- = O^c$, and $c^- = I^-$

Line 7: $a^- = O^c$, and $c^- = I^-$ or I^s

4.

	β-Galactosidase		Permease	
Part	No lactose	Lactose	No lactose	Lactose
a	+	+	−	+
b	+	+	−	−
c	−	−	−	−
d	−	−	−	−
e	+	+	+	+
f	+	+	−	−
g	−	+	−	+

5. a. A lack of only E_1 or only E_2 function indicates that both genes have enzyme products that are responsible for a conversion reaction. Because the two genes are in different linkage groups, they cannot be regulated by a single operator and promoter like the Z and Y genes of the *lac* operon. Type 3 mutants must be mutants of a site that produces a diffusible regulator of the E_1 and E_2 genes. The type 3 mutants identify a site that produces either a repressor (like I in the *lac* operon) or an activator (analogous to CAP) of the other two genes.

   b. Separate operator and promoter mutants might be found for each gene.

6.   If there is an operon governing both genes, then a frameshift mutation could cause the stop codon separating the two genes to be read as a sense codon. Therefore, the second gene product will be incorrect for almost all amino acids. However, there are no known polycistronic messages in eukaryotes. The alternative, and better, explanation is that both enzymatic functions are performed by the same gene product. Here, a frameshift mutation beyond the first function, carbamyl phosphate synthetase, will result in the second half of the protein molecule being nonfunctional.

7.   Nonpolar Z^- mutants cannot convert lactose to allolactose, and thus, the operon is never induced.

8. Because very small amounts of the repressor are made, the system as a whole is quite responsive to changes in lactose concentration. In the heterodiploids, repressor tetramers may form by association of polypeptides encoded by I^- and I^+. The operator binding site binds two subunits at a time. Therefore, the repressors produced may reduce operator binding, which in turn would result in some expression of the *lac* genes in the absence of lactose.

9. An operon is turned off by the mediator in negative control, and the mediator must be removed for transcription to occur. An operon is turned on by the mediator in positive control, and the mediator must be added for transcription to occur.

10. The *lacY* gene produces a permease that transports lactose into the cell. A *lacY⁻* gene could not transport lactose into the cell, so β-galactosidase will not be induced.

11. Activation of gene expression by *trans*-acting factors occurs in both prokaryotes and eukaryotes. In both cases, the *trans*-acting factors interact with specific sequences that control expression of *cis* genes.

In prokaryotes, proteins bind to a specific DNA sequence, which is regulated by the binding protein and which, in turn, regulates one or more downstream cistrons.

In eukaryotes, highly conserved sequences such as CCAAT and enhancers increase transcription controlled by the downstream TATA box promoter. Several proteins have been found to bind to the CCAAT sequence, upstream GC boxes, and the TATA sequence in *Drosophila*, yeast, and other organisms. Specifically, the Sp1 protein recognizes the upstream GC boxes of the SV40 promoter and many other genes; GCN4 and GAL4 proteins recognize upstream sequences in yeast; and many hormones bind to specific sites on the DNA (e.g., estrogen binding to a sequence upstream of the ovalbumin gene in chicken oviduct cells). Additionally, the structure of some of these trans-acting DNA-binding proteins is quite similar to the structure of binding proteins seen in prokaryotes. Further, protein-protein interactions are important in both prokaryotes and eukaryotes. For the above reasons, eukaryotic regulation is now thought to be very close to the model for regulation of the bacterial *ara* operon.

12. The bacterial operon consists of a promoter region that extends approximately 35 bases upstream of the site where transcription is initiated. Within this region is the promoter. Inducers and repressors, both of which are *trans*-acting proteins that bind to the promoter region, regulate transcription of associated cistrons in *cis* only.

The eukaryotic cistron has the same basic organization. However, the promoter region is somewhat larger. Also, enhancers up to several thousand nucleotides upstream or downstream can influence the rate of transcription. A major difference is that eukaryotes have not been demonstrated to have polycistronic messages.

   13.   The *araC* product has two conformations, which are determined by the presence and absence of arabinose. When it has bound arabinose, the *araC* product can then bind to the initiator site (*araI*) and activate transcription. When it is not bound to arabinose, the *araC* product binds to both the initiator (*araI*) and the operator (*araO*) sites, forming a loop of the intermediary DNA. When both sites are bound to the *araC* product, transcription is inhibited. The *araC* product is *trans*-acting.

   Many eukaryotic *trans*-acting protein factors also bind to promoters and/or enhancers that are upstream from the protein-encoding gene. These factors are required for the initiation of transcription. Additionally, some bind to other proteins, such as RNA polymerase II, in order to initiate transcription. Like their counterparts in the *ara* operon, the eukaryotic *trans*-acting protein factors can bind DNA at two sites, with the intermediary DNA forming a loop between the binding sites.

   14.   A reasonable model is that one dimer binds O_1 and one dimer binds O_2. The two dimers then bend the DNA when forming the tetramer complex, which results in a blocking of transcription.

   15.   Normally, the repressor searches for the operator by rapidly binding and dissociating from nonoperator sequences. Even for sequences that mimic the true operator, the dissociation time is only a few seconds or less. Therefore, it is easy for the repressor to find new operators as new strands of DNA are synthesized. However, when the affinity of the repressor for DNA and operator is increased, it takes too long for the repressor to dissociate from sequences on the chromosome that mimic the true operator, and, as the cell divides and new operators are synthesized, the repressor never quite finds all of them in time, leading to a partial synthesis of beta-galactosidase. This explains why in the absence of IPTG there is some elevated beta-galactosidase synthesis. When IPTG binds to the repressors with increased affinity, it lowers the affinity back to that of the normal repressor (without IPTG bound). Then, the repressor can rapidly dissociate from sequences in the chromosome that mimic the operator and find the true operator. Thus, beta-galactosidase is repressed in the presence of IPTG in strains with repressors that have greatly increased affinity for operator. In summary, because of a kinetic phenomenon, we see some type of reverse induction curve.

SELF-TEST

   1.   Using the standard format for the *lac* gene, identify which products are made and indicate whether they are induced or made constitutively.

   a. $I^s\ P^+\ O^+\ Z^+\ Y^+$
   b. $I^s\ P^+\ O^+\ Z^+\ Y^+$
   c. $I^s\ P^+\ O^c\ Z^+\ Y^+$

    d. $I^+ P^- O^+ Z^+ Y^+$

    e. $I^+ P^+ O^c Z^+ Y^+$

2. What is the mechanism of attenuation?

3. Can cells operate in a positive feedback loop?

4. It has been suggested that intron transcripts have the potential to control transcription of a gene through negative feedback. How could this occur?

5. What is the difference between positive control and positive feedback?

SOLUTIONS TO SELF-TEST

1.

	β-Galactosidase		Permease	
	No lactose	Lactose	No lactose	Lactose
a.	−	−	−	−
b.	−	−	−	−
c.	+	+	+	+
d.	−	−	−	−
e.	+	+	+	+

2. In the tryptophan operon, transcription pauses in the leader sequence. During this period, the ribosome that is translating the transcript (remember transcription is coupled to translation) proceeds through the leader to a given point in the presence of excess tryptophan. This forces the leader to assume a secondary configuration that causes termination of transcription. If there is a lack of excess tryptophan, the ribosome is halted at an earlier point, the leader assumes a different secondary structure as a consequence, and transcription continues. This is a negative feedback control.

3. A positive feedback loop means that the end product of a metabolic pathway would induce the formation of more of itself. This is a prescription for disaster in any system because it leads to uncontrolled behavior.

4. The intron transcripts would have to be complementary to the promoter region of the transcribed strand. By pairing with this region, they could block transcription.

5.   Positive control is the initiation of transcription of a gene by a protein factor transcribed off a different gene. Positive feedback is the initiation of transcription by the end product of transcription from the same gene.

18

Mechanisms of Genetic Change I: Gene Mutation

IMPORTANT TERMS AND CONCEPTS

A **mutation** consists of a change in DNA sequence. **Spontaneous** mutations occur at a low rate in all cells; the mechanisms for spontaneous mutations include errors in DNA replication and the action of transposable genetic elements. **Induced** mutations are caused by one or more environmental agents.

A **tautomeric shift** results in a **transition** mutation: a purine is substituted for a purine or a pyrimidine is substituted for a pyrimidine. **Transversion** mutations substitute a purine for a pyrimidine or a pyrimidine for a purine.

Frameshift mutations result in a change in the reading frame; they are caused by slipped mispairing during the replication of repeated sequences. **Deletion** and **duplication** mutations can be caused by replication errors or recombinational errors.

Depurination, the loss of the nitrogenous purine base from the nucleotide, can result in a mutation. **Deamination** of cytosine yields uracil, which pairs with adenine (a transition).

Base analogs induce mutation at a high rate; they are incorporated into the DNA and alter base pairing. **Alkylating agents** chemically modify the nitrogenous bases to cause mutations. **Intercalating agents** insert themselves between the nitrogenous bases, causing additions and deletions.

DNA is **repaired** by several different systems: the **SOS system**, **detoxification** by **superoxide dismutase**, the **photoreactivating enzyme**, **alkyltransferase**, **excision repair**, the **AP endonucleases**, the **DNA glycosylase repair pathway**, the **mismatch repair system**, and **recombinational repair**. A defect in one of these repair systems can produce a **mutator** phenotype; that is, a strain can have a very high rate of spontaneous mutation.

The **Ames test** is a screening test for possible mutagens.

Be sure that you have thoroughly read the entire chapter before you attempt any of the problems.

SOLUTIONS TO PROBLEMS

1. a. A transition mutation is the substitution of a purine for a purine or the substitution of a pyrimidine for a pyrimidine. A transversion mutation is the substitution of a purine for a pyrimidine, or vice versa.

    b. Both are base-pair substitutions. A silent mutation is one that does not alter the function of the protein product from the gene, because the new codon codes for the same amino acid as did the nonmutant codon. A neutral mutation results in a different amino acid that is functionally equivalent, and the mutation therefore has no adaptive significance.

    c. A missense mutation results in a different amino acid in the protein product of the gene. A nonsense mutation causes premature termination of translation, resulting in a shortened protein.

    d. Frameshift mutations arise from the addition of one or more bases which are not a multiple of three which alters the reading frame for translation and, therefore, the amino acid sequence from the site of the mutation to the end of the protein product of the gene. Frameshift mutations can result in nonsense (stop) mutations.

2. Frameshift mutations result in a protein that is altered in virtually every amino acid from the point of the mutation. This will rarely result in a protein with activity, unless the mutation is near the end of the gene. Also, frameshift mutations will often lead to chain termination, since nonsense mutations can occur in the wrong reading frame. Missense mutations change only a single amino acid. In many cases the single amino acid replacement will not affect the activity of the protein.

3.   The Streisinger model proposed that frameshifts arise when loops in single-stranded regions are stabilized by slipped mispairing of repeated sequences. In the *lac* gene of *E. coli*, a four-base-pair sequence is repeated three times in tandem, and this is the site of a hot spot.

The sequence is 5′ CTGG CTGG CTGG CTGG 3′. During replication the DNA must become single-stranded in short stretches for replication to occur. As the new strand is synthesized and becomes hydrogen-bonded to the template strand, it can pair out of register with that strand by a total span of four bases. Depending on which strand, new or template, loops out with respect to the other, there will be an addition or deletion of four bases, as diagramed below:

$$
\begin{array}{c}
\text{A--C} \\
\text{|} \quad \text{|} \\
\text{G} \quad \text{C} \\
\text{|} \quad \text{|} \\
\text{------G--A--C--C} \quad \text{G--A--C--C--G--A--C--C} \longrightarrow \\
5′ \longleftarrow \text{C--T--G--G--C--T--G--G--C--T--G--G--C--T--G--G---} \ 3′
\end{array}
$$

In this diagram, the upper strand looped out as replication was occurring. The loop is stabilized by base pairing on either strand. As replication continues at the 3′ end, an additional copy of GACC will be synthesized, leading to an addition of four bases. This will result in a frameshift mutation.

4.   **(1)** In Problem 3, had the lower strand looped, the result would have been a deletion in the newly synthesized upper strand.

   (2)   As with the bar-eye allele in *Drosophila*, misalignment of homologous chromosomes during recombination results in one chromosome with a duplication and the other with a deletion:

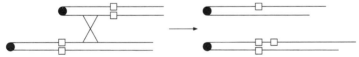

The above models are supported by DNA sequencing results.

5.   **(1)** Depurination results in the loss of adenine or guanine from the DNA. Since the resulting apurinic site cannot specify a complementary base, replication is blocked. Under certain conditions, replication proceeds with a near random insertion of a base opposite the apurinic site. In three-fourths of these insertions, a mutation will result.

   (2) Deamination of cytosine yields uracil. If left unrepaired, the uracil will be paired with adenine during replication, ultimately resulting in a transition mutation.

6.   5-Bromouracil is an analog of thymine. It undergoes tautomeric shifts at a higher frequency than does thymine and, therefore, is more likely to pair with G than is thymine during replication. At the next replication this will lead to a GC pair rather than the original AT pair. On the other hand, 5-bromouracil can also be incorporated into DNA by mispairing with Guanine. In this case it will convert a GC pair to an AT pair.

Ethylmethanesulfonate is an alkylating agent that produces O-6-ethylguanine. This will pair with thymine, which leads from a GC pair to an AT pair at the next replication.

7. An AP site is an apurinic or apyrimidinic site. AP endonucleases introduce chain breaks by cleaving the phosphodiester bonds at the AP sites. Some exonuclease activity follows, so that a number of bases are removed. The resulting gap is filled by DNA pol I and then sealed by DNA ligase.

When UV damage occurs in *E. coli*, several compounds may bind to the damaged site, resulting in the so-called bulky adducts. The *uvrA*, *uvrB*, and *uvrC* gene products recognize a distortion in the DNA helix. Again, excision is followed by gap-filling and ligation.

8. (1) Mismatch repair occurs if a mismatched nucleotide is inserted during replication. The new, incorrect base is removed and the proper base is inserted. The enzymes involved can distinguish between new and old strands because, in *E. coli*, the old strand is methylated.

(2) Recombination repair occurs if AP sites and UV photodimers block replication (there is a gap in the complementary strand). Recombination occurs with one strand from the sister DNA molecule, which is normal in both strands. This produces one DNA molecule with a gap across from a correct strand, and one with a photodimer across from a correct strand (refer to Figure 18-36a).

9. Leaky mutants are mutants with an altered protein product that retains a low level of function. Enzyme activity may, for instance, be reduced rather than abolished by a mutation.

10. The wild type contained a gene that increased the spontaneous mutation rate. This new gene seems to be unlinked to *ad-3*. Call the new gene B. Cross A (*ad-3 B+*) × wild type (*ad-3+ B*). The progeny should reflect independent assortment.

Progeny: 1/4 *ad-3 B*

1/4 *ad-3 B+*

1/4 *ad-3+ B*

1/4 *ad-3+ B+*

Further crosses should verify the above.

11.   a.   Because 5′ UAA 3′ does not contain G or C, a transition to a
           GC pair in the DNA cannot result in 5′ UAA 3′. 5′ UGA 3′
           and 5′ UAG 3′ have the DNA antisense-strand sequence of
           3′ ACT 5′ and 3′ ATC 5′, respectively. A transition to either of
           these stop codons occurs from the nonmutant 3′ ATT 5′,
           respectively. A DNA sequence of 3′ ATT 5′ results in an RNA
           sequence of UAA, itself a stop codon.

      b.   Yes. An example would be 5′ UGG 3′, which codes for Trp, to
           5′ UAG 3′.

      c.   No. In the three stop codons the only base that can be acted
           upon is G (in UAG, for instance). Replacing the G with an A
           would result in 5′ UAA 3′, a stop codon.

12.   a. and b.   *Mutant 1*: Most likely a deletion. It could be caused
           by radiation.

           Mutant 2:   Because proflavin causes either additions or dele-
           tions of bases and because spontaneous mutation can result
           in additions or deletions, the most probable cause was a
           frameshift mutation by an intercalating agent.

           Mutant 3:   5-BU causes transitions, which means that the
           original mutation was most likely a transition. Because HA
           causes GC-to-AT transitions and HA cannot revert it, the
           original must have been a GC-to-AT transition. It could have
           been caused by base analogs.

           Mutant 4:   The chemical agents cause transitions or
           frameshift mutations. Because there is spontaneous reversion
           only, the original mutation must have been a transversion. X-
           irradiation could have caused the original mutation.

           Mutant 5:   HA causes transitions from GC to AT, as does 5-
           BU. The original mutation was most likely an AT-to-GC tran-
           sition, which could be caused by base analogs.

      c.   The suggestion is a second-site reversion linked to the origi-
           nal mutant by 20 map units (m.u.) (prototrophs equal one-
           half of the recombinants).

13.   To understand these data, recall that half of the progeny should
come from the wild-type parent.

      a.   A lack of revertants suggests either a deletion or an inversion
           within the gene.

      b.   *Prototroph A*:   Because 100 percent of the progeny are prototrophic, a reversion at the original mutant site may have occurred.

    Prototroph B: Half of the progeny are parental prototrophs, and the remaining prototrophs, 28 percent, are the result of the new mutation. Notice that 28 percent is approximately equal to the 22 percent auxotrophs. The suggestion is that an unlinked suppressor mutation occurred, yielding independent assortment with the *nic* mutant.

    Prototroph C: There are 496 "revertant" prototrophs (the other 500 are parental prototrophs) and 4 auxotrophs. This suggests that a suppressor mutation occurred in a site very close (100% $[4 \times 2]/1000 = 0.8$ m.u.) to the original mutation.

14.   **a.**   To select for a nerve mutation that blocks flying, place *Drosophila* at the bottom of a cage and place a poisoned food source at the top of the cage.

    b.   Make antibodies against flagellar protein and expose mutagenized cultures to the antibodies.

    c.   Do filtration through membranes with various-sized pores.

    d.   Screen visually.

    e.   Go to a large shopping mall and set up a rotating polarized disk. Ask the passersby to look through the disk for a free evaluation of their vision and their need for sunglasses. People with normal vision will see light with a constant intensity through the disk. Those with polarized vision will see alternating dark and light.

    f.   Set up a Y tube (a tube with a fork giving the choice of two pathways) and observe whether the flies or unicellular algae crawl to the light or the dark pathway.

    g.   Set up replica cultures and expose one of the two plates to low doses of UV.

SELF-TEST

1.   Name two ways to increase the number of copies of a sequence.

2.   Many repeated sequences diverge over time, yet some remain absolutely unchanged. The process by which spontaneous changes in repeated sequences are reversed is known as rectification. No one knows how rectification occurs. Propose two mechanisms.

3.   If you wanted to introduce small deletions, how would you do it?

4.   Which chemical group distinguishes new DNA strands from old? Which chemical group is frequently added to a base to protect it from restriction endonuclease activity?

5.   What would constitute a secondary cure for the recessive human disorder xeroderma pigmentosum?

6.   Would you expect there to be a correlation between gene length and mutation rate?

SOLUTIONS TO SELF-TEST

1.   Mispairing during recombination and slipped pairing during replication.

2.   Recombinational repair; sister-chromatid exchange, if it occurs by the process of recombination.

3.   The easiest way would be through the use of intercalating agents.

4.   Methyl groups in both cases.

5.   Remaining out of the sun or using complete sun blockers.

6.   Yes. The longer the gene, the larger the number of sites available for mutation.

19

Mechanisms of Genetic Change II: Recombination

IMPORTANT TERMS AND CONCEPTS

Crossing-over occurs during prophase I of meiosis. It involves the **breakage and reunion** of DNA molecules. **Chiasmata** are the sites of crossing-over.

The **Holliday model** involves the creation of **heteroduplex** DNA, which can undergo **branch migration**. A number of enzymes are postulated to function in this process. The model accounts for **gene conversion, polarity**, and **co-conversion**.

Site-specific recombination occurs between two specific sequences that need not be homologous.

Be sure that you have thoroughly read the entire chapter before you attempt any of the problems.

SOLUTIONS TO PROBLEMS

1.   Gene conversion may result in a deviation from a 4 : 4 ratio, with the order unimportant. The following asci show gene conversion: 3, 6.

Ascus 4 is also produced by gene conversion. To recognize it as such, recall the sequence that gives rise to the eight meiotic products in *Neurospora*. The pattern generated could be produced only if the two DNA strands have a region of mismatch.

2.   In the first case, 1' is being converted to 1'+. In the second case, 1" is being converted to 1"+. The difference in frequency is due to polarity.

3.   A fixed break point is the point at which a DNA strand breaks and begins unwinding as the first step in recombination. The highest level of gene conversion is seen at this point.
     Gene conversion has occurred in cistrons 1, 2, and 3, and the conversions all are from mutant to wild type. Therefore, most likely one piece of heteroduplex DNA extended across the three cistrons:

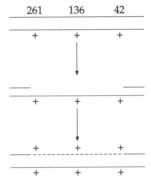

These data are compatible with the idea, but do not prove, that the heteroduplex DNA initiates from a site to the left of cistron 1, corresponding to a promoter of a polycistronic message.

4.   The actual mechanism of sister-chromatid exchange induction by mutagens is unknown but would be expected to vary with mutagen effects. The end point must be a break in a DNA strand, very likely as part of postreplication repair.

5.   First notice that gene conversion is occurring. In the first cross, a_1 converts (1 : 3). In the second cross, a_2 converts. In the third cross, a_3 converts. Polarity is obviously involved. The results can be explained by the following map, where hybrid DNA enters only from the left.

a_3 _____ a_1 _____ a_2

6.   Rewrite the cross and results so that it is clear what they are.

P A $(m_1\ m_2\ m^+)$ $B \times a\ (m^+\ m^+\ m_3)\ b$

F_1 A $(m_1\ m_2\ m^+)$ B parental

      A $(m_1\ m^+\ m^+)$ b recombinant

      a $(m_1\ m_2\ m^+)$ B recombinant

      a $(m^+\ m^+\ m_3)$ b parental

Next, note the frequency of each allele:

$m_1 : m^+ = 3 : 1$

$m_2 : m^+ = 1 : 1$

$m_3 : m^+ = 1 : 3$

Two gene conversion events have occurred, involving m_1 and m_3.

To understand this at the molecular level, consider the following diagram:

A	m_1 $m_3{}^+$ m_2 B				A	m_1 $m_3{}^+$ m_2 B			
A	m_1 $m_3{}^+$ m_2 B				A	$m_1{}^+$ m_3 $m_2{}^+$ b			
a	$m_1{}^+$ m_3 $m_2{}^+$ b				a	m_1 $m_3{}^+$ m_2 B			
a	$m_1{}^+$ m_3 $m_2{}^+$ b				a	$m_1{}^+$ m_3 $m_2{}^+$ b			

A m_1 $m_3{}^+$ m_2 B	A m_1 $m_3{}^+$ m_2 B
A $\qquad\qquad m_2{}^+$ b	A m_1 $m_3{}^+$ $m_2{}^+$ b
a m_1 $m_3{}^+$ m_2 B	a m_1 $m_3{}^+$ m_2 B
a $m_1{}^+$ m_3 $m_2{}^+$ b	a $m_1{}^+$ m_3 $m_2{}^+$ b

A single excision-repair event changed m^+ m_3 to m_1 m^+, and the other mismatches remained unrepaired.

7. The ratios for a_1 and a_2 are both 3 : 1. There is no evidence of polarity, which indicates that gene conversion as part of recombination is occurring. The best explanation is that two separate excision-repair events occurred and, in both cases, the repair retained the mutant rather than the wild type.

8. **a and b.** A heteroduplex that contains an unequal number of bases in the two strands has a larger distortion than does a simple mismatch. Therefore, the former would be more likely to be repaired. For such a case, both heteroduplex molecules are repaired (leading to 6 : 2 and 2 : 6) more often than one (leading to 5 : 3 or 3 : 5) or none (leading to 3 : 1 : 1 : 3). The preference in direction (i.e., adding a base rather than subtracting) is analogous to thymine dimer repair. In thymine dimer repair, the unpaired, bulged nucleotides are treated as correct and the strand with the thymine dimer is excised.

A mismatch more often than not escapes repair, leading to a 3 : 1 : 1 : 3 ascus.

Transition mutations would not cause as large a distortion of the helix, and each strand of the heteroduplex should have an equal chance of repair. This would lead to 4 : 4 (two repairs each in the opposite direction), 5 : 3 (1 repair), 3 : 1 : 1 : 3 (no repairs or two repairs in opposite directions), and, less frequently, 6:2 (two repairs in the same direction).

c. Because excision repair excises the strand opposite the larger buckle (i.e., opposite the frameshift mutation), the *cis* transition mutation will also be retained. The nearby genes are converted because of the length of the excision repair.

9. The easiest way to handle these data is to construct the following table, which shows the repair rates for 0, 1, and 2 hybrid DNA molecules.

	$0.5 +/+$	$0.3 +/g_1$	$0.2\, g_1/g_1$
$0.5 +/+$	0.25 (6 : 2)	0.15 (5 : 3)	0.1 (4 : 4)
$0.3 +/g_1$	0.15 (5 : 3)	0.09 (3 : 1 : 1 : 3)	0.06 (3 : 5)
$0.2\, g_1/g_1$	0.1 (4 : 4)	0.06 (3 : 5)	0.04 (2 : 6)

The aberrant asci are all those that are not 4 : 4. The 4 : 4 asci occur 20 percent of the time. Correcting for them,

a. $6 : 2 = 25\%/0.8 = 31.25\%$

b. $2 : 6 = 4\%/0.8 = 5\%$

c. $3 : 1 : 1 : 3 = 9\%/0.8 = 11.25\%$

d. $5 : 3 = 30\%/0.8 = 37.5\%$

e. $3 : 5 = 12\%/0.8 = 15\%$

10. The map is

trp   5   me-2   5   pan

(α, β)

Rewrite the crosses and results to be sure that you understand them.

Cross 1: *trp* $(\alpha\, \beta^+)$ *pan*$^+$ $\times$ *trp*$^+$ $(\alpha^+\, \beta)$ *pan*

Cross 2: *trp* $(\alpha^+\, \beta)$ *pan*$^+$ $\times$ *trp*$^+$ $(\alpha\, \beta^+)$ pan

Note that all progeny must be $\alpha^+\, \beta^+$, which requires a crossover between them, and that the order of α and β is unknown.

Consider the first cross. If the sequence is *trp* $\alpha\, \beta$ *pan*, then one crossover should lead to a high frequency of $+ + + +$. The conventional double crossovers $+ + + -$ and $- + + +$ should be equally frequent and of lower frequency than $+ + + +$. The pattern $- + + -$ would result from a triple crossover and would be least frequent. This is summarized in the tabulation below, along with the results if the opposite gene order is true.

		Number of Crossovers Required	
Pattern	Frequency	trp α β pan	trp β α pan
+ + + +	56	1 CO	3 CO
− + + +	26	DCO	DCO
+ + + −	59	DCO	DCO
− + + −	16	3 CO	1 CO

For the second cross, the patterns and their interpretation are

		Number of Crossovers Required	
Pattern	Frequency	trp α β pan	trp β α pan
+ + + +	15	3 CO	1 CO
− + + +	84	DCO	DCO
+ + + −	23	DCO	DCO
− + + −	87	1 CO	3 CO

Both crosses indicate that the sequence is *trp* α β *pan*, but these results are, on the surface, confusing. We see that a double-crossover event does not lead to reciprocal results and, in fact, one double-crossover product occurs as frequently as the single-crossover product. The difficulty is not in the cross but in thinking of the results in terms of a conventional Mendelian cross rather than in terms of gene conversion. Double crossovers are not occurring in the Mendelian sense. In both crosses, "crossing-over" between β and the *pan* allele is occurring at a much higher frequency than expected, which means that β is being converted at a higher level than is α. By convention, that means the polarity runs from *pan* toward *trp*. The asymmetry due to polarity is also seen in the *trp* + : + *pan* ratios in each cross.

11. Rewrite the original cross:

P A x y^+ $\times$ a x^+ y

The progeny of parental genotypes will be like either of the two parents. The backcrosses are as follows, with the prime indicating progeny generation.

Cross 1: a' x^+ y $\times$ A x y^+ $\longrightarrow$ 10^{-5} prototrophs

Cross 2a: A' x y^+ $\times$ a x^+ y $\longrightarrow$ 10^{-5} prototrophs

Cross 2b: A' x y^+ $\times$ a x^+ y $\longrightarrow$ 10^{-2} prototrophs

Recombination is allowing for the higher rate of appearance of prototrophs. Cross 2 is obviously a backcross for some gene affecting the rate of recombination. Whatever that gene is, the allele in the A parent blocks recombination (cross 1 and cross 2a), and the allele in the a parent allows recombination (cross 2b). It is unlinked to the *his* gene since cross 2 yields results in a 1 : 1 ratio. The allele that blocks recombination (in A) is dominant, while the allele that allows recombination is recessive. This is demonstrated by the original cross, in which prototrophs occurred at the lower rate, and by cross 1.

To test this interpretation, one-fourth of the crosses between the A x y^+ and a x^+ y progeny should yield a high rate of recombination and therefore have a high frequency of prototrophs.

SELF-TEST

1. Can the Holliday model be applied to sister-chromatid exchange? If yes, what initial assumption must you make?

2. Some mutagens, in addition to causing sister-chromatid exchange, cause mitotic recombination between homologs. What does this suggest about the interphase location of homologous chromosomes?

3. Which of the following linear asci show gene conversion?

1	2	3	4	5	6
+	+	+	+	+	+
+	+	+	+	+	+
met	met	+	+	+	met
met	met	+	+	+	+
met	+	+	+	met	met
met	met	met	+	met	met
met	met	met	met	met	+
met	met	met	met	met	+

4. If branch migration occurs, what is the relationship between the initial break point and the chiasma that results? What do the data of Tease and Jones suggest about branch migration?

SOLUTIONS TO SELF-TEST

1. The Holliday model can account for sister-chromatid exchange. It must be assumed that a break caused by a mutagen signals an enzyme with endonuclease function to cause a break in the homologous site on the sister chromatid.

2. It suggests that homologous chromosomes are located near each other in mitotic interphase. Although it is generally assumed that the distribution of chromosomes during interphase is random, there are several studies that indirectly indicate that chromosome distribution is non-random during interphase.

3. All asci except ascus 5 show gene conversion.

4. There is not necessarily any relationship between an initial break point and the resulting chiasma. As branch migration proceeds, the center of the recombination intermediate can be at any point along the length of a chromosome. The probability is very large that resolution of the recombination intermediate will not occur at the exact site of the initial break point.

Because Tease and Jones found that the dark-light transition occurred right at the chiasma, the tentative suggestion is either that branch migration does not occur or that it occurs for a limited distance not detectable by light microscopy.

20

Mechanisms of Genetic Change III: Transposable Genetic Elements

IMPORTANT TERMS AND CONCEPTS

Transposable genetic elements exist in both prokaryotes and eukaryotes. They move from location to location within the genome. Both the DNA sequence from which they are removed and the DNA sequence into which they are inserted are altered, potentially causing phenotypic changes that are scored as mutations.

Prokaryotic **insertion sequences**, termed **IS elements**, usually block the expression of all genes downstream in the operon from the site of insertion. These are **polar mutations.**

Prokaryotic **transposons** possess **inverted repeat (IR) sequences**, which are IS elements that flank one or more genes. If they are located on a plasmid, they can be passed during conjugation from organism to organism within a species or between closely related species. The transposon can move from plasmid to plasmid or between a plasmid and a bacterial chromosome. Transposition can be **replicative** or **conservative.**

There are several types of eukaryotic transposable genetic elements: the yeast **Ty elements**; the *Drosophila copia*-like elements, **fold-back elements (FB)**, and **P elements**; and the maize **controlling elements.**

Retroviruses are RNA viruses that integrate into host chromosomes as a DNA copy of the viral genome made using **reverse transcriptase.** When integrated, they are termed **proviruses.** They possess long terminal repeats like those of prokaryotic transposons.

In eukaryotes the transposable elements use an RNA intermediate, while in prokaryotes transposition occurs at the DNA level.

Be sure that you have thoroughly read the entire chapter before you attempt any of the problems.

SOLUTIONS TO PROBLEMS

1. Isolate a λ dgal phage from the wild-type and cross the mutant allele into it. Then determine the density of each phage in a CsCl gradient. If there is an insertion in the mutant phage, the phage will band at a higher density than for the wild-type. Also, the phage can be used as a source of DNA for heteroduplex mapping, hybridizing separated strands of the wild-type and mutant phage and then reannealing and observing the molecules under the electron microscope. As Figure 20-3 shows, a looped out segment will result at the position of the insertion.

Another method would be to use restriction enzymes to cut the DNA from both the wild-type and the mutant. One can do a Southern blot from each and probe with sequence from the gal region. With some enzymes, particularly those that give large fragments, one should be able to detect a larger fragment in the mutant than in the wild-type.

2. Polar mutations affect the transcription or translation of the part of the gene or operon on only one side of the mutant site, usually described as downstream. Examples are nonsense mutations, frameshift mutations, and IS-induced mutations.

3. In replicative transposition a new copy of the transposable element is generated during transposition. The experiment by Ljungquist and Bukhari first demonstrated this by using restriction enzyme digests to show that new Mu-bacterial chromosome junctions appeared during Mu transposition while the presence of the original Mu could still be detected.

In conservative transposition no replication occurs. The element is excised from its location and integrated into the new site. Kleckner and co-workers demonstrated this by constructing heteroduplexes of a transposon carrying different alleles of *lacZ* and using them to transpose. The resulting cells formed sectored colonies, indicating that they received heteroduplex DNA.

4. R plasmids are the main carriers of drug resistance. They acquire these genes by transposition of drug-resistance genes located between IR (inverted repeat) sequences. Once in a plasmid, the transposon carrying drug resistance can be transferred upon conjugation if it stays in the R plasmid, or it can insert into the host chromosome.

5. Boeke, Garfinkel, Fink, and their co-workers demonstrated that transposition of the Ty element in yeast involved an RNA intermediate. They constructed a plasmid using the Ty element. It had a promoter near the end of the element that could be activated by galactose, and it had an intron inserted into the Ty transposon–coding region. After transposition, they found that the new transposon lacked the intron sequence. Because intron splicing occurs only in RNA, there must have been an RNA intermediate.

6. P elements are transposons (genes flanked by inverted repeats, allowing for great mobility). Because they are transposons, they can insert into chromosomes. By inserting specific DNA between the inverted repeats of the P elements and injecting the altered transposons into cells, a high frequency of gene transfer will occur.

7. The a_1a_1 $DtDt$ plant has the A (target gene) inactivated by the insertion of a receptor element into it. The regulator is at the Dt locus. When crossed with an a_1a_1 $dtdt$ tester, the progeny should be a_1a_1 $Dtdt$, colorless.

Excision of the receptor element restores the A gene function.

Black kernels would arise if the receptor element excises from the chromosome prior to fertilization. Dotted kernels arise from sporadic excision at a later stage in development of the kernel.

8. The best explanation is that the mutation is due to an insertion of a transposable element.

9. The sn^+ patches in an sn background and the occurrence of sn^+ progeny from an $sn \times sn$ mating mean that the sn^+ allele is appearing at a fairly high frequency. The sn allele is unstable, suggesting that an insertion element in the sn^+ gene results in sn.

10. **a.** The expression of the tumor is blocked in plant B. This suggests either that plant B can suppress the functioning of the plasmid that causes the tumor, or that plant A provides something to the tissue with the tumor-causing plasmid that plant B does not provide.

b. Tissue carrying the plasmid, when grafted to plant B, appears normal, but the graft produces tumor cells in synthetic medium. This indicates that the plasmid sequences are present and capable of functioning in the right environment. However, the production of normal type A plants from seeds from the graft suggests a permanent loss of the plasmid during meiosis.

11.   *Cross 1:*

P $C/c^{Ds}\ Ac/Ac^+ \times c/c\ Ac^+/Ac^+$

F_1 1 $C/c\ Ac/Ac^+$ (solid pigment)

   1 $C/c\ Ac^+/Ac^+$ (solid pigment)

   1 $c^{Ds}/c\ Ac/Ac^+$ (unstable colorless or spotted)

   1 $c^{Ds}/c\ Ac^+/Ac^+$ (colorless)

Cross 2:

P $C/c^{Ac} \times c/c$

F_1 1 C/c (solid pigment)

   1   c/c^{Ac} (spotted)

Cross 3:

P $C/c^{Ds}\ Ac/Ac^+ \times C/c^{Ac}\ Ac^+/Ac^+$

F_1 1 $C/C\ Ac/Ac^+$ (solid pigment)

   1   $C/c^{Ac}\ Ac/Ac^+$ (solid pigment)

   1   $C/C\ Ac^+/Ac^+$ (solid pigment)

   1   $C/c^{Ac}\ Ac^+/Ac^+$ (solid pigment)

   1   $C/c^{Ds}\ Ac^+/Ac^+$ (solid pigment)

   1   $C/c^{Ds}\ Ac^+/Ac$ (solid pigment)

   1   $c^{Ds}/c^{Ac}\ Ac^+/Ac^+$ (spotted)

   1   $c^{Ds}/c^{Ac}\ Ac^+/Ac$ (spotted)

SELF-TEST

1.   What evidence indicates that transposable elements in prokaryotes do not literally jump from one location to another?

2.   A retrovirus has 27 percent G. When it is in the provirus state, what will be its percentage of G?

3.   Consider the following genetic units: episome, lysogenic virus, plasmid, retrovirus, and lytic virus. Arrange them on a continuum and justify the arrangement. The answer to this question requires a creative approach.

4.   The virus causing AIDS is a retrovirus. Suggest a way that it could be detected in humans.

5.   Some retroviral infections are associated with a high rate of malignancy. List several mechanisms that could account for this.

SOLUTIONS TO SELF-TEST

1.   If transposable elements did jump, there would be a correlation between loss at one location and gain at another. This is not observed. Also, intermediate cointegrate structures have been observed during transposition of some elements.

2.   There is no way to predict the percentage of G in the DNA copy of the retrovirus, because a retrovirus is single-stranded and the percentage of C is not known.

3.   Several different schemes could be proposed. One follows.

plasmid	an episome that has lost the ability to integrate
episome	a virus that has lost the ability to exist extracellularly
lytic virus	a virus that has lost the ability to undergo lysogeny
retrovirus	a virus that has lost the ability to cause lysis
lysogenic virus	a complete virus

4.   Restriction analysis should be able to detect the AIDS virus. Another possibility would be the detection of reverse transcriptase. A third would be the detection of viral antigens.

5.   If the virus specifically integrates into cells of the immune system, the functioning of the immune system is impaired. Thus, the immune system is unable to destroy the malignant cells, which are always being formed in multicellular organisms.

By integrating into specific genes that repair DNA lesions, the virus can eliminate repair functions. Thus, the genome can become more and more altered over time, eventually leading to malignancy.

The virus may itself carry genes that cause malignancy.

By causing chromosome breaks, a vital regulatory gene for such processes as control of cell division may be disrupted, leading to malignancy.

21

The Extranuclear Genome

IMPORTANT TERMS AND CONCEPTS

Extranuclear genes exist in eukaryotes. These genes are located in organelles. They do not show Mendelian patterns of inheritance.

Organelles such as **chloroplasts** and **mitochondria** contain circular DNA. The phenotypes coded for by organelle DNA generally show a **maternal inheritance** pattern. **Segregation** is commonly seen among the progeny when two or more genetically different chloroplast or mitochondrial DNAs exist in the mother. **Recombination** and **extranuclear mutation** exist in organelle DNA. Organelle DNA can be mapped.

Most organelle-encoded polypeptides unite with nucleus-encoded polypeptides to form active proteins. These proteins function in the organelle.

Maternal inheritance does not always indicate extranuclear inheritance. For some characteristics, the maternal nuclear genome determines a progeny phenotype. This is called **maternal effect**.

Be sure that you have thoroughly read the entire chapter before you attempt any of the problems.

SOLUTIONS TO PROBLEMS

1. Most organelle-encoded polypeptides unite with nucleus-encoded polypeptides to produce active proteins, and these active proteins function in the organelle.

2.   Reciprocal crosses reveal cytoplasmic inheritance. Cytoplasmic inheritance also can be demonstrated by doing a series of backcrosses, using hybrid females in each case, so that the nuclear genes of one strain are functioning in cytoplasm from the second strain. A heterokaryon test will also demonstrate cytoplasmic inheritance.

3.   Maternal inheritance of chloroplasts results in the green-white color variegation observed in *Mirabilis*.

Cross 1: variegated female × green male ———→ variegated progeny

Cross 2: green female × variegated male ———→ green progeny

4.   Stop-start growth for the first cross; normal growth for the reciprocal cross.

5.   Both yeast parents contribute mitochondria to the cytoplasm of the resulting diploid cell. Subsequent meiosis shows uniparental inheritance for mitochondria. Therefore, 4 : 0 and 0 : 4 asci will be seen.

6.   **a.**   The ant^R gene may be mitochondrial.

      b.   Some of the petites must have been neutral petites, in which all mitochondrial DNA, including the ant^R gene, was lost. Other petites were suppressive, in which the ant^R gene was retained.

7.   The genetic determinants of R and S are cytoplasmic and are showing maternal inheritance.

8.   The cpDNA from mt^- *Chlamydomonas* is lost. The results of the crosses are

Cross 1: all morph 1; 2 kb and 3 kb bands

Cross 2: all morph 2; 3 kb and 5 kb bands

9.   Both yeast parents contribute mitochondria to the cytoplasm of the resulting diploid cell. Subsequent meiosis shows uniparental inheritance for mitochondria. If no crossing-over occurs in the diploid fusion cell, asci will be of two types:

      4 oli^R cap^R

      4 oli^S cap^S

If crossing-over occurs, the recombinants will be of two types:

      4 oli^R cap^S

      4 oli^S cap^R

10.   Both crosses show maternal inheritance of a chloroplast gene. The rare variegated phenotype is probably due to a minor male contribution to the zygote. Variegation must result from a mixture of normal and prazinizan chloroplasts.

11. If the mutation is in the chloroplast, reciprocal crosses will give different results, while if it is in the nucleus and dominant, reciprocal crosses will give the same results.

12. This pattern is observed when a maternal recessive nuclear gene determines phenotype. The crosses are

P   *dd* dwarf female × *DD* normal male

F_1 *Dd* dwarf (all dwarf because mother is *dd*)

F_2 3/4 *D*– : 1/4 *dd* normal (all normal because mother is *Dd*)

F_3 3/4 normal (mother is *D*–) : 1/4 dwarf (mother is *dd*)

13. After the initial hybridization, a series of backcrosses using pollen from B will result in the desired combination of cytoplasm A and nucleus B. With each cross the female contributes all of the cytoplasm and one-half the nuclear contents, while the male contributes one-half the nuclear contents.

14. **a.** Maternal inheritance is suggested.

b. "Why" can never be inferred. However, the net result was that a line carrying the nuclear genes of *E. hirsutum* contained the cytoplasm of *E. luteum*. This demonstrated that the very tall progeny were not the result of a hybrid nucleus.

15. Let male sterility be symbolized by MS.

a. A line that was homozygous for *Rf* and contained the male-sterility factor would result in fertile males. When this line was crossed for two generations with females from a line not carrying the restorer gene, the male-sterility trait would reappear.

b. The F_1 would carry the male-sterility factor and would be heterozygous for the *Rf* gene. Therefore, it would be fertile.

c. The cross is *Rf/rf* MS × *rf/rf* (no cytoplasmic transmission). The progeny would be 1/2 *Rf/rf* MS (fertile) and 1/2 *rf/rf* MS (sterile).

d. i.   P   *Rf-1/rf-1 Rf-2/rf-2* × *rf-1/rf-1 rf-2/rf-2* MS

F_1 1/4 *Rf-1/rf-1 Rf-2/rf-2* MS   fertile

1/4 *Rf-1/rf-1 rf-2/rf-2* MS   fertile

        1/4 *rf-1/rf-1 Rf-2/rf-2* MS   fertile

        1/4 *rf-1/rf-1 rf-2/rf-2* MS   male sterile

  ii. P   *Rf-1/Rf-1 rf-2/rf-2* × *rf-1/rf-1 rf-2/rf-2* MS

     F$_1$ 100% *Rf-1/rf-1 rf-2/rf-2* MS fertile

  iii. P   *Rf-1/rf-1 rf-2/rf-2* × *rf-1/rf-1 rf-2/rf-2* MS

     F$_1$ 1/2 *Rf-1/rf-1 rf-2/rf-2* MS   fertile

        1/2 *rf-1/rf-1 rf-2/rf-2* MS   male sterile

  iv. P   *Rf-1/rf-1 Rf-2/Rf-2* × *rf-1/rf-1 rf-2/rf-2* MS

     F$_1$ 1/2 *Rf-1/rf-1 Rf-2/rf-2* MS   fertile

        1/2 *rf-1/rf-1 Rf-2/rf-2* MS   fertile

16. The suggestion is that the mutants were cytoheterozygotes for streptomycin resistance.

17. Realize that the closer two genes are, the higher the rate of cosegregation. A rough map of the results is as follows:

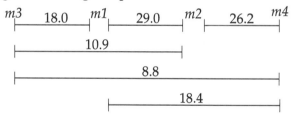

18. The red phenotype in the heterokaryon indicates that the red phenotype is caused by a cytoplasmic organelle allele.

19. (1) Injection of normal mitochondria into wild-type *Neurospora*. This should result in the wild-type phenotype in several generations unless there is an injection effect.

    (2) Injection of physiological saline solution into wild-type *Neurospora*. This also should result in the wild-type phenotype in several generations unless there is an injection effect.

    (3) In order to be sure that a cytoplasmic factor rather than a nuclear gene is being transferred, all donor material should be derived from organisms with many alleles variant from the wild type.

20. a–c. Notice that the results are not reciprocal, which indicates an extranuclear gene. Notice also that in the first cross, there is a 1 : 1 ratio of phenotypes, indicating a nuclear gene. This may be a case where the same function has a different location in different species. The two genes are incompatible in the hybrid. Let cy = cytoplasmic factor in *N. sitophila*, A^c = the nuclear allele in *N. crassa*, and A = the nuclear allele in *N. sitophila*. Aconidial is then $A^c cy$. The crosses are

$A cy \times A^c \longrightarrow 1/2\ A\ cy$ (normal) : $1/2\ A^c\ cy$ (aconidial)

$A^c \times A$ (no cy contribution from male) $\longrightarrow$ all normal (A and A^c)

Neither parent was aconidial, because the sporeless phenotype requires the interaction of a nuclear allele A^c from one species with a cytoplasmic factor (cy) from the other species.

21.   Let poky be symbolized by (c). Let the nuclear suppressor of poky be symbolized by n. To do these problems, you cannot simply do the crosses in sequence. For instance, the parental genotypes in cross a must be written taking cross c into consideration.

Cross	Progeny
a. $(+) + \times (c) +$	all $(+) +$
b. $(+) n \times (c) +$	$1/2 (+) c : 1/2 (+) +$
c. $(c) + \times (+) +$	all $(c) +$
d. $(c) + \times (+) n$	$1/2 (c) + (= D) : 1/2 (c) n (= E)$
e. $(c) n \times (+) n$	all $(c) n$
f. $(c) n \times (+) +$	$1/2 (c) n : 1/2 (C) +$

22.   **a. and b.**   Each meiosis shows uniparental inheritance, suggesting cytoplasmic inheritance.

   c.   Because ant^r is probably mitochondrial and because petites have been shown to result from deletions in the mitochondrial genome, ant^r may be lost in some petites.

23.   **a.**   The first tetrad shows a $2:2$ pattern, indicating a nuclear gene, while the second tetrad shows a $0:4$ pattern, indicating maternal inheritance and a cytoplasmic factor (mitochondrial).

   b.   The nuclear gene should always show a $1:1$ segregation pattern. The mitochondrial gene could produce an ascus that is all $cyt2^+$.

   c.   Both produce proteins involved with the cytochromes. Either the products of the two genes affect different steps in mitochondrial function or they affect the same step if the two proteins interact to form one enzyme.

24.   Consider the following hypothetical situation of three genes:

$$\underline{\qquad\quad a \qquad\qquad\quad b \qquad\qquad\quad c \qquad\quad}$$

If a deletion of one of them occurred, b by itself would be least likely to be the only gene deleted if the genes were closely linked. The closer a is to b, the less likely it is that a will be deleted if b is retained.

Applying the above logic to the data, the *apt-cob* pair had the lowest rate of loss (45 total), and the *apt-bar* pair had the highest rate of loss (207 total). This puts *cob* between *apt* and *bar*. The relative rate of loss is *apt-cob* : *cob-bar*, or 45 : 117 = 1 : 2.6.

apt	*cob*	*bar*
1	2.6	

25.   Remember that petites arise by deletion. Hybridization with any fragment means that the gene being tested is on that fragment.

Culture 1:   *cap* and rRNA$_{large}$ are on the same fragment

Culture 2:   tRNA$_4$ is not next to *cap, ery, oli,* or *par*

Culture 3:   tRNA$_2$ and tRNA$_5$ are on the same fragment

Culture 4:   *oli*, rRNA$_{large}$, and rRNA$_{small}$ are on the same fragment

Culture 5:   *ery*, rRNA$_{large}$, and rRNA$_{small}$ are on the same fragment

Culture 6:   *cap* and tRNA$_3$ are on the same fragment

Culture 7:   *oli, par,* and tRNA$_2$ are on the same fragment

Culture 8:   rRNA$_{small}$, tRNA$_4$, and tRNA$_5$ are not next to *cap, ery, oli,* or *par*

Culture 9:   *ery* and rRNA$_{large}$ are on the same fragment

Culture 10: tRNA$_1$ and tRNA$_3$ are on the same fragment

Culture 11: *ery* and rRNA$_{large}$ are on the same fragment

Culture 12: *ery*, rRNA$_{large}$, and rRNA$_{small}$ are on the same fragment

Once you have identified each fragment, begin arranging them in overlapping order. For example,

Culture 1:   *cap* $\underline{\text{rRNA}_{large}}$

Culture 9: $\underline{\text{rRNA}_{large} \qquad\qquad ery}$

Culture 5: $\underline{\text{rRNA}_{large} \qquad\qquad ery \quad \text{rRNA}_{small}}$

gives you *cap*–rRNA$_{large}$–*ery*–rRNA$_{small}$. The entire sequence is a circle:

$cap-rRNA_{large}-ery-rRNA_{small}-tRNA_4-tRNA_5-tRNA_2-par-oli$
$-tRNA_1-tRNA_3-cap.$

26. Some tetrads will show strain-1 type, some will show strain-2 type, and some will be recombinant.

27. **a.** No; during diploid budding all the progeny receive one type of mtDNA.

b. Most likely it is a plasmid or episome.

28.

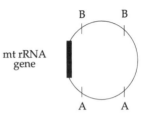

mt rRNA gene

29. First, prepare a restriction map of the mtDNA using various restriction enzymes. Using the assumption of evolutionary conservation, Southern blot hybridize equivalent fragments from yeast or another organism in which the genes have already been identified.

30. **a.** The cytoplasm from senescent cultures is a mixture of normal and abnormal mitochondria. The mitochondrial types are distributed in different ratios to different spores. The abnormal mitochondria appear to have a replicative advantage over the normal since senescence seems, ultimately, to "win out" over normal nonsenescence. The rapidity of the onset of senescence seems to be related to the ratio of normal-to-abnormal mitochondria.

b. The mutation is an insertion of about 10 kb. It carries bands E and G and splits the original fragment into two fragments, B and C.

31. **a.** The plant is a mosaic: one cell line is normal and the other cell line has both cpDNAs. Assume that the plant is self-fertilizing.

Recall endosperm formation from Chapter 3. The endosperm is derived from two identical haploid female nuclei and one haploid male nucleus. In order for four bands to appear on the gel, lane 3, the cytoplasm of the meiocyte giving rise to the seed must have contained a mixture of both cpDNAs. This could occur only if a progenitor cell contained the original mutant and normal cpDNA, and segregation of the two types of chloroplasts did not occur.

In order to get homozygous cpDNA, seen in lanes 1 and 2, segregation of chloroplasts had to occur. Lane 1 is derived from normal cpDNA, which could have come from the normal cell line or the mutant line, through segregation. Lane 2 is derived from mutant cpDNA, through segregation.

b. Both *Gryllus* and *Drosophila* would be expected to have segregation of mitochondria, but it is not being seen in these rare females. Therefore, it must be hypothesized that their mitochondria all contain two genomes, one of which carries the mutation and one of which is normal. In other words, they are the products of a segregation of mitochondria that occurred in an earlier generation. In this case, all of their progeny would be expected to show the mixture seen in the rare females. Alternatively, segregation of mitochondria may not occur in these species.

32. The two repeats, center to center, are separated by 83 kb. If the two direct repeats lined up as below and then experienced a recombination event, the two smaller circles would be 83 kb and 135 kb, each containing a single copy of the direct repeat:

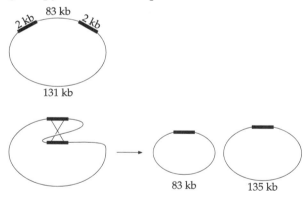

33. **a.** Both the gametophyte and the sporophyte are closer in shape to the mother than the father. Note that a size increase occurs in each type of cross.

b. Gametophyte and sporophyte morphology are affected by extranuclear factors. Leaf size may be a function of the interplay between nuclear genome contributions.

c. If extranuclear factors are affecting morphology while nuclear factors are affecting leaf size, then repeated backcrosses could be conducted, using the hybrid as the female. This would result in the cytoplasmic information remaining constant while the nuclear information becomes increasingly like that of the backcross parent. Leaf morphology should therefore remain constant while leaf size would decrease toward the size of the backcross parent.

34.   a.   The complete absence of males is the unusual aspect of this pedigree. In addition, all progeny that mate carry the trait for lack of male offspring. If the male lethality factor were nuclear, the male parent would be expected to alter this pattern. Therefore, cytoplasmic inheritance is suggested.

   b.   If all females resulted from chance alone, then the probability of this result is $(1/2)^n$, where n = the number of female births. In this case n is 72. Chance is an unlikely explanation for the observations.

   The observations can be explained by cytoplasmic factors by assuming that a new mutation in mitochondria is lethal only in males.

   Mendelian inheritance cannot explain the observations, because all the fathers would have had to carry the male-lethal mutation in order to observe such a pattern. This would be highly unlikely.

SELF-TEST

1.   *Limnaea peregra* is a hermaphroditic snail that can reproduce either by crossing or by self-fertilization. Shell coiling in progeny is controlled by a maternal gene. A right-handed shell pattern is caused by the dominant gene s^+. The left-handed shell pattern is recessive. A snail homozygous for the right-handed shell pattern is fertilized by a snail homozygous for the left-handed shell pattern.

   a.   What is the phenotype of the offspring?

   b.   If the offspring self-fertilize, what are the genotypes and phenotypes in the F_2?

   c.   If the F_2 offspring self-fertilize, what are the genotypes and phenotypes in the F_3?

2.   In the *Limnaea* described in the previous problem, if a snail heterozygous for the left-handed shell pattern is fertilized by a snail homozygous for the left-handed shell pattern, what will be the phenotype of the progeny?

3.   Heroin-addicted mothers give birth to heroin-addicted babies, whether or not the father is heroin-addicted. Nonaddicted mothers fertilized by addicted fathers give birth to nonaddicted babies. This maternal effect is not caused by a nuclear or a cytoplasmic gene. Suggest a mechanism for the maternal effect.

4.   A strain of *Chlamydomonas* requires streptomycin in the culture medium for survival. Most strains are sensitive to streptomycin. How can you determine if the streptomycin-dependence is due to a cytoplasmic or a nuclear gene?

5.   In mice, certain strains have a high rate of breast cancer, and other strains have a low rate of breast cancer. A cross between high-rate females and low-rate males results in breast cancer in approximately 90 percent of the females when they begin to nurse their offspring. The reciprocal cross does not result in breast cancer in the female offspring. However, if high-rate males are crossed with low-rate females and the female progeny are nursed by high-rate females, approximately 90 percent of the female progeny develop breast cancer when they begin nursing their own offspring. How can you explain these results?

SOLUTIONS TO SELF-TEST

1. **a.** The cross is

    P $s^+s^+ \times ss$

    F_1 s^+s (right-handed)

   b. F_1 $s^+s \times s^+s$

    F_2 $1\ s^+s^+ : 2\ s^+s : 1\ ss$ (all right-handed)

   c. *Cross 1*:

    F_2 $s^+s^+ \times s^+s^+$

    F_3 s^+s^+ (all right-hand)

    Cross 2:

    F_2 $s^+s \times s^+s$

    F_3 $1\ s^+s^+ : 2\ s^+s : 1\ ss$ (all right-handed)

    Cross 3:

    F_2 $ss \times ss$

    F_3 all ss (all left-handed)

2.   all right-handed

3.   The heroin in the mother's blood passes through the placenta, enters the baby's blood system, and causes addiction.

4.   Cross a male-sensitive with a female-dependent. If the gene is cytoplasmic, nearly all of the progeny should be streptomycin-dependent. If the gene is chromosomal, one-half should be streptomycin-dependent.

5.   Something is transmitted through the high-rate mother's milk to the female offspring that causes breast cancer. In mice, it is thought to be a virus in the milk. However, the nursing of offspring seems to be required for the appearance of breast cancer, suggesting a hormonal trigger.

22

Developmental Genetics: Cell Fate and Pattern Formation

IMPORTANT TERMS AND CONCEPTS

The **totipotent** egg gives rise to the mature adult through the sequence of **determination** and then **differentiation**. In humans and many other, but not all, species, the genetic information contained in each cell remains unchanged throughout this process. Some differentiated cells in some species also retain totipotency, which leads to **regeneration**.

Fate maps show the destinies of the descendants of specific cells during embryogenesis. Cells can also be marked genetically through the use of **mosaics**. In species with an invariant pattern of cell division, it is possible to derive a complete **lineage** of every cell from fertilized egg to the mature adult. **Cell lineage** studies in *C. elegans* have revealed that development is invariant for that organism.

The **pattern of determination** is apparently established in the cytoplasm of the egg in many species and is under the control of the maternal genotype.

Embryonic genes affecting determination for relatively large segments of the embryo do so within the restrictions imposed by the maternal genotype. Other embryonic genes affecting determination do so within the restrictions imposed for the large segment in which they function.

Determination studies in **Drosophila** have demonstrated that the egg is initially asymmetric because of maternal contributions. This chemical asymmetry is then followed by differential gene activity in the egg in response to the localized chemical asymmetry, which results in physical asymmetry as development proceeds. There is a **hierarchy** of gene expression that divides the embryo continually in ever more refined sub-divisions on the anterior-posterior axis. The order is **maternal *bcd* gene, gap genes, pair-rule genes** and **segment-polarity genes.** The **homeotic genes** are responsible for segment identity. This cascade of determination in part sets **cell fate.** Communication between cells is also required for this process because fixed cell lineage is not involved as it is in *C. elegans.*

The **homeobox** is a 180–base-pair DNA sequence that results in a 60–amino-acid polypeptide, the **homeodomain.** All homeotic genes share a similar homeobox sequence. The homeodomain binds DNA, altering transcription. The homeotic genes also maintain segmental iden-tity in *Drosophilia* after differentiation is completed.

Communication between cells can be **inductive**, leading to the acqui-sition of a new fate, or it can be **inhibitory,** suppressing the ability of a cell to adopt the same fate as that of its neighbor. In cases where the process has been defined at the molecular level, it has turned out to involve modulation of transcription factors.

The developmental principles discovered in *C. elegans* and *Drosophila* also can be found to apply in other organisms, including humans.

Be sure that you have thoroughly read the entire chapter before you attempt any of the problems.

SOLUTIONS TO PROBLEMS

1. Human development, like the development of all multicellular organisms, is a process that continues throughout life and ends only when death occurs. It is a result of the complex interaction of genetics, the environment, developmental noise (see Chapter 1), and chance. There is no "final phenotype" *per se.* The production of human clones in the laboratory would be the first step in an experiment that would have to last for the life span of all the clones, and it would be virtually impos-sible to tease out the various factors impinging upon each of the clones. Therefore, clonal reproduction of humans would likely be useless in determining the relative effects of heredity and environment, even though the clones are genetically identical.

2. a. Regeneration is controlled by the nucleus.

   b. The hat-forming substance, produced by the nucleus, is concentrated in the upper part of the stem. An enucleated cell cannot synthesize more of this substance when the upper part of the stem is removed.

   c. The hat-forming substance cannot function in the presence of a hat.

3. a. There must be a diffusible substance produced by the anchor cell that affects development of the six PVCs. The 1° has the strongest response to the substance, and 3° represents a lack of response due to a low concentration or absence of the diffusible substance.

   b. Remove the anchor cell and the six Pn.p cells. Arrange the Pn.p cells in a circle around the anchor cell. All six Pn.p cells will develop the same phenotype, which will depend on the distance from the anchor cell.

4. a. The results suggest that ABa and ABp are not determined at this point in their development. Also, future determination and differentiation of these cells is dependent upon their position within the developing organism.

   b. Because an absence of EMS cells leads to a lack of determination and differentiation of AB cells, the EMS cells must be at least in part responsible for AB-cell development, either through direct contact or by the production of a diffusible substance.

   c. Most descendants of the AB cells do not become muscle cells when P2 is present; all descendants of the AB cells become muscle cells when P2 is absent. Therefore, P2 must prevent some AB descendants from becoming muscle cells.

5. The R8 cell makes a *boss*⁺ product that influences R7 but not R3 and R4. Therefore, the expression of *sev* plus contact with the *boss*⁺ product is required to turn a cell into a photoreceptor.

Alternatively, R3 and R4 produce some product that prevents the *sev*⁺ product from functioning properly despite its expression. For this possibility, contact with the *boss*⁺ product, whether or not it occurs, would be irrelevant to the R3 and R4 cells.

6. It may be that the wild-type allele in the embryo produces a gene product that can inhibit the gene product of the rescuable maternal-effect lethal mutations while the nonrescuable maternal-effect lethal mutations produces a product that cannot be inhibited.

Alternatively, the nonrescuable maternal-effect lethal mutations may produce a product that is required very early in development, before the developing fly is producing any proteins, while the rescuable maternal-effect lethal mutations may act later in development when embryo protein production can compensate for the maternal mutation.

7. a. The determination of anterior-posterior portions of the embryo is governed by a concentration gradient of *bcd*. The concentration is highest in the anterior region and lowest in the posterior region. The furrow develops at a critical concentration of *bcd*. As *bcd*$^+$ gene dosage decreases, the furrow shifts anteriorly; as the gene dosage increases, the furrow shifts posteriorly.

b.

	hb (high *bcd* expression)	*Kr* (intermediate *bcd* expression)	*kni* (low *bcd* expression)
$2n - 1$			
$2n$			
$2n + 1$			
$2n + 4$			

8. The anterior/posterior axis would be reversed.

9. Proper *ftz* expression requires *Kr* in the fourth and fifth segments and *kni* in the fifth and sixth segments.

10. If you diagram these results, you will see that deletion of a gene that functions posteriorly allows the next-most anterior segments to extend in a posterior direction. Deletion of an anterior gene does not allow extension of the next-most posterior segment in an anterior direction. The gap genes activate *Ubx* in both thoracic and abdominal segments, whereas the *abd-A* and *Abd-B* genes are activated only in the middle and posterior abdominal segments. The functioning of the *abd-A* and *Abd-B* genes in those segments somehow prevents *Ubx* expression. However, if the *abd-A* and *Abd-B* genes are deleted, *Ubx* can be expressed in these regions.

11. A number of experiments could be devised. A comparison of amino acid sequence between mammalian gene products and insect gene products would indicate which genes are most similar to each other. Using cloned cDNA sequences from mammalian genes for hybridization to insect DNA would also indicate which genes are most similar to each other.

SELF-TEST

1. In embryo fusion experiments using mammals, the fused embryos cannot be sexed prior to fusion. When XX and XY embryos, as later determined by chromosome analysis, are fused, all the embryos develop into males. What does this say about the Y chromosome in mammals? In birds, in which the female is the heterogametic sex, what would be the result of fusion of embryos that are of different sexes?

2. Why are all mammalian females mosaics?

3. When twin cattle share one placenta, all females develop as males if their twin is a male. What does this suggest? How would you test your explanation?

4. If the circulatory systems of two embryonic rats are surgically connected and three kidneys are removed, the growth of the remaining kidney proceeds quite vigorously. What does this suggest? What type of mutants would be useful?

5. Tissues and organs take shape, in part, through differential cell death. If cells destined to die in the normal course of events at stage 24 in the wing of a chick are removed at stage 17 and grafted to a region of muscles, they die on schedule. If they are grafted to the dorsal side of the limb bud, they survive. However, if they are grafted at stage 22 rather than at stage 17 to the dorsal side of the limb bud, they die. What seems to be occurring here? What type of mutants would be useful?

6. Female mammals do not go through estrus or menstruation if their percentage of body fat is too low. Transgenic pigs produced by the injection of the human growth hormone gene into eggs are considerably leaner than controls. This is thought to be because the growth hormone favors the conversion of nutrients to protein rather than fats. The females never go into estrus and are sterile. What is the cause of the sterility, and what approaches might be made to overcome it?

7. Large quantities of specific human gene products can be produced in bacteria. However, some of the gene products normally contain sugar additions that bacteria cannot duplicate. For this reason, researchers are putting these genes into such animals as cows and sheep, hoping that the gene products will be secreted into the milk of these animals. What is required for production of these gene products in milk?

8. If the vegetal pole of eggs from the frog *Rana* is irradiated with UV light, the mature frog is normal in every way except that it does not have any germ cells. What does this finding suggest?

9. What is the easiest way to demonstrate maternal inheritance?

SOLUTIONS TO SELF-TEST

1. The mammalian studies suggest that the Y contains one or more genes that are responsible for sex determination. In birds, if the W chromosome contains one or more genes that determine sex, the fused embryos should develop as females.

2. Because of X-inactivation, which occurs randomly in each cell, each female has two genetically distinct cell lines.

3. The blood of cattle contains some factor that alters development toward the male phenotype. The best guess is that the female tissue is responding to testosterone produced by the male twin. Injection of that hormone into the placenta of developing females should confirm that idea. If so, then the gene coding for testosterone could be cloned and introduced into early embryos by injection. A shift in the sex ratio should be observed. It might be better to do this experiment in mice rather than in cattle, however.

4. Either the remaining kidney is responding to some humoral factor that controls kidney growth or the organ somehow monitors the amount of body to be served and adjusts its size accordingly. Mutants that have altered size for the kidney would be useful.

5. The experiments suggest that, although a "death clock" is set by stage 17 for these cells, it can be turned off by the imposition of external controls in the appropriate environment until stage 22. After stage 22, the clock cannot be turned off. Mutants that show abnormal development of the wing would be required for any genetic testing.

6. The data suggest that the females are sterile because their body fat content is too low. One approach to overcoming this might be to feed the females a high-fat diet. Another might be to select a strain with very high body fat and use eggs from it for the injections. A third approach would be to attach regulatory sequences to the growth hormone gene that would reduce the level of transcription from the gene or would turn off transcription of the growth hormone gene after a specific developmental stage.

7. The gene would have to be linked to regulatory sequences of a gene that functions only in milk-producing cells. The regulatory sequences that have been tried are from the β-lactoglobin gene. This has resulted in low secretion of the exogenous gene product into the milk.

8. The vegetal pole contains some cytoplasmic factor that is required for germ cell production.

9. Do reciprocal crosses.

23

Developmental Genetics: Topics in Gene Regulation and Differentiation

IMPORTANT TERMS AND CONCEPTS

The types and relative amounts of **proteins** in a cell determine the characteristics of that cell. Because both transcription and translation are involved, the **regulation of gene expression** through transcription and translation is ultimately responsible for the differentiated state of each cell. In turn, the coordinated development of each differentiated cell gives rise to the final organism.

The regulation of protein synthesis occurs by a number of processes: **modification of gene structure, modulation of transcription rate, modulation of processing of the primary transcript into mature RNA, modulation of translation rate, and modulation of protein modifications.**

Modification of gene structure occurs by a number of processes, including **gene amplification** (histones), **DNA rearrangement** (the immune system), and **methylation** of genes.

Modulation of transcription rate occurs through **tissue-specific enhancers** controlled by **transcription factors** and coordinated by **hormones.**

The modulation of processing of the primary transcript into mature RNA can occur through regulation of the splicing of introns.

Sex determination can occur through environmental, chromosomal or gene differences in those species that have two sexes. A combination of genetic and environmental control determines sex in some species. In *Drosophila*, the state of sexual differentiation is established and maintained through regulation of transcription and splicing. At the cellular level, each cell is autonomous for sex. In mammals, each cell is not autonomous for sex, and sexual differentiation is established and maintained by the transcription of androgens. **Dosage compensation** in mammals is accomplished by **X-inactivation** and in *Drosophila* by **hyperactivation of X chromosome genes.**

Cancer, defined as unregulated growth, results from multiple mutations within a single cell. **Oncogenes** are genes in viruses that cause cancer in multicellular organisms. The oncogenes are mutated cellular **proto-oncogenes** that entered the virus through improper excision. Mutations in the proto-oncogenes can result in cancer. Many tumors of the same type possess the same oncogene. Different types of tumors contain different oncogenes. The normal cellular functions of the proto-oncogenes involve transcription factors, parts of the system that convert signals received by a cell into a change in gene activity, and parts of the system that involve communication between cells. Dominant oncogenic mutations activate proto-oncogenes. They result in the expression of a protein in an active form, at too high a level, or in the wrong tissue. Recessive oncogenic mutations inactivate the inhibitory function of a proto-oncogene. Presumably, a protein product that is required for normal cellular function is then not made .

Be sure that you have thoroughly read the entire chapter before you attempt any of the problems.

SOLUTIONS TO PROBLEMS

1. a. If the number of copies of a transcription factor is increased, transcription will occur at a higher rate. That could lead to an acceleration of cellular growth, which would be cancer.

    b. A nonsense mutation would lead to a decrease of the normal protein product. If that protein were part of the receptor for a growth factor, then growth could become less regulated or absent, which would be cancer. This is unlikely to be dominant, however.

    c. If the mutant protein blocks the binding action of an inhibitory protein, then transcription would be increased. An increase in transcription rate could lead to unregulated growth, which is cancer.

   d. Cytoplasmic tyrosine-specific protein kinase phosphorylates proteins in response to signals received by the cell. Phosphorylation of the proteins presumably alters their activity. If the active site is disrupted, then phosphorylation will not occur. That could result in unregulated cell growth, which would be cancer. This is unlikely to be dominant, however.

2. a. Because female flies do not accomplish dosage compensation through X-inactivation, both alleles would be expressed within the same cell.

   b. Because female humans undergo X-inactivation in all their somatic cells, only one allele would be expressed in each cell although the woman would express both alleles at the organismal level.

3. Sex determination in *Drosophila* is autonomous at the cellular level. The *Sxl* gene is permanently turned on or remains off early in development in response to the concentration of X : A transcription factor. Because the X : A ratio is established by the interaction of gene products made in the ovary and in the early zygote, a chemical gradient would be expected to exist that would be sufficiently high in some cells to result in femaleness but low enough in other cells to result in maleness, making the individual an intersex.

4. To induce excision of the P[Δ2,3] element in a specific tissue of a fly, use a copy of the P element with a weak promoter and a tissue specific enhancer.

5. a. If more than one light- or heavy-chain rearrangement were to occur within a cell, the cell would then lose its ability to respond specifically to an antigen that it had already encountered in its environment and might produce deleterious antibodies.

   b. The possible number of different antibody molecules is

   $300 \times 4 \times 1{,}000 \times 4 \times 12 = 57{,}600{,}000.$

6. Dominant gain-of-function mutations can result from the fusion of enhancers with transcription units that they do not normally control. These mutations could be reverted by any agent that could disrupt the illicit fusion or inactivate either gene.

7. All cells of the tumor should express the same alleles of all the X-linked genes that are heterozygous within the organism and not express the alternative set of alleles.

8. Construct a set of reporter genes with the promoter region, the introns, and the region 3' to the transcription unit of the gene in question containing different alterations that do not disrupt transcription or processing. Use these reporter genes to make transgenic animals by germ line transformation. Assay for expression of the reporter gene in various tissues and the kidney of both sexes.

9. a. In *Drosophila* males, the genes on the X chromosome are normally expressed at a rate twice as high as the same genes in the female. If the *tra* homozygotes transform chromosomally female flies into phenotypically male flies, then hyperactivity of X must not be a necessary prerequisite for male development even though it normally is part of male development.

  b. Normally, the *tra* gene in the female is active, while in the male it is not active. The active *tra* form of the gene product results in a change in the *dsx* product, shifting development towards the female. If the *dsx* product is not altered, development proceeds along the male line. A mutation in the gene that results in chromosomal females developing as phenotypic, but sterile, males must involve an inactive *tra* product. Homozygotes for the *tra* mutation could be transplanted with male germ cells very early in development, which should result in normal gonad development.

10. In humans, a single copy of the Y chromosome is sufficient to shift development towards normal male phenotype. The extra copy of the X chromosome is simply inactivated. Both mechanisms seem to be all-or-none rather than to be based upon concentration gradients.

11. Because maleness is based upon the presence of androgens produced by the developing testes and femaleness is based upon the absence of those androgens, what seems to be crucial here is whether the migrating germ cells organize a testes. Although the determinator is unknown, it may be that a minimal number of XY cells are required to organize a testes. If, in the mosaic, not enough exist, then development will be female. If a sufficient number exist, development will be male.

12. The transformation assay requires expression of the gene in order to identify an oncogene. Because the oncogene is recessive, it cannot be identified unless it is homozygous. It is highly unlikely that two copies of the gene would be picked up by the same cell and integrated into homologous sites to knock out the normal wild-type copies.

13. The concentration of *Sxl* is crucial for female development and dispensable for male development. The dominant *Sxl*^{M} male-lethal mutations may not actually kill all males but simply produce an excessive amount of gene product so that only females (fertile XX and XY) result. The reversions may eliminate all gene product, resulting in XX (sterile) and XY males. The reversions would be recessive because, presumably, a single normal copy of the gene may produce enough gene product to "toggle the switch" in development to female.

SELF-TEST

1. When genes are introduced into recipient eukaryotic cells through one of several techniques available, how likely is it that these genes will be regulated properly?

2. Muscular dystrophy in mice has been observed. When normal and mutant embryos are fused, wild-type muscle cells enervated by nerve cells from the dystrophic strain have muscular dystrophy. If adult mice from the two strains are surgically linked (parabiosis), wild-type muscle cells enervated by nerve cells from the dystrophic strain are normal. What do these results indicate?

3. How would you select for the following behavioral mutants in *Drosophila*? Note: flies taste with their feet.

   a. blindness

   b. inability to fly

   c. abnormal feeding responses

SOLUTIONS TO SELF-TEST

1. The answer to this question could go one of several ways, and it might vary with the gene being introduced. It is known that position effect does occur in translocated material. A similar effect would most likely occur for introduced genes. Thus, a gene normally functioning within the context of euchromatin would be expected to function at a lower rate when located within heterochromatin, and vice versa. Genes that normally are regulated in *cis* are unlikely to be regulated in a normal fashion simply because the chance that they will be located close to their *cis* regulator in the new cell is low. Genes that normally are regulated by *trans*-acting factors are more likely to be properly regulated in their new locations.

2. The studies suggest that muscular dystrophy is caused by defects in the nerves that subsequently cause muscular defects. The parabiosis

studies show that the muscular defects cannot be induced in adult muscle. Therefore, the effects of the nerves on the muscles must occur during development.

3. a. The wild-type flies are attracted to light. Select flies that do not move toward a light at the end of a tube.

   b. Select for flies that do not fly by placing a poisoned food source high enough in a fly cage so that the flies can only reach it by flying. Alternatively, place mutagenized flies on a window ledge and scare them. The ones that do not fly away are very brave, are very stupid, or are the mutants that you want.

   c. Add a tasteless toxic compound to a sugar solution on filter paper in the bottom of the cage. Those flies that cannot taste sugar will not eat it, and those that can taste sugar will eat it and die.

24

Quantitative Genetics

IMPORTANT TERMS AND CONCEPTS

The **genotype** can be identified and studied only through its **phenotypic** effects. The study of **genetics** is the study of allelic substitutions that cause **qualitative** differences in the phenotype. However, the actual variation among organisms is usually **quantitative** rather than qualitative. Quantitative variation gives rise to **continuous** variation among members of a species, rather than discrete differences.

Continuous variation is the result of a **norm of reaction** for each genotype and the fact that most traits are controlled by more than one locus. Two individuals with the same genotype can have different phenotypes. Two individuals with different genotypes can have the same phenotype.

Quantitative traits have a **statistical distribution.** This can be presented as a **frequency histogram** or a **distribution function.** A distribution of phenotypes can be described by its **mode,** which is the most frequent class. Some distributions are **bimodal.** The distribution can also be described by the **mean,** the arithmetic average. The **variance** is the spread around the central class. The **standard deviation** is the square root of the variance. Two variables may be described by their **correlation.**

A collection of observations constitutes a **sample** from the **universe** of all observations. This sample may be **biased** or **unbiased.**

The **heritability** of a trait is the proportion of phenotypic variation that can be attributed to genetic variation. The estimates of genetic and environmental variance are specific to the population and environment in which the estimates were made.

Be sure that you have thoroughly read the entire chapter before you attempt any of the problems.

SOLUTIONS TO PROBLEMS

1. Continuous variation can be represented by a bell-shaped curve. Examples are height and weight. Discontinuous variation results in easily classifiable, discrete entities. Examples are red versus white and taster versus nontaster.

2. **a.** Broad heritability is $H^2 = s_g^2/(s_g^2 + s_e^2)$. Narrow heritability is $h^2 = s_a^2/(s_a^2 + s_d^2 + s_e^2)$, where $s_g^2 = s_a^2 + s_d^2$.

Shank length:

$H^2 = (46.5 + 15.6)/(46.5 + 15.6 + 248.1) = 0.200$

$h^2 = 46.5/(46.5 + 15.6 + 248.1) = 0.150$

Neck length:

$H^2 = (73.0 + 365.2)/(73.0 + 365.2 + 292.2) = 0.600$

$h^2 = 73.0/(73.0 + 365.2 + 292.2) = 0.010$

Fat content:

$H^2 = (42.4 + 10.6)/(42.4 + 10.6 + 53.0) = 0.500$

$h^2 = 42.4/(42.4 + 10.6 + 53.0) = 0.400$

b. The larger the h^2 value, the more that characteristic will respond to selection. Therefore, fat content would respond best to selection.

c. The formula needed is

$h^2 \times$ (selection differential) = (selection response)

Therefore, selection response = $(0.400)(4.0) = 1.6\%$ decrease in fat content, or 8.9% fat content.

3. **a.** Homozygotes at one locus can be homozygotic at A or at B or at C. The probability of being homozygotic is $1/2$ (for A/a: AA or aa), and the probability of being heterozygotic is $1/2$. Putting this all together,

p(homozygotic at 1 locus) $= 3(1/2)^3 = 3/8$

p(homozygotic at 2 loci) $= 3(1/2)^3 = 3/8$

p(homozygotic at 3 loci) $= (1/2)^3 = 1/8$

b. p(0 capital letters) = p(all homozygous recessive)

$= (1/4)^3 = 1/64$

p(1 capital letter)

= p(1 heterozygote and 2 homozygous recessive)

= $3(1/2)(1/4)(1/4) = 3/32$

p(2 capital letters)

= p(1 homozygous dominant and 2 homozygous recessive)

or = p(2 heterozygotes and 1 homozygous recessive)

= $3(1/4)^3 + 3(1/4)(1/2)^2 = 15/64$

p(3 capital letters)

= p(all heterozygous)

or = p(1 homozygous dominant, 1 heterozygous, and 1 homozygous recessive)

= $(1/2)^3 + 6(1/4)(1/2)(1/4) = 10/32$

p(4 capital letters)

= p(2 homozygous dominant and 1 homozygous recessive)

or = p(1 homozygous dominant and 2 heterozygous)

= $3(1/4)^3 + 3(1/4)(1/2)^2 = 15/64$

p(5 capital letters)

= p(2 homozygous dominant and 1 heterozygote)

= $3(1/4)^2(1/2) = 3/32$

p(6 capital letters)

= p(all homozygous dominant) = $(1/4)^3 = 1/64$

4.   For three genes there are a total of 27 genotypes that will occur in predictable proportions. For example, there are three genotypes that have two heterozygotes and a homozygote recessive (*Aa Bb cc, Aa bb Cc, aa Bb Cc*). The frequency of this combination is $3(1/2)(1/2)(1/4) = 3/16$, and the phenotypic score is $3 + 3 + 1 = 7$. The distribution of scores is as follows:

Score	Proportion
3	1/64
5	6/64
6	3/64
7	12/64

8	12/64
9	11/64
10	12/64
11	6/64
12	1/64

5. The population described above would be distributed as follows:

2 bristles   43/64

1 bristle   1/63

Note that the 3-bristle class contains 7 different genotypes, the 2-bristle class contains 19 different genotypes, and the 1-bristle class contains only 1 genotype. It would be very difficult to determine the underlying genetic situation by doing controlled crosses and determining progeny frequencies.

6. a. First, solve the formula for values of x over the range for each genotype. Plot those values. Next, add the three values, one for each genotype, for each phenotypic value and plot these summed values. This will give you the overall population distribution.

Phenotypic Value	Genotype 1	Genotype 2	Genotype 3	Total
0.03	0.9037			0.9037
0.04	0.9147			0.9147
0.05	0.9250			0.9250
0.06	0.9347			0.9347
0.07	0.9437			0.9437
0.08	0.9520			0.9520
0.09	0.9597			0.9597
0.10	0.9667		0.9020	1.8687
0.11	0.9730		0.9155	1.8885
0.12	0.9787	0.0000	0.9280	1.9067
0.13	0.9837	0.1900	0.9395	2.1132
0.14	0.9880	0.3600	0.9500	2.2980
0.15	0.9917	0.5100	0.9595	2.4612

(continued on next page)

Phenotypic	Genotype			Total
Value	1	2	3	
0.16	0.9947	0.6400	0.9680	2.6027
0.17	0.9970	0.7500	0.9755	2.7225
0.18	0.9987	0.8400	0.9820	2.8207
0.19	0.9997	0.9199	0.9875	2.8972
0.20	1.0000	0.9600	0.9920	2.9520
0.21	0.9997	0.9900	0.9955	2.9852
0.22	0.9987	1.0000	0.9980	2.9967
0.23	0.9970	0.9900	0.9995	2.9865
0.24	0.9947	0.9600	1.0000	2.9547
0.25	0.9917		0.9995	1.9912
0.26	0.9880		0.9980	1.9860
0.27	0.9837		0.9955	1.9792
0.28	0.9787		0.9920	1.9707
0.29	0.9730		0.9875	1.9605
0.30	0.9667		0.9820	1.9487
0.31	0.9597		0.9755	1.9352
0.32	0.9520		0.9680	1.9200
0.33	0.9437		0.9595	1.9032
0.34	0.9347		0.9500	1.8847
0.35	0.9250		0.9395	1.8645
0.36	0.9147		0.9280	1.8427
0.37	0.9037		0.9155	1.8192
0.38			0.9020	0.9020

b. The overall population distribution will not result in three distinct modes. With sufficient variation within genotypes, there is a continuous distribution of phenotypes.

7. mean = sum of all measurements/number of measurements

$$= \frac{1 + 2(4) + 3(7) + 4(31) + 5(56) + 6(17) + 7(4)}{1 + 4 + 7 + 31 + 56 + 17 + 4}$$

$$= \frac{564}{120} = 4.7$$

variance = average squared deviation from the mean

$$= 1/120 \, \Sigma \left[\begin{array}{l} (1-4.7)^2 + (2-4.7)^2 + (3-4.7)^2 \\ + (4-4.7)^2 + (5-4.7)^2 + (6-4.7)^2 \\ + (7-4.7)^2 \end{array} \right]$$

$$= 31.43/120 = 0.2619$$

standard deviation = square root of variance = 0.5117

8.

   a. 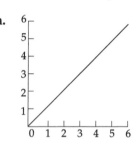   **b.**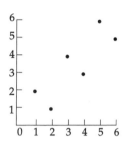

   c. 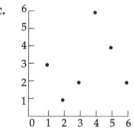   **d.**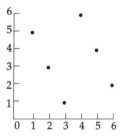

Use the following formula to calculate the correlation between x and y:

$$\text{correlation} = r_{xy} = \frac{\text{cov } xy}{s_x s_y},$$

where

$$\text{cov } xy = \frac{1}{N} \, \Sigma \, x_i y_i - \overline{xy}$$

  a.   cov xy = 1/6[(1)(1) + (2)(2) + (3)(3) + (4)(4) + (5)(5) + (6)(6)

                                                                         – (21/6)(21/6)]

               = 13.125

$$s_x = \sqrt{\frac{1}{N}\Sigma x_i^2 - \bar{x}^2} = \sqrt{\frac{1}{6}\left[1^2 + 2^2 + 3^2 + 4^2 + 5^2 + 6^2 - \left(\frac{21}{6}\right)^2\right]}$$

$$= 3.623$$

$$s_y = \sqrt{\frac{1}{N}\Sigma x_i^2 - \bar{x}^2} = \sqrt{\frac{1}{6}\left[1^2 + 2^2 + 3^2 + 4^2 + 5^2 + 6^2 - \left(\frac{21}{6}\right)^2\right]}$$

$$= 3.623$$

Therefore, r_{xy} = 13.125/(3.623)(3.623) = 1.0. The other correlation coefficients are calculated in a like manner.

    b.   0.83

    c.   0.66

    d. −0.20

9.   a. H^2 has meaning only with respect to the population that was studied in the environment in which it was studied. Otherwise, it has no meaning.

    b. Neither H^2 nor h^2 are reliable measures that can be used to generalize from a particular sample to a "universe" of the human population. They certainly should not be used in social decision making (as implied by the terms "eugenics" and "dysgenics").

    c. Again, H^2 and h^2 are not reliable measures and they should not be used in any decision making with regard to social problems.

10.   The following are unknown: (1) norms of reaction for the genotypes affecting IQ; (2) the environmental distribution in which the individuals developed; and (3) the genotypic distributions in the populations. Even if the above were known, because heritability is specific to a specific population and its environment, the difference between two different populations cannot be given a value of heritability.

11.   First, define alcoholism in behavioral terms. Next, realize that all observations must be limited to the behavior you used in the definition and all conclusions from your observations are applicable only to that behavior. In order to do your data gathering, you must work with a population in which familiarity is distinguished from heritability. In practical terms, this means using individuals who are genetically close but who are found in all environments possible.

12.   Before beginning, it is necessary to understand the data. The first entry, h/h h/h, refers to the II and III chromosomes, respectively. Thus,

there are four h sets of alleles in two or more genes on separate chromosomes. The next entry is $h/l \; h/h$. Chromosome II is heterozygous and chromosome III is homozygous.

The effect of substituting a low for a high chromosome II can be seen within each row. In the first row, the differences are $25.1 - 22.2 = 2.9$ and $22.2 - 19.0 = 3.2$. In the second row the differences are 3.1 and 5.2. They are 2.7 and 6.8 in the third row. The average difference is $23.9/6 = 3.98$, which actually tells you very little.

The effect of substituting one l chromosome for an h chromosome in chromosome II, and therefore going from homozygous hh to heterozygous hl, can be seen in the differences along the rows in the first two columns. The average change is $(2.9 + 3.1 + 2.7)/3 = 2.9$. When chromosome II goes from heterozygous hl to homozygous ll, the average change is $(3.2 + 5.2 + 6.8)/3 = 5.1$.

The effect of substituting one l chromosome for an h chromosome in chromosome III, and therefore going from homozygous hh to heterozygous hl, can be seen in the differences between rows: $25.1 - 23.0 = 2.1$; $22.2 - 19.9 = 2.3$; $19.0 - 14.7 = 4.3$; $23.0 - 11.8 = 11.2$; $19.9 - 9.1 = 10.8$; $14.7 - 12.4 = 12.4$. When chromosome III goes from homozygous hh to heterozygous hl, the average change is $(2.1 + 2.3 + 4.3)/3 = 2.9$. When it goes from heterozygous hl to homozygous ll, the average change is $(11.2 + 10.8 + 12.4)/3 = 11.5$.

Here is a summary of these results:

	Chromosome II	Chromosome III	Total
hh to hl	2.9	2.9	5.8
hl to ll	5.1	11.5	16.6

Now it should be clear that each set of alleles for both chromosomes is expressed in the phenotype, but that expression varies with the chromosome. Chromosome III appears to have a stronger affect on the phenotype than does chromosome II (compare total amount of change). There is some dominance of h over l for both chromosomes because the change from hh to hl is less than the change from hl to ll. Finally, there is definitely some epistasis occurring. Compare $h/h \; h/h$ with both $l/l \; h/h$ and $h/h \; l/l$. The difference in the first case is 6.0 and, in the second case, 13.3. The expected amount of change in going from $h/h \; h/h$ to $l/l \; l/l$ is therefore $6.0 + 13.3 = 19.3$. The $l/l \; l/l$ phenotype should be $25.1 - 19.3 = 5.8$, but the observed value is 2.3.

13.

a.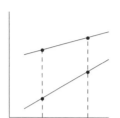

b.

c.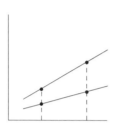

d.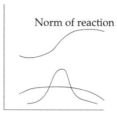

Norm of reaction

14. **a.** If you assume that individuals at the extreme of any spectrum are homozygous, then their offspring are more likely to be heterozygous than are the original individuals. That is, they will be less extreme.

b. For Dalton's data, regression is an estimate of heritability (h^2), assuming that there were few environmental differences between father and son.

SELF-TEST

1. In a study of body weight among Labrador retrievers, the total variance is 4.80. The covariance between half-siblings is 0.76. Estimate the narrow-sense heritability of body weight in this population.

2. Two inbred lines of sheep are intercrossed. The variance in the weight of the F_1 is 3.2. The F_1 are crossed, and the variance in the F_2 is 7.3. What is the estimate of broad-sense heritability in sheep weight?

3. In Maine, there is a fairly high frequency of cats with excess claws on one or more feet. This genetic abnormality is called "double-paws". Below, each "double-paw" on a cat is counted as two paws. Calculate the mean, variance, and standard deviation of the distribution of paws observed in one community. Does it make sense to characterize the observations in this fashion?

Paw number/Cat	Number of individuals
4	93
5	0
6	4
7	0
8	3

4. The accident rate among human males aged twenty is much higher than among females. List some of the hypotheses that might be tested experimentally.

5. The number of eye facets in *Drosophila* was measured at various temperatures. What is the correlation between numbers of facets and temperature?

Temperature, °C	Facets
15	200
20	150
25	90
30	70

SOLUTIONS TO SELF-TEST

1. The covariance for half-siblings is 1/4 of the additive genetic variance (page 722 in Chapter 24):

$$s_a^2 = 4 \times \text{cov} = (4)(0.76) = 3.04$$

Heritability in the narrow sense is

$$h^2 = s_a^2 / s_p^2$$

so that $h^2 = 3.04/4.80 = 0.63$, or 63%.

2. $s_e^2 = 3.2$

$s_e^2 + s_g^2 = 7.3$

$s^2 = 7.3 - 3.2 = 4.1$

$H^2 = 4.1/7.3 = 0.56$, or 56%

3. mean = (4)(93) + (6)(4) + (3)(8) = 4.2

variance $= s^2 = 1/100[(4 - 4.2)^2 + (5 - 4.2)^2 + (6 - 4.2)^2 + (7 - 4.2)^2 + (8 - 4.2)^2]$

$= 0.262$

standard deviation $= s = 0.512$

Although the population can be categorized in this fashion, the number of paws on a cat is not a continuous distribution. It would make more sense to study this trait by traditional Mendelian methods, using statistical analysis such as χ^2. Recall from Chapter 2 the distinction between continuous and discontinuous variation. "Mean," "variance," and "standard deviation" are appropriate for traits showing continuous variation. χ^2 is appropriate for traits showing discontinuous variation.

4.   Many hypotheses could be proposed. The following are a subset of them.

Males are genetically more susceptible to accidents than are females.

Males are environmentally conditioned to take more risks than are females.

There is a familial component to risk-taking among males and females. This component varies among families.

Males have poorer reaction times than do females.

Males have poorer vision than do females.

5.   mean temperature, $\bar{x} = 22.5$

mean facets, $\bar{y} = 121.7$

standard deviation temperature, $s_x = 20.27$

standard deviation facets, $s_y = 121.7$

$\text{cov}_{xy} = -281.25$

correlation $= r_{xy} = -0.114$

25

Population Genetics

IMPORTANT TERMS AND CONCEPTS

Among individuals in a population, there is **phenotypic variation**, or **polymorphism.** Offspring are phenotypically closer to their parents than they are to unrelated individuals. Some phenotypes **survive** to reproduce better than other phenotypes in a given environment. **Natural selection** of these more successful phenotypes in a given environment leads to a **reproductive advantage**, or an increased **fitness**, for them. This results in a change of allelic frequency. **Evolution** is a change in genotypic frequencies.

All variation ultimately comes from **mutation**.

The frequency of a given allele in a specific population is affected by recurrent mutation, selection, migration, and random sampling effects. In an idealized, randomly interbreeding population not subjected to any forces that alter genotypic frequencies, the genotypic frequencies do not change. They can be represented by the **Hardy-Weinberg equilibrium** equation, $p^2 + 2pq + q^2 = 1.0$.

Be sure that you have thoroughly read the entire chapter before you attempt any of the problems.

SOLUTIONS TO PROBLEMS

1. The frequency of an allele in a population can be altered by selection, mutation, migration, inbreeding, and random genetic drift.

2. There are a total of $(2)(384) + (2)(210) + (2)(260) = 1708$ alleles in the population. Of those, $(2)(384) + 210 = 978$ are *A1* and $210 + (2)(260) =$

730 are *A2*. The frequency of *A1* is $978/1708 = 0.57$, and the frequency of *A2* is $730/1708 = 0.43$.

3. The given data are $q^2 = 0.04$ and $p^2 + 2pq = 0.96$. If $q^2 = 0.04$, $q = 0.2$ and $p = 0.8$. To check this, use these numbers in the second equation: $(0.8)^2 + (2)(0.8)(0.2) = 0.64 + 0.32 = 0.96$. The frequency of *BB* is 0.64, and the frequency of *Bb* is 0.32.

4. This problem assumes that there is no backward mutation. Use the following equation: $p_n = p_o e^{-n\mu}$. That is,

$$p_{50,000} = (0.8)e^{-(5\times10^4)(4\times10^{-6})} = (0.8)(0.81873) = 0.65$$

5. a. If the variants represent different alleles of gene *X*, a cross between any two variants should result in a $1 : 1$ progeny ratio. All the variants should map to the same locus. Amino acid sequencing of the variants should reveal differences of one to just a few amino acids.

   b. There could be another gene (gene *Y*), with five variants, that modifies the gene *X* product post-transcriptionally. If so, the easiest way to distinguish between the two explanations would be to find another mutation in *X* and do a dihybrid cross. For example, if there is independent assortment,

   P $X^1 Y^1 \times X^2 Y^2$

   F_1 $1 X^1 Y^1 : 1 X^1 Y^2 : 1 X^2 Y^1 : 1 X^2 Y^2$

   If the mutation in *X* led to no enzyme activity, the ratio would be

   2 no activity : 1 variant one activity : 1 variant two activity
   The same mutant in a one-gene situation would yield 1 active : 1 inactive.

6. a. If the population is in equilibrium, $p^2 + 2pq + q^2 = 1$. Use *p* from the data to predict the frequency of *q*, and then check the calculated values against the observed.

   $p = [406 + 1/2(744)]/1482 = 0.5249$

   $q = 1 - p = 0.4751 =$ predicted value

   The phenotypes should be distributed as follows if the population is in equilibrium:

   $L^M L^M = p^2(1482) = 408$

   $L^M L^N = 2pq(1482) = 739$

   $L^N L^N = q^2(1482) = 334$

   The population is in equilibrium.

b. If mating is random with respect to blood type, then the following frequency of matings should occur.

$$L^M L^M \times L^M L^M = (p^2)(p^2)(741) \qquad = 56.25$$

$$L^M L^M \times L^M L^N = (2p^2)(2pq)(741) \quad = 203.6$$

$$L^M L^M \times L^N L^N = (2p^2)(q^2)(741) \qquad = 92$$

$$L^M L^N \times L^M L^N = (2pq)(2pq)(741) \quad = 184.28$$

$$L^M L^N \times L^N L^N = (2)(2pq)(q^2)(741) = 166.8$$

$$L^N L^N \times L^N L^N = (q^2)(q^2)(741) \qquad = 37.75$$

The mating is random with respect to blood type.

7. **a.** When the allelic frequency differs between sexes for an X-linked gene, $p = 1/2(1/3 p_m + 2/3 p_f)$. At generation 0, $p = 1/2[1/3(0.8) + 2/3(0.2)] = 0.2$.

  In generation 1, all males get their X from their mother, and therefore, the frequency of p in the males will be the same as it is in the mother, 0.2. All females get an X from each parent at the allelic frequency in each parent. Therefore, the daughters will have a frequency of $p_1 = (1/2)(p_m + p_f) = (1/2)(0.8 + 0.20) = 0.5$. The following table provides information for further generations.

Generation	p male	p female
0	0.8	0.2
1	0.2	0.5
2	0.5	0.35
3	0.35	0.425
.	.	.
.	.	.
.	.	.
n	$p_{f(n-1)}$	$p_{1/2[m(n-1) + f(n-1)]}$

where m = male and f = female.

b. Let p = frequency in males and p' = frequency in females. For any generation, $p_n = p'_{n-1}$ and $p'_n = (1/2)(p_{n-1} + p'_{n-1})$. The difference between these two, d, is

$$d = (1/2)(p_{n-1} + p'_{n-1}) - p'_{n-1}$$
$$= (1/2)(p_{n-1} - p'_{n-1})$$

Given the initial values of p_0 and p'_0,

$$d_n = (1/2)^n (p_0 - p'_0)$$

8.   a. and b.

Population	p	q	Equilibrium?
1	1.0	0.0	yes
2	0.5	0.5	no
3	0.0	1.0	yes
4	0.625	0.375	no
5	0.3775	0.625	no
6	0.5	0.5	yes
7	0.5	0.5	no
8	0.2	0.8	yes
9	0.8	0.2	yes
10	0.993	0.007	yes

   c. $4.9 \times 10^{-6} = 5 \times 10^{-6}/s; s = 0.102$

   d.

Genotype	Frequency	Fitness	Gametes	A	a
AA	0.25	1.0	0.25	0.25	0.0
Aa	0.50	0.8	0.40	0.20	0.20
aa	0.25	0.6	0.15	0.0	0.15
				0.45	0.35

$p = 0.45/(0.45 + 0.35) = 0.56$

$q = 0.35/(0.45 + 0.35) = 0.44$

9.   a.   Assuming equilibrium, if $q = 0.1$, $q^2 = 0.01$.

   b.   10 times

   c.   Marriages in which one-half of the children of both sexes would be colorblind are $X^B X^b \times X^b Y$. Such marriages occur with a frequency of $(2pq)(q) = 2pq^2 = 2(0.9)(0.1)^2 = 0.018$.

   d.   All children would be normal if the female were homozygous normal. The frequency of such marriages is $p^2(p + q) = (0.9)^2(0.5 + 0.5) = 0.81$.

e. Colorblind females result from two types of matings:

$$X^B X^b \times X^b Y = (2pq)(q') = 2(0.2)(0.8)(0.6) = 0.192$$

$$X^b X^b \times X^b Y = (q)^2(q') = (0.2)^2(0.6) = 0.024$$

Half the females from the first mating and all the females from the second will be colorblind, so the frequency of color-blind female progeny is $(1/2)(0.192) + 0.024 = 0.12$.

Colorblind males will result when the mother is either heterozygous (half the male offspring) or homozygous recessive (all the male offspring), regardless of the father's genotype. Therefore, the frequency of color blind male progeny is

$$(1/2)(2pq) + q^2 = (1/2)(2)(0.8)(0.2) + (0.2)^2 = 0.2$$

f. The male frequency will be 0.2 (frequency of the female in the previous generation) and the female frequency will be $(1/2)(0.2 + 0.6) = 0.4$.

10. The frequency of a phenotype in a population is a function of the frequency of alleles that lead to that phenotype in the population. To determine dominance and recessiveness, do standard Mendelian crosses.

11. Assume that proper function results from the right gene products in the proper ratio to all other gene products. A mutation will change the gene product, eliminate the gene product, or change the ratio of it to all other gene products. All three outcomes upset a previously balanced system. While a new balance may be achieved, this is unlikely.

12. Dominance is usually wild type because most detectable mutations in enzymes result in lowered or eliminated enzyme function. To be dominant, the heterozygote has approximately the same phenotype as the homozygote dominant. This will be true only when the wild-type allele produces a product and the mutant allele does not.

The chromosomal rearrangements are dominant mutations because so many genes are affected that it is highly unlikely that all of their alleles will be dominant and "cover" for them.

13. Prior to migration, $q^A = 0.1$ and $q^B = 0.3$. Immediately after migration, $q^{A+B} = (1/2)(q^A + q^B) = (1/2)(0.1 + 0.3) = 0.2$. The frequency of affected males is 0.2 and the frequency of affected females is $(0.2)^2 = 0.04$.

14. The probability of homozygous by descent (f) is $f = (1/2)^n$, where n = number of ancestors in a closed loop.

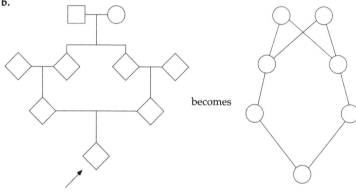

a. $f = (1/2)^3 = 1/8$

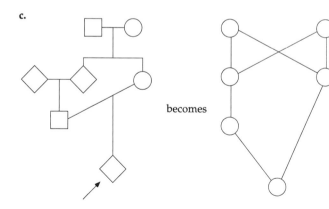

b. $f = (1/2)^5 + (1/2)^5 = 1/16$

c. $f = (1/2)^4 + (1/2)^4 = 1/8$

15. Albinos may have been considered lucky and encouraged to breed at very high levels in comparison to nonalbinos. They may also have been encouraged to mate with each other. Alternatively, in the tribes with a very low frequency, albinos may have been considered very unlucky and destroyed at birth or prevented from marriage.

16.   The allele frequencies are

A: $0.2 + (1/2)(0.60) = 50\%$

a: $(1/2)(0.60) + 0.2 = 50\%$

Positive assortive mating: The alleles will randomly unite within a phenotype. For A–, the mating population is 0.2 *AA* + 0.6 *Aa*. The allele frequencies within this population are

A $[0.2 + (1/2)(0.6)]/0.8 = 0.625$

a: $(1/2)(0.6)/0.8 = 0.375$

The phenotypic frequencies that result are

$$A\text{--}: p^2 + 2pq = (0.625)^2 + 2(0.625)(0.375) = 0.3906 + 0.4688$$

$$= 0.8594$$

$$aa:\ q^2 = (0.375)^2 = 0.1406$$

However, because this subpopulation represents 0.8 of the total population, these figures must be adjusted to reflect that by multiplying by 0.8:

A–: $(0.8)(0.8594) = 0.6875$

aa: $(0.8)(0.1406) = 0.1125$

The *aa* contribution from the other subpopulation will remain unchanged because there is only one genotype, *aa*. The contribution to the total phenotypic frequency is 0.20. Therefore, the final phenotypic frequencies are A– = 0.6875 and *aa* = 0.20 + 0.1125 = 0.3125. These frequencies will remain unchanged over time, but the end result will be two separate populations, *AA* and *aa*, which will not interbreed.

Negative assortive mating: If assortive mating is between unlike phenotypes, the two types of progeny will be *Aa* and *aa*. *AA* will not exist. *Aa* will result from all *AA* × *aa* matings and one-half of the *Aa* × *aa* matings. The matings will occur with the following frequencies:

AA × aa = $(0.2)(0.2) = 0.04$

Aa × aa = $(0.6)(0.2) = 0.12$

Because these are the only matings that will occur, they must be put on a 100 percent basis by dividing by the total frequency of matings that occur:

$AA \times aa$: $0.04/0.16 = 0.25$, all of which will be Aa

$Aa \times aa$: $0.12/0.16 = 0.75$, half Aa and half aa

The phenotypic frequencies in the next generation will be

Aa: $0.25 + 0.75/2 = 0.625$

aa: $0.75/2 = 0.375$

In the second generation, the same method will result in a final ratio of 0.5 Aa : 0.5 aa. These values will remain unchanged after the second generation of negative assortive mating.

17. Many genes affect bristle number in *Drosophila*. The artificial selection resulted in lines with mostly high-bristle-number alleles. Some mutations may have occurred during the 20 generations of selective breeding, but most of the response was due to alleles present in the original population. Assortment and recombination generated lines with more high-bristle-number alleles.

Fixation of some alleles causing high bristle number would prevent complete reversal. Some high-bristle-number alleles would have no bad effects on fitness, so there would be no force pushing bristle number back down due to those loci.

The low fertility in the high-bristle-number line could have been due to pleiotropy or linkage. Some alleles that caused high bristle number may also have caused low fertility (pleiotropy). Chromosomes with high-bristle-number alleles may also carry alleles at different loci that caused low fertility (linkage). After artificial selection was relaxed, the low-fertility alleles would have been selected against through natural selection. A few generations of relaxed selection would have allowed low-fertility-linked alleles to recombine away, producing high-bristle-number chromosomes that did not contain low-fertility alleles. When selection was reapplied, the low-fertility alleles had been reduced in frequency or separated from the high-bristle loci, so this time there was much less of a fertility problem.

18. **a.** The needed equation is $p' = p\overline{W}_a/\overline{W}$, where $\overline{W}_a = p\overline{W}_{AA} + q\overline{W}_{Aa}$ and $\overline{W} = p^2 W_{AA} + 2pq W_{Aa} + q^2 W_{aa}$.

$$p' = \frac{(0.5)[(0.5)(0.9) + (0.5)(1.0)]}{(0.5)^2(0.9) + 2(0.5)(0.5)(1.0) + (0.5)^2(0.7)} = 0.528$$

b. $\hat{p} = (W_{aa} - W_{Aa})/[(W_{aa} - W_{Aa}) + (W_{AA} - W_{Aa})]$

$$\hat{\mu p} = \frac{0.7 - 1.0}{(0.7 - 1.0) + (0.9 - 1.0)} = 0.75$$

19. The equation needed is $\hat{q} = \sqrt{\mu/s}$

or $s = \mu/\hat{q}^2 = \mu/\text{recessive frequency} = 10^{-5}/10^{-3} = .01$

20. Affected individuals $= Bb = 2pq = 4 \times 10^{-6}$. Because q is almost equal to 1.0, $2p = 4 \times 10^{-6}$. Therefore, $p = 2 \times 10^{-6}$.

$$\mu = hsp = (1.0)(0.7)(2 \times 10^{-6}) = 1.4 \times 10^{-6}$$

21. The probability of not getting a recessive lethal genotype for one gene is $1 - 1/8 = 7/8$. If there are n lethal genes, the probability of not being homozygous for any of them is $(7/8)^n = 13/31$. From log tables, $n = 6.5$, or an average of 6.5 recessive lethals in the human genome.

22. **a.** $\hat{q} = \sqrt{\mu/s} = \sqrt{10^{-5}/0.5} = 4.47 \times 10^{-3}$

$sq^2 = 0.5(4.47 \times 10^{-3})^2 = 10^{-5}$

b. $\hat{q} = \sqrt{\mu/s} = \sqrt{2 \times 10^{-5}/0.5} = 6.32 \times 10^{-3}$

$sq^2 = 0.5(6.32 \times 10^{-3})^2 = 2 \times 10^{-5}$

c. $\hat{q} = \sqrt{\mu/s} = \sqrt{10^{-5}/0.3} = 5.77 \times 10^{-3}$

$sq^2 = 0.3(5.77 \times 10^{-3})^{-2} = 10^{-5}$

SELF-TEST

1. In a population, the alleles A and a are at initial frequencies of p and q. Prove that the gene frequencies and the zygotic frequencies do not change from generation to generation as long as no forces for change are acting on the population.

2. At what allelic frequency is the heterozygous genotype frequency one-half the homozygous recessive genotype frequency?

3. A strongly odorous substance, mathanethiol, is secreted in some humans. Secretion is recessive. If the frequency of the secretor allele, m, is 0.6, what is the probability of a mating between two heterozygous nonsecretors?

4. In the previous problem, what is the probability among all matings of having a secreting girl?

5. In humans, an index finger shorter than the ring finger is autosomal dominant in males and recessive in females. Of 1000 males in a population, 510 had a short index finger. What is the expected frequency of long and short index fingers in 1000 females from this population?

6. If the fitness of a population is 0.85 and the mutation rate to the recessive allele is 6×10^{-6}, what is the equilibrium frequency?

SOLUTIONS TO SELF-TEST

1. Random mating results in the following zygotic frequencies:

$p^2(AA) + 2pq(Aa) + q^2(aa) = 1.0$

All the gametes of AA individuals and half the gametes of Aa individuals will be A. The frequency of A in the next generation will be

$p^2 + pq = p^2 + p(1-q) = p^2 + p - p^2 = p$

Therefore, the frequency of all a alleles in the next generation will be $1 - p = q$.

2. $1/2(q^2) = 2pq$

$q^2 = 4pq$

$= 4q(1-q)$

$= 4q - 4q^2$

$0 = 4q - 5q^2$

Either $q = 0$, which is not correct, or $0 = 4 - 5q$, $q = 4/5 = 0.8$, and $p = 0.2$.

3. The frequencies are $q = 0.6$ and $p = 0.4$. The heterozygous population is $2pq$. The frequency of matings between heterozygotes is $(2pq)(2pq) = 4p^2q^2 = 4(0.16)(0.36) = 0.23$.

4. A secretor could result from the following matings:

$Aa \times Aa \longrightarrow 1/4\ aa$

$Aa \times aa \longrightarrow 1/2\ aa$

$aa \times Aa \longrightarrow 1/2\ aa$

$aa \times aa \longrightarrow$ all aa

The probability of a girl is $1/2$. The probability of a secreting girl is $(1/2)(1/4)(2pq)(2pq) + 2(1/2)(1/2)(2pq)(q^2) + 1/2(q^2)(q^2)$

$= (1/2)(1/4)(2)(0.4)(0.6)(0.4)(0.6) = 0.029$

$2(1/2)(1/2)(2)(0.4)(0.6)(0.36) = 0.086$

$(1/2)(0.36)(0.36) = \underline{0.065}$

0.180

5. The frequencies are $q^2 = 490/1000$, $q = 0.7$, and $p = 0.3$. Among females, however, p is recessive. Therefore, $1000\ p^2$ females will have a ring finger that is shorter than the index finger, or 90. The remaining 910 females will have a long index finger.

6. $\hat{q} = \sqrt{\mu/s}$, $q = 6 \times 10^{-6}$, $s = 1 - W = 1.0 - 0.85 = 0.15$

$\hat{q} = \sqrt{6 \times 10^{-6}/0.15} = 0.0063$

$p = 0.9937$